FERRIES 2017
BRITISH ISLES AND NORTHERN EUROPE EDITION

GW00775659

Scandlines HYBRID FERRY

Berlin

ISBN 978-1-911268-01-7

Ferry Publications, PO Box 33,
Ramsey, Isle of Man IM99 4LP

Email: ferrypubs@manx.net   Website: www.ferrypubs.co.uk

Europe's **Leading** Guide To The Ferry Industry

Contents...

Sound of Scarba *(Miles Cowsill)*

Europe's **Leading** Guide To The Ferry Industry

Introduction...

This is the twenty-ninth edition of this book, which first appeared in 1983 as the 24-page 'home published' *Car Ferries from Great Britain and Ireland'*. The book aims to list every passenger/vehicle ferry in Great Britain and Ireland, ro-ro freight vessels which operate regular services between Great Britain and Ireland and to nearby Continental destinations and major passenger/vehicle ferries in other parts of Northern Europe. The coverage of Northern Europe is not fully comprehensive (to make it so would probably triple the size of the book) and does not include freight-only operations and vessels – although freight-only vessels have been included where the operators also run passenger services. This year I have included some ro-ro operators who convey only private traffic in new Section 4.

Each operator is listed alphabetically within sections – major operators, minor operators, freight-only operators, chain, cable and float ferries, passenger-only ferries, other North European passenger operators and vehicle/passenger vessels owned by companies not currently engaged in operating services. After details relating to each company's management, address, telephone numbers, email, website and services, there is a fleet list with technical data and then a potted history of each vessel with previous names and dates.

Each operator was sent the draft text relating to them in March. Where they have not responded, I have attempted to ensure that any telephone, fax and email details match what is quoted on their website but management details may not be 100% accurate.

Whitstable, Kent   **Nick Widdows**

August 2016

Stena Adventurer *(Gordon Hislip)*

Foreword...

Forward by Helen Deeble, CEO, P&O Ferries

I am delighted to be supporting Ferries 2017, which is rightly seen as an essential and must read book for our industry.

The most topical subject around boardrooms and dinner tables is Brexit. Irrespective of EU membership, P&O Ferries is a vital part of the European transport infrastructure, employing 4,000 people, transporting 10 million passengers a year, and delivering services of the highest quality and professionalism.

We are also a key part of the transport infrastructure of individual European countries, most obviously France, Belgium, Holland and the Republic of Ireland, but also

Helen Deeble

across central and eastern Europe, where manufacturers rely on our services across land and sea to export goods to Britain.

We employ people of many different nationalities – we do not expect this to change.

I also welcomed the assurance from Prime Minister Theresa May and French President Francois Hollande that the Le Touquet Agreement, a bilateral treaty that allows British border force officers to carry out passport checks in Calais and vice versa, will remain in place – an agreement that benefits both the UK and the EU.

As Brexit discussions begin, we are maintaining a close dialogue with Government ministers, trade bodies, suppliers and customers to ensure our voice is heard when the UK's transport arrangements with the EU are renegotiated. Our priorities are minimising disruption and ensuring secure, safe and efficient passage through our ports.

The focus on the safety and security of our passengers and crew has become even greater, given the nature of terrorist attacks seen in Europe recently. Security will continue to be a major theme for 2017 and beyond. The ferry industry has faced challenges over recent years, from the financial crisis and global recession, low cost airlines, competition from fixed links and environmental legislation, to name but a few. The list can seem endless, but the industry has overcome these challenges by listening and adapting to its customers, improving its service and value for money proposition.

I am sure we will face up to these latest challenges in a similar way to ensure that we can continue to invest and grow for the future. We are energised and determined, like the UK, to make a success of Brexit and are confident for the future of our industry. It is truly an exciting time.

August 2016

Spirit of France *(Miles Cowsill)*

A Guide To Using

This Book

A GUIDE TO USING THIS BOOK

Sections Listing is in seven sections. **Section 1** – Services from Great Britain and Ireland to the Continent and between Great Britain and Ireland (including services to/from the Isle of Man and Channel Islands), **Section 2** – Domestic services within Great Britain and Ireland, **Section 3** – Freight-only services from Great Britain and Ireland and domestic routes, **Section 4** – Minor vehicle ferries in Great Britain and Ireland (chain and cable ferries etc), **Section 5** – Major passenger-only operators, **Section 6** – Major car ferry operators in Northern Europe, **Section 7** – Companies not operating regular services possessing vehicle ferries which may be chartered or sold to other operators.

Order The company order within each section is alphabetical. Note that the definite article and words meaning 'company' or 'shipping company' (eg. 'AG', 'Reederei') do not count. However, where this is part of a ship's name it does count. Sorting is by normal English convention eg. 'Å' is treated the same as 'A' and comes at the start, not as a separate character which comes at the end of the alphabet as is the Scandinavian convention. Where ships are numbered, order is by number whether the number is expressed in Arabic or Latin digits.

Listing of Ships When a ship owned by a company listed in this book is on charter to another company listed, then she is shown under the company which operates her. When a ship owned by a company listed in this book is on charter to another company not listed, then she is shown under the company which owns her.

IMO Number All ships of 100t or greater (except vessels solely engaged in fishing, ships without mechanical means of propulsion (eg. chain ferries), pleasure yachts, ships engaged on special service (eg. lightships), hopper barges, hydrofoils, air cushion vehicles, floating docks and structures classified in a similar manner, warships and troopships, wooden ships) are required to be registered by the International Maritime Organisation (IMO), an agency of the United Nations. The number is retained by the ship throughout her life, however much the vessel is rebuilt. This number is now required to be displayed on the ship externally and on top so that it can be read from the air. The scheme is administered by Lloyd's Register-Fairplay, who maintain a database of all ships in excess of 100t (with some exceptions), not just those classified through them.

Company Information This section gives general information regarding the status of the company. That is, nationality, whether it is public or private sector and whether it is part of a larger group.

Management The Managing Director and Marketing Director or Manager of each company are listed. Where these posts do not exist, other equivalent people are listed. Where only initials are given, that person is, as far as is known, male.

Address This is the address of the company's administrative headquarters. In the case of some international companies, British and overseas addresses are given.

Telephone and Fax Numbers are expressed as follows: + [*number*] (this is the international dialling code which is dialled in combination with the number dialled for international calls (00 in the UK, Ireland and most other European countries); it is not used for calling within the country), ([*number*]) (this is the number which precedes area codes when making long-distance domestic calls – it is not dialled when calling from another country or making local calls (not all countries have this)), [*number*] (this is the rest of the number including, where appropriate, the area dialling code). UK '08' numbers are sometimes not available from overseas and the full number must be dialled in all circumstances.

Internet Email addresses and **Website** URLs are given where these are available; the language(s) used is shown. The language listed first is that which appears on the home page when accessed from a UK based computer; the others follow in alphabetical order. In a few cases Email facility is only available through the Website. To avoid confusion, there is no other punctuation on the Internet line.

Routes operated After each route there are, in brackets, details of **1** normal journey time, **2** regular vessel(s) used on the route (number as in list of vessels) and **3** frequencies (where a number per day is given, this relates to return sailings). In the case of freight-only sailings which operate to a regular schedule, departure times are given where they have been supplied. Please note that times are subject to quite frequent change and cancellation.

Winter and Summer In this book, Winter generally means the period between October and Easter while Summer means Easter to October. The peak Summer period is generally June, July and August. In Scandinavia, the Summer peak ends in mid-August whilst in the UK it starts rather later and generally stretches into the first or second week of September. Dates vary according to operator.

Spelling The convention is used in respect of town and country names is that English names are used for towns and areas of countries where such names exist (eg. Gothenburg rather than Göteborg) and English names for countries (eg. Germany rather than Deutschland). Otherwise local names are used, accented as appropriate. In a few cases, English names have slipped out of common usage and the local name is more commonly used in Britain, ie Dunkerque not Dunkirk, Helsingør not Elsinore and Vlissingen not Flushing. Many towns in Finland have both Finnish and Swedish names; we have used the Finnish name except in the case of Åland which is a Swedish-speaking area. In the case of Danish towns, the alternative use of 'å' or 'aa' follows local convention. The following towns, islands and territories are expressed using their English names – the local name is shown following: Antwerp – Antwerpen/Anvers, Fyn – Funen, Genoa – Génova, Ghent – Gent, Gothenburg – Göteborg, Hook of Holland – Hoek van Holland, Jutland – Jylland, Copenhagen – København, Ostend – Oostende, Oporto – Porto, Seville – Sevilla, Sealand – Sjælland and Venice – Venezia.

Terms The following words mean *'shipping company'* in various languages: Redereja (Latvian), Rederi (Danish, Norwegian, Swedish), Rederij (Dutch), Reederei (German) and Zegluga (Polish). The following words mean *'limited company'*: AB – Aktiebolaget (Swedish) (Finnish companies who use both the Finnish and Swedish terms sometimes express it as Ab), AG – Aktiengesellschaft (German), AS – Aksjeselskap (Norwegian), A/S – Aktie Selskabet (Danish), BV – Besloten Vennootschap (Dutch), GmbH – Gesellschaft mit beschränkter Haftung (German), NV – Naamloze Vennootschap (Dutch), Oy – (Finnish), Oyj – (Finnish (plc)) and SA – Société Anonyme (French).

Types of Ferry

These distinctions are necessarily general and many ships will have features of more than one category.

Car Ferry Until about 1970, most vehicle ferries were primarily designed for the conveyance of cars and their passengers and foot passengers. Little regard was paid to the conveyance of lorries and trailers, since this sort of traffic had not begun to develop. Few vessels of this type are still in service.

Multi-purpose Ferry From about 1970 onwards vehicle ferries began to make more provision for freight traffic, sharing the same ship with passengers and cars. Features usually include higher vehicle decks, often with retractable mezzanine decks, enabling two levels of cars or one level of freight and coaches, and separate facilities (including cabins on quite short crossings) for freight drivers.

Cruise Ferry In the 1980s the idea of travelling on a ferry, not just to get from A to B but for the pleasure of the travel experience, became more and more popular and ferries were built with increasingly luxurious and varied passenger accommodation. Such vessels also convey cars and freight but the emphasis is on passenger accommodation with a high level of berths (sometimes providing berths for all passengers).

Ro-pax Ferry A vessel designed primarily for the carriage of freight traffic but which also carries a limited number of ordinary passengers. Features generally include a moderate passenger capacity – up to about 500 passengers – and a partly open upper vehicle deck. Modern ro-pax vessels are becoming increasingly luxurious with facilities approaching those of a cruise ferry.

Ro-ro Ferry A vessel designed for the conveyance of road freight, unaccompanied trailers and containers on low trailers (known as 'Mafis' although often made by other manufacturers). Some such vessels have no passenger accommodation but the majority can accommodate up to 12 passengers – the maximum allowed without a passenger certificate. On routes where there is a low level of driver-accompanied traffic (mainly the longer ones), ordinary passengers, with or without cars, can sometimes be conveyed. On routes with a high level of driver-accompanied traffic, passenger capacity will sometimes be higher but facilities tend to be geared to the needs of freight drivers eg. lounge with video, high level of cabins on routes of three hours or more. Technically such vessels are passenger ferries (having a passenger certificate).

Con-ro Many ro-ro vessels are capable of having ISO (International Standards Organisation) containers crane-loaded on the upper 'weather' deck. In this book the term con-ro applies only to vessels whose upper deck can only take containers and has no vehicle access.

Fast Ferry Streamlined vessel of catamaran or monohull construction, speed in excess of 30 knots, water jet propulsion, generally aluminium-built but some have steel hulls, little or no freight capacity and no cabins.

Timescale Although the book goes to press in August 2016, I have sought to reflect the situation as it will exist in early Summer 2016 with regard to the introduction of new ships or other known changes. Vessels due to enter service after July 2016 are shown as '**Under Construction**'. This term does not necessarily man that physical work has started but an order has been placed with a shipyard. The book is updated at all stages of the production process where this is feasible, although major changes once the text has been paginated are not possible; there is also a 'Late News' section on page 219 for changes which cannot be incorporated into the text.

List of vessels

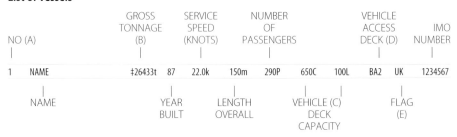

(A) **>>** = fast ferry, • = vessel laid up, F = freight-only vessel (max 12 passengers), F+ = freight-only vessel (with passenger certificate), p = passenger-only vessel.

(B) C = Cars, L = Lorries (**15m**), T = Trailers (**13.5m**), r = can also take rail wagons, – = No figure quoted.

(C) B = Bow, A = Aft, S = Side, Q = Quarterdeck, R = Slewing ramp, 2 = Two decks can be loaded at the same time, C = Vehicles must be crane-loaded aboard, t = turntable ferry.

(D) The following abbreviations are used:

AG	= Antigua and Barbuda	DK	= Denmark	IR	= Republic of Ireland	PT	= Portugal
AL	= Åland Islands	EE	= Estonia			PL	= Poland
BB	= Barbados	ES	= Spain	LU	= Luxembourg	RU	= Russia
BE	= Belgium	FO	= Faroes	LT	= Lithuania	SG	= Singapore
BM	= Bermuda	FI	= Finland	LV	= Latvia	SE	= Sweden
BS	= Bahamas	FR	= France	MT	= Malta	TR	= Turkey
CY	= Cyprus	GI	= Gibraltar	NL	= Netherlands	UK	= United Kingdom
DE	= Germany	IM	= Isle of Man	NO	= Norway		
		IT	= Italy	PA	= Panama		

In the notes ships are in CAPITAL LETTERS, shipping lines and other institutions are in *italics*.

Capacity In this book, capacities shown are the maxima. Sometimes vessels operate at less than their maximum passenger capacity due to reduced crewing or to operating on a route on which they are not permitted to operate above a certain level. Car and lorry/trailer capacities are the maximum for either type. The two figures are not directly comparable. Some parts of a vessel may allow cars on two levels to occupy the space that a trailer or lorry occupies on one level, some may not; some parts of a vessel with low headroom may only be accessible to cars. All figures have to be approximate.

Ownership The ownership of many vessels is very complicated. Some are actually owned by finance companies and banks, some by subsidiary companies of the shipping lines, some by subsidiary companies of a holding company of which the shipping company is also a subsidiary and some by companies which are jointly owned by the shipping company and other interests like a bank, set up specifically to own one ship or a group of ships. In all these cases the vessel is technically chartered to the shipping company. However, in this book, only those vessels chartered from one shipping company to another or from a ship-owning company unconnected with the shipping line are recorded as being on charter. Vessels are listed under the current operator rather than the owner. Charter is 'bareboat' (without crew) unless otherwise stated. If chartered with crew, vessels are 'time-chartered'.

Gross Tonnage This is a measure of enclosed capacity rather than weight, based on a formula of one gross ton = 100 cubic feet. Even small alterations can alter the gross tonnage. Under old measurement systems, the capacity of enclosed car decks was not included but, under the 1969 Convention, all vessels laid down after 1982 have been measured by a new system which includes enclosed vehicle decks as enclosed space, thereby considerably increasing the tonnage of vehicle ferries. Under this Convention, from 1st January 1995 all vessels were due to be re-measured under this system. Tonnages quoted here are, where possible, those given by the shipping companies themselves.

The following people are gratefully thanked for their assistance with this publication, many of them in ferry companies in the UK and abroad: Gary Andrews, John Bryant, Andrew Cooke, Matthew Davies, Ian Hall, Peter Therkildsen, Matthew Punter, Ian Smith (The Camrose Organisation), and Gomer Press.

Whilst every effort has been made to ensure that the facts contained here are correct, neither the publishers nor the writer can accept any responsibility for errors contained herein. We would, however, appreciate comments from readers, which we will endeavour to reflect in the next edition which we plan to publish in summer 2017.

P&O FERRIES AND ITS PREDECESSORS AT DOVER

A BRIEF HISTORY OF THE P&O GROUP

Although P&O Ferries is a relative newcomer to the world of shipping, the origins of The Peninsular and Oriental Steam Navigation Company can be traced as far back as 1815.

By 1823 the firm was known as Willcox and Anderson, and the business had expanded to include the operation of small sailing vessels to Spain and Portugal, as agents for the owners. In the early 1830s the partners began to charter steamers, soon adopting the trading name Peninsular Steam Navigation Company and the company's first owned ship, the newly built *Iberia,* entered service on the route to Spain and Portugal.

The partners had raised loans, chartered steamers for use as troopships and warships, and engaged in gun running for the Royal Houses in both the Spanish and Portuguese Civil Wars in the early 1830s and as a result, were granted the right to fly both sets of Royal colours. The famous P&O house flag showing the red and yellow of Spain and the blue and white of Portugal, is still proudly worn today by the ships of P&O Ferries.

By 1971, the activities of more than 100 subsidiary companies were amalgamated into operating divisions within P&O. All of the cargo ships formerly operated by P&O and its subsidiaries were put into the General Cargo Division, the liners, along with British India's educational cruise ships formed the Passenger Division, and the tankers, bulk carriers and gas carriers became the fleet of the Bulk Shipping Division. From this time the ships of constituent companies flew the P&O flag and began to adopt a corporate identity. Following this reorganisation, the fleet consisted of 239 ships, including 136 general cargo liners, 27 coasters, 18 passenger liners, 17 ferries, 17 tankers and 6 bulk carriers.

The 1970s were years of diversification away from shipping. A large network of road haulage operations was built up under the Ferrymasters, Pandoro, P&O Roadways and P&O Roadtanks names and construction group Bovis was acquired in 1974. By March 1999, the Group, including joint ventures and associates, was again a major force to be reckoned with in the shipping world, controlling some 276 ships.

At the same time P&O's Chairman announced that it was his Board's intention to refocus the Group on the three core businesses: cruising, ferries, and ports and logistics. Disposal of property and service company interests began and by early October almost £1 billion had been realised from the sale of investment properties, Bovis Construction, Laing (Canada), service companies in Australia, and the London exhibition halls of Earls Court and Olympia.

It was known that P&O was prepared to move out of the container trades by floating P&O Nedlloyd on the stock-market but the announcement in February 2000 that the Company would rid itself of its cruise business was a total surprise.

On 23rd October 2000, P&O Princess Cruises de-merged from the Peninsular and Oriental Steam Navigation Company (P&O) to become an independent trading company. Then, during April 2003 the Miami-based Carnival Corporation merged with P&O Princess Cruises to form Carnival Corporation & plc, the world's largest cruise company.

Although former Prime Minister Mrs Margaret Thatcher is quoted as saying of P&O: "It's not just a company but the very fabric of the Empire," the company's 168 years of independence was coming to an end and following a period of uncertainty, on 29th November 2005 they announced that Dubai Ports (DP World) had taken them over in a deal worth £3.3 billion. P&O stated that it was not actively looking for a takeover bid but the offer proved too attractive to resist and shareholders agreed to the takeover on 13th February 2006. DP World was one of several Dubai Government-linked firms looking for assets to invest in, backed by huge cash piles from the Gulf emirate's resources. Compared with the ports division, which was the principal prize that DP World was interested in adding to its portfolio, P&O Ferries proved to be very small in terms of the total package that the Dubai-based company acquired and was really outside their area of expertise or even interest. After a period of uncertainty during which time the future direction of the ferry company was in doubt, the new owners were able to allay fears when they announced that P&O Ferries was not for sale.

n.f. Panter. *(FotoFlite)*

Free Enterprise II *(FotoFlite)*

Free Enterprise IV *(FotoFlite)*

Thus P&O Ferries continues to be managed and operated from its Channel House Headquarters at Dover, high on a hill above the town and overlooking both the harbour and the Dover Strait.

THE DOVER STORY

TOWNSEND CHANNEL FERRY

The ancestry of the P&O involvement at Dover goes back to 1928 when Mr Stuart M. Townsend chartered the 368-ton collier *Artificer* for a brief summer season to offer motorists a cut-price motor car ferry service linking Dover with Calais. Townsend's original plan was to end the monopoly then enjoyed by the Southern Railway Company, undercut their fares by half and force them to reduce their rates after which he would withdraw. His initial success saw a profit of £80 in the first season which prompted a further charter during 1929 after which the former minesweeper *HMS Ford* was purchased and converted for merchant use after being inspected at the scrap yard at Dover's Eastern Docks.

Renamed *Forde*, the 11-year-old steamer started her seasonal service in April 1930 carrying up to 168 passengers and 28 cars. She was an immediate success and throughout the thirties the family-owned 'Townsend Channel Ferry' blossomed.

Townsend had seen from an early time that the drive-on method of loading was the way ahead but the authorities on both sides of the Channel were reluctant to allow the construction of linkspans over which cars could be driven between ship and shore. The *Forde* was actually rebuilt with a stern gate and when in June 1936 a French General Strike paralysed the cranes at Calais, at high water she simply presented her stern to the quay and allowed her vehicles to drive directly onto French soil. All those who witnessed this historic occasion saw the foundations laid for a transport revolution.

Success continued after the war and the elderly *Forde* was sold for further service at Gibraltar. Her replacement was another former Royal Navy vessel, the 'River' class frigate *HMS Halladale*. After her conversion at Cork, she took up service in April 1950 and in the following June opened the drive-on ramp at Calais although she was not able to use similar facilities at Dover until April 1953.

In 1956, continued growth prompted Townsend to go public but the share issue was launched on the very day that President Nasser announced the nationalisation of the Suez Canal. Trade on the Stock Exchange slumped and few shares were sold.

At this time the Coventry-based Mr George Nott and his associates were scouring the market looking for a small company with large assets which they could transfer to their own. A controlling interest in Townsend Bros. Car Ferries was duly secured after which the Townsend family's involvement eventually ceased. It was initially Nott's intention to strip the ferry company of its assets and to wind-up the ferry service but sense prevailed and the *Halladale* continued to make handsome profits for her new owners.

The new regime was far more aggressive and now looked further afield than the traditionally seasonal car ferry traffic. Some of its ideas were very forward-looking and were amply illustrated when in 1959 a subsidiary company European Ferries was formed and the former tank-landing craft *Empire Shearwater* was taken on long-term charter to provide a service for lorries and heavy vehicles. Sadly the climate was not then right for such a link and after just six months it ended in failure.

The first of the well-known green-hulled ferries, the £1 million *Free Enterprise* entered service in April 1962 and was followed in May 1965 by the *Free Enterprise II* – the first British-registered drive-through ferry. She opened the Dover-Zeebrugge link in March 1966 after which time, expansion – especially of freight – was tremendous and between 1966 and 1974 six more larger 'Free Enterprise' vessels were added to the fleet.

TOWNSEND-THORESEN IS BORN

The year 1968 had seen the acquisition of the Norwegian-owned Thoresen Car Ferries after which the European Ferries Group was created and eventually the combined fleets adopted the orange hulls of the Thoresen ships but with Townsend's green funnels. The enlarged company was the largest independent ferry concern in Europe and was further strengthened in 1971 by the purchase of the Atlantic Steam Navigation Company and (as mentioned later) in 1985 of the Dover-Boulogne operators P&O Ferries.

The continuing demand for freight space particularly on the Zeebrugge link saw the introduction of three 'European' class roll on – roll off freighters in 1975, 1976 and 1978. The *Free Enterprise VI* and *Free Enterprise VII* both underwent major surgery in 1985 when they were raised and lengthened to increase their lorry capacity from 24 to 60 units. The result was not a pretty sight but this clever piece of engineering allowed two well-tried ships to continue their successful careers at a time when the cost of building replacements would have been prohibitive.

P&O FERRIES MARK I

P&O moved into Dover in 1976 with a single ship operation between Dover and Boulogne using the *Lion*. This vessel had been built in 1967 for subsidiary Burns and Laird Ltd to operate between Ardrossan and Belfast but the troubles which broke out in Northern Ireland 1969 had damaged the tourist market and it became increasingly clear that there was no room for this sort of ship – which had limited freight capacity – on the route. Rather than attempt to sell her, they decided to launch the new Dover services branded as Normandy Ferries, which was the name of their successful Southampton – Le Havre operation (although Boulogne is not in Normandy). In 1978 a second ship was acquired for the route in the form of the former Danish internal ferry *N F Tiger* and a sister vessel – the *N F Panther* – was acquired the following year. In 1980 it was decided that all P&O passenger ferry operations should be rebranded as 'P&O Ferries'.

In 1985 P&O's ferry operations in Dover and Southampton were sold to European Ferries. The *Lion* was soon withdrawn and sold but the Dover – Boulogne service continued with the *N F Tiger* and *N F Panther* on a reduced frequency. In due course they were repainted into TT's orange, green and white livery and continued to serve until they were replaced by the *Free Enterprise IV* and *Free Enterprise V* in 1986.

THE LAST DAYS OF TOWNSEND THORESEN

In 1980, Townsend Thoresen had introduced a completely new generation of cross-Channel ferries. The *Spirit of Free Enterprise* and her two sisters offered 75-minute crossings which enabled as many as five daily round sailings to be operated between Dover and Calais by each ship. They were the first Channel ferries to be built with twin vehicle decks both capable of carrying freight. Such was the success of the concept that when plans for the present fixed cross-Channel link were unveiled, Townsend Thoresen soon declared their intention of offering their own 'Chunnel Beaters' – twin giant ferries (with double the lorry capacity of the previous 'Spirit' class) which they claimed would threaten the financial viability of the tunnel.

The £85 million *Pride of Dover* and *Pride of Calais* both entered service during 1987 but prior to this (in January 1986) the P&O Group had acquired a controlling interest in a company holding almost 21% of the European Ferries Group shares. P&O Chairman Sir Jeffrey Sterling was invited to join the Board and from that time the future of the EFG was always in doubt. By this time the company had accrued large land holdings in the United States where a drop in oil prices eventually brought the EFG to its knees. The Board invited P&O to act as their life raft and this was duly accomplished in January 1987.

P&O RETURNS

The ferry division continued to trade as Townsend Thoresen but following the 'Herald' disaster off Zeebrugge in March, P&O acted decisively to distance themselves from the former regime and duly created P&O European Ferries in October 1987.

Following the change, the ships bearing 'Free Enterprise' names were all given 'Pride' names and the freighter *European Enterprise* was renamed the *European Endeavour*. During 1991-93, four more vessels were added to the Dover-based fleet in the form of the three 'Super-European' class freighters for the Zeebrugge link and their half sister the *Pride of Burgundy* which entered service in April 1993. With the stretching of the *Pride of Kent* (formerly the *Spirit of Free Enterprise*) in June 1992, the P&O European Ferries fleet of super ferries now numbered five. The fitting of Club Class and luxury lounges on all ships set a standard which was the envy of others and the company carried three times more traffic from Dover and Calais than their nearest competitor.

During the preparation for the opening of the tunnel, the secondary passenger routes to Zeebrugge (in December 1991) and Boulogne (in January 1993) were closed although Zeebrugge continued in a freight-

The Viking II operated at Dover after the merger of Townsend and Thoresen Car Ferries. *(FotoFlite)*

European Seaway. *(FotoFlite)*

The Pride of Bruges and Pride of Burgundy at Dover. *(John Hendy)*

The Pride of Kent following her conversion at Calais. *(John Hendy)*

only capacity until December 2002 (and for about a year before the route closed, a limited number of car passengers began to be carried). It was important that all efforts should be directed at the premier route against the tunnel and so services that weakened that position were terminated. As it was, P&O European Ferries had its own Channel Shuttle service up and running by summer 1993 a whole year and a half before the tunnel eventually opened.

P&O STENA LINE

During July 1996 the Department of Trade and Industry gave both P&O European Ferries and Stena Line UK Ltd the 'amber' light allowing them to adopt some form of co-operation in response to the Channel Tunnel. A Memorandum of Understanding was signed that October when it was agreed that both companies would supply 14 vessels (8 from P&OEF and 5 from Stena in addition to a fast craft) for the Dover-Zeebrugge, Dover-Calais and Newhaven-Dieppe routes. After further delays, Government permission for the 'Joint Venture' was given in November 1997 and the new company was officially launched on 9th March 1998. The vessels concerned were as follows:

Pride of Dover – *P&OSL Dover*

Pride of Calais – *P&OSL Calais*

Pride of Bruges (I)- *P&OSL Picardy* but withdrawn February 2000

Pride of Burgundy – *P&OSL Burgundy*

Pride of Kent – *P&OSL Kent*

European Seaway

European Pathway

European Highway

Stena Empereur – *P&OSL Provence*

Stena Fantasia – *P&OSL Canterbury*

Stena Invicta – chartered and renamed *Color Viking*

Stena Cambria – withdrawn in January 1999

Stena Antrim – withdrawn in March 1998

Elite (fast craft) – handed back to Stena in October 1998

The original plan was for the *Pride of Bruges* to be switched to the Newhaven-Dieppe service and trials were duly made. However, the *Stena Antrim* was withdrawn and sold and sister vessel *Stena Cambria,* with her more modern interior, was placed on the link to operate with the fast craft, *Elite* (formerly the *Stena Lynx III*). The 'Invicta' was immediately dispensed with, as with only one freight deck her use would be limited on the Calais link and so she never operated for the new company. The Dieppe link continued to lose money and the *Elite* was withdrawn from service as being unreliable and prone to delays or cancellations in bad weather. P&O Stena Line eventually closed the link on 31st January 1999 after which the French crews from the *Stena Cambria* were switched to the Zeebrugge freighter *European Pathway*.

At the time, this vessel was enduring a prolonged period off service with a broken gearbox and finding themselves a ship short for the Zeebrugge link duly chartered the *Stena Royal* which had been laid up at Dunkirk since the closure of RMT's Ostend-Ramsgate link in February 1997. As the *Prins Filip*, the former flagship of the Belgian Government's fleet, this vessel represented that concern's last effort to save the ailing link. She was a splendid vessel which had entered service in 1992 and was built with the finest materials that the Belgian taxpayer could afford. One of Stena's numerous companies had purchased the idle vessel in June 1998 and this was her first service since the Ostend link had closed. Although much mechanical work was required, it was soon realised that the *Stena Royal* was too good a ship to lose and her charter was duly extended (with an option to purchase) at which time she was renamed *P&OSL Aquitaine*. After a major internal and mechanical refit, the ship took up sailings to Calais during November

1999 replacing the smaller *P&OSL Picardy* in the fleet. After a brief lay-up at Dunkirk, the latter vessel was sold to TransEuropa Ferries at Ramsgate.

The Stena side of the partnership held a 40% stake in the joint-venture company. Stena Line of Gothenburg in Sweden had taken over the former Sealink fleet following a hostile takeover battle with Sea Containers in April 1990. Sealink had been de-nationalised and sold for just £66 million in July 1984 after which the company traded as Sealink British Ferries. No purpose-built tonnage was added to any route apart from those to the Isle of Wight (which Sea Containers retained in 1990) but Stena's purchase of the company for £259 million severely stretched the Swedes and amongst the early casualties was the historic Folkestone-Boulogne link.

While Townsend Thoresen and then P&O European Ferries were constructing new super ferries and upgrading their service, Sealink Stena Line continued to run with converted and second-hand vessels introducing the *Fantasia* in 1990 followed by the *Stena Invicta* with the ro-pax ferry *Stena Challenger* in 1991. After an £8 million refit the *Stena Empereur* (ex *Stena Jutlandica*) joined the Calais service in July 1996 after which the 'Challenger' sailed to the Holyhead station.

The Sealink and then Stena operation at Dover was always run as a joint venture with French partners Sealink SNAT but due to increased friction between them, this ceased at the end of 1995 when the French floated their own company known as SeaFrance. This company became MyFerryLink when SNAT disposed of it and closed down in 2015.

P&O FERRIES RETURNS (AGAIN)

The P&O Stena Line joint venture duly ended during autumn 2002 when P&O purchased Stena's share of the business for £150 million. Following this, all name prefixes reverted to 'Pride of' rather than 'P&OSL' although for a brief period this was modified to just 'PO'. At the same time P&O Irish Sea, P&O North Sea Ferries and P&O Portsmouth merged with the now 100% P&O-owned P&O Stena Line to become simply P&O Ferries.

Although in 2001, car traffic was again taken on the Zeebrugge link, a decision to convert the sisters *European Pathway* and *European Highway* to dual-purpose mode for the Dover-Calais service saw the service end on 15th December 2002. Both ships were sent to Bremerhaven for conversion and were renamed *Pride of Canterbury* (II) and *Pride of Kent* (II) in a double naming ceremony at Dover's Admiralty Pier. They replaced the earlier ships with those names, the former Stena ship *PO Canterbury* (ex *Fantasia*) and *PO Kent* (ex *Pride of Kent*) which were both sold to Greek owners GA Ferries although after a single season in the Mediterranean, the former *Fantasia* was resold to Polish operators Polferries. The last member of the eclectic former Stena fleet, the *Pride of Provence* (ex *Stena Empereur*) was also sold to GA Ferries in 2004 but was quickly passed on to the Norwegian company Kystlink for service between Norway and Denmark.

With the closure of the Zeebrugge service, the remaining freighter *European Seaway* was switched to the Calais route but serious financial problems followed by a thorough re-evaluation and reorganisation of the fleet in 2004 saw the ship laid up in Birkenhead and offered for sale during which time the *Pride of Burgundy* operated in a freight-only mode. However, in the following year it was decided to recall the 'Seaway' and lay up the more expensive to operate vessel *Pride of Aquitaine* which was on charter from one of the many Stena Line subsidiaries and which was duly passed on to the French LD Lines for their Portsmouth-Le Havre link. She now operates again between Dover and Calais for DFDS Seaways as the *Calais Seaways*. Since then the 'Seaway' has spent spells laid up and chartered out as a windfarm accommodation vessel, but returned to traffic in August 2015 following the ending of the rival MyFerryLink operation.

There had been much discussion in recent years concerning new tonnage for the Calais service and an order was finally made in June 2008 for twin 49,000 gross ton Finnish-built sister ships which entered service during in 2011 and 2012. With space for more than 170 lorries (or 800 cars) and facilities for up to 2,000 passengers, these latest trendsetting ships, the *Spirit of Britain* and *Spirit of France*, set completely new standards on the English Channel.

The Spirit of Britain arriving at Dover from her builders in Finland. *(John Hendy)*

The Spirit of France leaving Calais. *(Matthew Punter)*

The delivery of these new ships lead to the withdrawal of the original 'Chunnel Beaters', the *Pride of Calais* and *Pride of Dover*. Because of their specialised design, they were unable to find buyers and both ended up being scrapped on the beach at Aliaga, Turkey – first the *Pride of Dover* in December 2012 and later the *Pride of Calais*, after a brief but unsuccessful stint with TransEuropa Ferries at Ramsgate as the *Ostend Spirit*, in November 2013.

Further newbuilds could be delivered in a few years time. In an interview with the Daily Telegraph in May 2016, CEO Helen Deeble said "We were previously thinking about newbuild orders coming on stream in 2020-21. Now what we're going to do is see if we can bring them forward by a year or two, which means we have got to start really at the end of this year with a new build project.

The Pride of Canterbury on her 90 minute crossing to Dover. *(George Holland)*

SCANDLINES FERRY BERLIN IN SERVICE AT LAST

O n 3rd May 2016, Scandlines' new Rostock – Gedser ferry Berlin was christened in the port of Rostock. Words and expressions were full of relief that day since the vessel had been delivered no less than four years behind schedule a few days earlier. Three different shipyards had dealt with building, de-constructing and rebuilding the ship, a process that resulted in countless delays in delivery.

After Scandlines had been forced recently to also cancel their latest proposed introduction date, Easter 2016, the Berlin was finally able to embark on sea trials in mid-April, completing these successfully shortly later at the end of the month. 150 guests were invited to join the christening ceremony on 3rd May which, rather untypically, was held on the open aft part of the vessel's upper car deck. The ceremony started off with a short speech by Søren Poulsgaard Jensen, the Scandlines CEO, followed by another few words referring to the history of the Warnemünde – Gedser train ferry route by Ines Rehberg, the ship's Godmother. Ines is the wife of Eckhardt Rehberg, the Commissioner for Maritime Affairs in the German conservative party, the CDU and member of the German parliament, the Bundestag. Ines Rehberg dutifully spoke of the vessel just as 'hull number 502' before naming the ship after the German capital and smashing a bottle of champagne against the steel wall which divides the ferry's upper car deck. In German language, the traditional christening of a ship includes the wish that the vessel named may always have a 'handful of water beneath her keel' and in the case of the Berlin, no wish could better express the ups and downs surrounding the (almost) never-ending story of her construction. Also the fact that, apart from the bottle of champagne, the whole apparatus constructed to hold it was also smashed, fits perfectly into the history of a ship which has seen numerous incarnations and reincarnations even before being put into service.

FROM STRALSUND TO MUNKEBO

The famous 'handful of water beneath her keel' was indeed crucial to the Berlin being delivered or not; in fact NOT having enough of it meant that the ship was not taken over by Scandlines from the building yard in the first place. Ordered in March 2010, the Berlin and her sister ship Copenhagen had originally been due for delivery in spring 2012. But in early 2012, it became apparent that the yard awarded the contract, P + S Werften in Stralsund, would not be able to keep the schedule. And soon it also became clear what the reason was: The two ships were too heavy, exceeding their contractual draught. Basically, the Berlin and Copenhagen would not have had the necessary amount of water beneath their keels when entering or leaving the shallow port of Gedser at low tide. P + S Werften in August 2012 even had to file for insolvency in the course of the two ferries not being delivered on schedule and having to pay heavy penalties.

The Berlin and Copenhagen at that time were in advanced stages of construction, but nevertheless still too heavy. In November 2012, Scandlines therefore withdrew from the building contract and turned its mind to STX Finland instead for a modified version of the pair. A letter of intent was signed with the Finnish yard in July 2013, but STX too at that time was in financial difficulties. A fixed building contract was never signed, leaving Scandlines to continue to operate the Rostock – Gedser with the elderly former DSB InterCity ferries Kronprins Frederik (built in 1981) and Prins Joachim (built in 1980), with support from the Mercandia VIII during the summer weekends. In an interesting twist of fate, Scandlines now turned its attention back to Stralsund where the Berlin and Copenhagen were now available from the receiver at what media called a bargain. Scandlines in fact bought the hulls in March 2014, but a bargain they were not since the difficult task now was to find a shipyard which was willing and able to rebuild these ships in a way that they would turn out light enough in the end to reach the original contract draft. For that purpose, the two unfinished hulls were towed from Stralsund to Blohm & Voss Repair in Hamburg in April 2014, but Scandlines and the German yard according to media reports could not agree on the price or a delivery schedule either. The Danish-German ferry operator (since 2007 majority-owned by the British investment fund 3i Group) went for the Danish shipyard Fayard A/S instead and the unfinished hulls were moved once more. From Hamburg, they were towed to Munkebo near Odense in July 2014, but the Danes too had underestimated the many challenges that this contract held for them. Succeeding in stripping down most of the ships' upper decks and building them anew from lighter materials, delivery dates came and went again after Scandlines had even invited the press to the site of the yard to watch the Berlin and Copenhagen taking shape in spring 2015. At the beginning of 2016 was there a light at the end of the

Berlin *(Peter Therkildsen)*

Berlin *(John Bryant)*

Berlin *(John Bryant)*

Aft Lounge - Berlin *(Kai Ortel)*

Food Xpress - Berlin *(Kai Ortel)*

Food Xpress - Berlin *(Kai Ortel)*

Good to Go - Berlin *(Kai Ortel)*

tunnel, with the *Berlin* nearing completion at last. Her sister vessel *Copenhagen* was due 'in a few months' when the *Berlin* was christened in May, but a press release only a few days later named 'Autumn 2016' as a more precise date. The ill-fated second vessel will thus miss its fifth summer season in a row. However, the *Kronprins Frederik* will not only remain in service for the time being, but Scandlines has also announced it will keep the DSB stalwart in its fleet as a spare vessel even after the delivery of the *Copenhagen*. Looking on the history of the *Berlin* and *Copenhagen* so far, this may be a wise decision.

FOUR FERRIES TEN YEARS AHEAD?

Scandlines needed the two ferries desperately. On the Rostock – Gedser route alone, car numbers were up by 9.6 % in 2015 compared to 2014, while passenger numbers had also risen by 6.3 %. How the company succeeded in doing so operating two ships that had been regarded as too small and too old already in 2012, remains quite a mystery, but as Gernot Tesch from the Rostock port operator HERO pointed out on the day of the christening, Scandlines has also lost traffic volumes to the ferry companies operating out of Świnoujście in Poland due to temporary capacity bottlenecks at Rostock. Scandlines' aim is therefore to regain lost business once the two new ships are delivered and fully operational.

The importance to Scandlines of the Eastern European market is also a reason for not having renamed the *Berlin* and *Copenhagen*, which have received more than their fair share of media attention during those troubled four year between 2012 and 2016. Scandlines' strategic focus now is on the Rostock – Gedser route, and it firmly believes in a promising future for this Germany – Denmark route in particular and the importance of the line for customers in Scandinavia and especially Eastern Europe. Both Rostock's mayor Roland Methling and his Danish counterpart John Braedder in their speeches even dreamed of four ferries operating on the route ten years ahead, remarking jokingly that they also had proposals in mind for the names of ships no. 3 and 4. However, until this dream comes true, the *Berlin* (and later the *Copenhagen*) now has to prove in daily operation that the wait for her was worth it.

On a different note, it may be of interest that the *Berlin* is not owned by Scandlines outright, but by Scandferries, a related firm also fully controlled by the 3i Group. The *Berlin* and *Copenhagen* are thus sailing on charter from Scandferries. Scandlines in a press release clarifies that 'due to high charter rates' it expects an overall drop in revenues for 2016 compared to 2015.

HYBRID FERRY

The good thing about the 'long and stony road' (Poulsen) leading to the delivery of the *Berlin* is that Scandlines has been able to turn the rather conventional ferry it had designed in 2009 (with just a vague option to reconvert her to LNG use at a later stage) into one of the most environmentally advanced Baltic ferries when delivered in 2016. By removing one of her five original diesel engines, Scandlines gained enough space within the vessel's hull to allow for powerful batteries to be installed, making the *Berlin* a so-called 'hybrid ferry' (as is prominently displayed on her hull). Surplus energy generated by the remaining four diesel engines is now used to charge those batteries when the ship is in service. The extra power gained is feeding other onboard systems, thus helping to reduce fuel consumption. However, this is only one step along the way towards what Scandlines calls 'emission-free ferries'.

The next step will be to turn the hybrid ferries into 'plug-in hybrid ferries'. As soon as the necessary infrastructure in the ports of Rostock and Gedser is installed, the vessels' batteries will be charged during the 15 minutes the ferries spend in port being loaded and unloaded (when they are 'plugged in'). The ships will then be able to leave port on battery power, change to diesel once at sea (where the batteries are charged again) and enter the port on the other side using battery power again. The ferries would thus become emission-free ferries while not at sea. However, the long distance between Rostock and Gedser makes it impossible to use battery power solely, but on the shorter Puttgarden – Rødby route, the operation is due to become completely emission-free in the next few years. Scandlines is already working out plans to achieve this 'green vision for the future'. Proud of the environmental achievements accomplished so far, Søren Poulsgaard Jensen in his post-christening speech remarked that this was homework that other operators still have to do. On this occasion, he also thanked the German environmental organization Naturschutzbund Deutschland (NABU) which had accompanied the design and building process of the *Berlin* in a constant dialogue with Scandlines.

ON BOARD

The building and conversion of the *Berlin* and *Copenhagen* has cost Scandlines more than €140m per ship which made them more expensive in the end than originally contracted in 2010. Even the interior design of the ships was affected by the necessary reconstruction using lighter materials once the vessels' superstructure had been broken up down to deck 7 in order to reduce weight. But the final result can be regarded as pleasant. The main passenger deck (deck 7) features a large buffet restaurant at the front, offering a spectacular view ahead and to the sides of the ship through large panoramic windows. Amidships, passengers will find the 'FoodXpress' cafeteria on port side which opens to a long arcade at which upholstered seats and benches invite them to have a rest while watching the sea. Also amidships is the 'Good to go' snack bar, while the aft part of deck 7 accommodates the vessel's large onboard shop and (again at the arcade on portside) a children's play area.

Deck 8 above houses the crew mess and cabins as well as the 'Xpresso', a caféteria cum lounge which will be opened on busier sailings only. Next to it is the small 'Scandlines Lounge', a quiet retreat with WiFi access and a TV screen the use of which comes at an extra cost. The Scandlines Lounge can also turn into a small conference room on request. All seating in the public areas is fitted with USB slots so that passengers can recharge their mobile phones, tablets and other electronic devices during the crossing.

Overall, the interior design of the *Berlin* is typically Scandinavian, featuring down-to-earth colour tones and using easy-to-clean materials. But orientation is easy and all public rooms are of an open design so that passengers can stroll through the ship without opening and closing doors all the time. There may have been more spectacular ferry new builds in the past years, but for the two hour route between Rostock and Gedser, the *Berlin* at first glance appears to be a day ferry which is very well laid-out and pleasantly designed. For Scandlines, her introduction into service is definitely a milestone. So much so that even Steven Ridgeway, Scandlines' Chairman of the Board and Chairman at the 3i Group, addressed the guests invited to the christening, remarking that it had been 'a tough job getting here'. Let's hope that the *Berlin* will slip into service trouble-free and that the tough job getting her built and delivered will be forgotten once she and her sister ship are there for a long time on the historic Rostock – Gedser route.

Immediately after her christening ceremony on 3rd May, the *Berlin* remained idle at the port of Rostock with a number of certificates and permissions still missing. On 20th May however, the vessel embarked on a last set of berthing trials and carried out her first commercial sailing from Rostock to Gedser at 06.00 on 23rd May. During her first days of service, she was only allowed to use her lower car deck (deck 3) since the ramps on the upper car deck (deck 5) still needed approval. But that was only for a matter of days. One thing at least is for sure: At 5.50 meters draught, the *Berlin* now does have the necessary 'handful of water beneath her keel' when entering and leaving Gedser harbour. At last!

Technical data MS Berlin:

Building yard	*P + S Werften, Stralsund and Fayard A/S, Munkebo*		
Owner	*Scandferries ApS, Copenhagen*		
Operator	*Scandlines ApS, Copenhagen*		
Flag	*Germany*	**Homeport**	*Rostock*
IMO number	*9587855*	**Call Sign**	*OXHC2*
Length	*169,50m*	**Beam**	*25,40m*
Draft	*5,50m*		
Tonnage	*22,319 GT*		
Power	*18,000 kW*		
Engines	*4xMaK type 9M32CCR*		
Speed	*20.5 knots (maximum 22)*		
Cars	*460*	**Lorries** *96*	
Cargo	*1,600 lane metres*		
Passengers	*1,300*		

Kai Ortel

Restaurant - Berlin *(Kai Ortel)*

ROUND BRITAIN REVIEW 2015/16

The following is a review of passenger and freight ferry activities during 2015 and the first half of 2016. Some events occurring in the first half of 2015 will have also been mentioned in 'Ferries 2016'.

EAST COAST & THAMES

During Summer 2015, DFDS Seaways and Forth Ports signed an agreement to secure the long term future of the Rosyth – Zeebrugge freight route. The service is operated twice weekly by the former Finnlines vessel *Finlandia Seaways*.

In January the chartered *Estraden* took over P&O's Middlesbrough – Rotterdam service from the *Norsky* (which was a short-term stand in for Cobelfret's *Wilhemine*, whose charter had ended in November 2014). In February, at the end of the refit period, the *Mistral* became second ship on the Middlesbrough – Zeebrugge route. Both ships were chartered from Bore Shipowners of Finland. During the 2016 refit period, DFDS's *Patria Seaways* was chartered to provide freight cover on the Hull – Zeebrugge and Middlesbrough – Zeebrugge routes. She later operated between Vlaardingen and Immingham for her owners before returning to the Baltic in mid March.

In November 2015 Sea-Cargo ended their charter of the *Marfret Niolon* and she was replaced on the service from various Norwegian ports to Immingham by their own *SC Astrea*. This vessel had previously been deployed on the carriage of windfarm equipment.

Booming traffic on Vlaardingen – Immingham had led DFDS Seaways to switch the *Anglia Seaways* to the route in September 2014 as third vessel. This lasted until March 2015 when the company redeployed the *Ficaria Seaways*, one of the lengthened 'flower class' vessels, from Gothenburg – Immingham to the Vlaardingen – Immingham route. Other switches enabled capacity to be more evenly matched to traffic and the *Anglia Seaways* to be placed on the charter market. She served with P&O from March until May and then returned to the Vlaardingen – Felixstowe route, covering for the *Britannia Seaways*. Although the *Ark Dania* and *Ark Germania* were specifically designed for NATO charters, the *Britannia Seaways* continued in this role during 2015. However, in 2016 the *Ark Germania* undertook her first NATO charter.

In March 2016, DFDS announced that the *Petunia Seaways* would be lengthened by 30m to provide an additional 800 lane metres, taking it to 4,600 lane metres (approximately another eighty 13.5m trailers). The lengthening, which is similar to that undertaken on the *Begonia Seaways*, *Freesia Seaways* and *Ficaria Seaways* in 2009, took place in July at MWB Motorenwerke Bremerhaven AG, the yard which undertook the work on the other three vessels. She returned to service in early August.

In May 2016 DFDS placed an order for two 209.6m ro-ro ferries from the Flensburg shipyard. They will be long term chartered to DFDS by the year's owners with an option to purchase.

In May 2015 the *Flandria Seaways*, a regular on the Vlaardingen – Felixstowe service, was sold to Mexican owners.

Mann Lines' replacement for the *Estraden*, chartered to P&O Ferries from the beginning of January 2015, was the larger *Stena Foreteller*. At the same time, Mann Lines entered into an agreement with Stena Line to act as their sales agent and give them an access to the Northern Baltic market.

At the end of 2015, Finnlines took delivery of the *Carrier* and *Trader*, which had been on charter to Transfennica. They renamed them the *Finncarrier* and *Finnmaster*. In turn, the charter of the *Misada* and *Misima* ended and they were taken up by Transfennica. Both of these vessels are on a three year charter to Stena RoRo, but continue to be owned by Godby Shipping.

In June 2015 CLdN chartered the Turkish ro-ro *Cemil Bayulgen* from UN Ro-Ro. She is used primarily on the Rotterdam – Purfleet service. Built by Flensburger Schiffbau-Gesellschaft, Flensburg, Germany, she is similar to the company's vessels purchased from the same yard in the last decade.

In September 2014, CLdN placed an order for two 580 trailer vessels from Hyundai Mipo Dockyard, Ulsan, South Korea. They will be convertible to LPG propulsion and are designed to be useable on deep sea ro-ro services as well as CLdN's current short sea routes. In March 2016 an order was placed for two smaller

Cemil Bayulgen *(John Bryant)*

Pride of Burgundy *(Miles Cowsill)*

Côte des Dunes *(Matthew Punter)*

Mont St Michel *(Darren Holdaway)*

vessels from Uljanik Shipyard, Pula, Croatia (with an option for four more). These will operate on the company's North Sea routes when delivered in 2018. Both classes of ships will be convertible to LNG propulsion.

In October 2015, CLdN inaugurated a new service between the UK, Belgium and Portugal. The triangular route operated Purfleet – Zeebrugge – Leixoes on a weekly basis. Usually the service was generally operated by the 2012 built *Wilhelmine*. The service was then integrated with the Rotterdam – Leixoes route, with two ships operating Rotterdam – Leixoes – Purfleet – Rotterdam.

In February 2016, CLdN launched a new weekly service between Zeebrugge and Hirtshals. As well as serving northern Denmark, the service offers connections to Kristiansand and Larvik via Color Line and Stavanger and Bergen via Fjord Line.

In Autumn 2015, SOL Continent Line, which won the contract to operate the Gothenburg – Zeebrugge service for the Stora Enso Paper Group earlier in the year, expanded its North Sea fleet by the charter of the 1990 built *Baltica* and 1999 built *Elisabeth Russ* to run along side the *TransPulp* and *TransTimber* on their Oulu-Kemi – Lübeck – Antwerp – Zeebrugge – Tilbury service.

In January 2016, SCA Transforest added Sheerness to their schedules. At the end of June Tilbury was dropped from the schedule. At the same time Kiel replaced Lübeck as the German port of call.

MBNA Thames Clippers' two new vessels *Galaxy Clipper* and *Neptune Clipper* were delivered from Australia in October 2016. The Incat built vessels are slightly smaller than the earlier Brisbane Ship Constructions craft and were ordered to supplement the older vessels rather than replace them.

EASTERN CHANNEL

Ramsgate ferry port saw no traffic during 2015 but in January 2016 a ro-ro vessel returned – not a ferry as such but the car carrier *Autopremier* of UECC. A once weekly service from Zeebrugge was started, conveying Citroën and Peugeot cars.

DFDS Seaways' Dover – Calais service was reduced to a single ship operation between December 2014 and June 2015, following the ending of the charter of the *Dieppe Seaways*. In April, a second vessel arrived – the *Stena Nordica*, the vessel that the *Dieppe Seaways* had replaced on the Holyhead – Dublin route. Renamed the *Malo Seaways*, she enabled the *Calais Seaways* to go to Gdansk for a refit and the replacement of one of her engines. A two ship service resumed in June.

MyFerryLink's problems continued to dominate the situation at Dover. Despite the Supreme Court overturning the Competition and Markets Authority's ruling that the Eurotunnel backed service was anti-competitive, Eurotunnel decided to go ahead with plans cease its backing for the co-operative run company and to, instead, charter the *Rodin* and *Berlioz* to DFDS Seaways. On 23rd June, this provoked a 'strike' by MyFerryLink workers (strike in the French context meaning blockades, occupation of vessels, burning car tyres and general mayhem!). The port was closed, leading to enormous queues of lorries, which in turn attracted the attention of migrants attempting to enter the UK. The Channel Tunnel also experienced problems both from migrants attempting to board trains and ferry workers trying to blockade the tunnel, compounding the problems. After a few days P&O began operating to Boulogne, although the service was less frequent than the normal Calais service. DFDS switched the *Calais Seaways* to Dunkerque but, due to linkspan incompatibility, the *Malo Seaways* had to be laid up. Meanwhile on the UK side, 'Operation Stack' had to be implemented on the M20, leading to gridlock on the nearby A20.

The strikers 'allowed' P&O to return to Calais on 2nd July but DFDS ships were excluded until 29th July. P&O hurriedly brought the *European Seaway* back into traffic; she had been used as a wind farm support vessel and bow modifications meant that she could only operate as a stern loader until entering dry dock for a refit in early 2016.

Agreement was eventually reached on 31st August (some MFL staff to be employed by DFDS and others employed by Eurotunnel as extra security staff) and the two MyFerryLink ships were handed over to DFDS on 2nd September. Both ships moved to Dunkerque, initially at lay by berths but later moving to the shipyard. In February 2016, following a repaint and a major internal refit, the vessels re-entered service between Dover and Calais as the *Côte des Dunes (Rodin)* and *Côte des Flandres (Berlioz)*. The intention was that when the second ship entered traffic, a three ship service would operate, with the *Malo Seaways* being retained long enough to cover for the *Calais Seaways'* refit. However, the *Malo Seaways* had a problem with her prop-shaft and a full three ship service was not possible until the *Calais Seaways* returned from refit in March. In May 2016 the *Nord Pas-de-Calais* was chartered to FRS Iberia to operate between Spain and Morocco and renamed *Al Andalus Express*.

At the end of 2015, DFDS introduced a new darker blue livery with a simplified logo and sans serif lettering. All three Calais ships, as well as the three Dunkerque vessels, were repainted in this style.

The future of the Newhaven – Dieppe route has fluctuated over the period. In the first half of 2015 it looked as though the Syndicat Mixte de L'Activité Transmanche were to resume direct operation of the service themselves but they subsequently abandoned this idea and, after initially asking them to continue for three month, in December 2015 reached agreement with DFDS Seaways to continue to operate the service indefinitely. Revised subsidy arrangements were agreed. However, in March 2016 a French court decreed that the agreement broke competition rules and the route should be put out for tender again. The two ship, three sailings each way per day timetable introduced in 2015 continues into 2016. It now looks as though the future of the route is secure.

WESTERN CHANNEL AND SOLENT

In May 2015 Brittany Ferries introduced a new vessel to the fleet. She was the DFDS Seaways' vessel *Sirena Seaways*, renamed the *Baie de Seine*. The chartered ship now operates each week round trips between Portsmouth to both Bilbao and Santander as well as an overnight round trip from Portsmouth to Le Havre. She was repainted in a 'wavy line' livery, similar to the former LD Lines vessel *Etretat*, a variation on the livery inherited from that company. Her services are marketed as 'économie', with fewer facilities than other members of the fleet.

Early 2016, the *Pont Aven* was fitted with scrubbers in order to continue to use lower grade fuel and meet new environmental regulations. This resulted in a very enlarged funnel which was as wide as the ship.

In January 2016, Brittany Ferries chartered the freighter *MN Pelican* from Maritime Nantaise of France. She operates a twice weekly service between Poole and Bilbao. She is the first 12 passenger freighter to be operated by the company since the *Normandie Shipper* was withdrawn in 1995.

In August 2014, Condor Ferries purchased *Austal Hull 270* from builders Austal Ships of Australia. Built speculatively in 2010, she had not until then attracted a buyer. She was moved to the builder's yard in Cebu, Philippines for further work before arriving at Poole at the end of December. Renamed the *Condor Liberation*, she entered service between Poole and The Channel Island in late March 2015. Replacing both the *Condor Express* and *Condor Vitesse*, her arrival meant the ending of services from Weymouth whose berth, repaired at some expense in 2013, was unsuitable for the new vessel. Her arrival proved controversial, with numerous cancellations due to technical problems and complaints about her sea-keeping qualities. This was not helped by one of the windiest autumns and winters in recent years, resultant from a succession of Atlantic storms tracking in across the country. The *Condor Rapide* was retained to operate service from the Channel Islands to St Malo but occasionally had to be switched to the UK route. The *Condor Liberation* operated two round trips per day on some days during summer 2015, but this led to some very early departure times and it proved impossible to keep to schedule so in 2016 only one trip per day is being run.

In April 2015 Wightlink moved the *Wight Light*, one of the Lymington ships, to Portsmouth to replace the *St. Helen*, which was withdrawn from service and sold to Delcomar of Italy. The *St. Helen* was the last British Rail Sealink ship still sailing in UK waters. The *Wight Light* was later replaced by sister vessel, the *Wight Sun*.

In early 2016 Wightlink published plans for a new generation of Portsmouth – Fishbourne ferries which would incorporate double deck loading from substantially rebuilt terminals. In May an order was placed with the Cemre Shipyard, Yalova, Turkey for one new ship. In February 2016 the *St. Clare* was modified for double deck loading. The 1980s built *St. Cecilia* and *St. Faith* would be replaced by the new vessels. In

Condor Liberation *(Nicolas Levy)*

Stena Superfast X *(Matthew Punter)*

February 2015 Balfour Beatty Infrastructure Partners LP purchased Wightlink from Macquarie European Infrastructure Fund.

New operator Scoot Ferries launched a Lymington – Yarmouth passenger service in September (after operating an experimental Hamble – Cowes service during Cowes Week in August) using the 12 passenger *Scoot 1*. In November they launched a Cowes – Portsmouth service using two 41 seated catamarans. However, in December, following substantial losses, the services ceased and the company was liquidated.

During spring 2015 Red Funnel Lines' *Red Osprey* received a major revamp similar to that give to the *Red Falcon* in 2014. However, the third ship of this series, the *Red Eagle* did not receive the same treatment in 2016.

In May 2015, Red Funnel ordered a new catamaran from Shemara Refit of Cowes. Named *Red Jet 6*, she entered service in July 2016, replacing the *Red Jet 5*, which was sold.

Hovertravel introduced two new hovercraft on their Sandown – Ryde service in summer 2016. They are 22m Griffon Hoverwork 12000TD/AP models. Both the builder and the operator are subsidiaries of the Gibraltar based Bland Group. The new craft are 88 seaters – slightly less than the 95 seat BHC models they are to replace but are much more efficient.

Gosport Ferry's new *Harbour Spirit*, built by Tehnomont of Pula in Croatia was delivered by cargo ship in March 2015. She is similar to the 2001 built *Spirit of Gosport*. She entered service In May. The *Portsmouth Queen* was sold in February 2016 for use as a party cruise boat on the Thames.

In March 2016, the Isle of Wight Council announced that they had ordered a replacement for the 1976 built chain ferry *No 5*. The new craft will be 3.5m longer than the existing craft.

The 2000 year old Hayling Ferry ceased operation in March 2015 when the operating company filed for administration. A crowd funded trust has been formed by local residents with the aim of restoring the service. Financial assistance has been received from the Virgin Group.

IRISH SEA

In May, Irish Ferries announced the order of a new 50,000 ton vessel from Flensburger Schiffbau-Gesellschaft, Flensburg, Germany for delivery in 2018. She is likely to replace the chartered *Epsilon*, which operates between Dublin and Holyhead with a weekend trip to Cherbourg.

In May 2015 Stena Line introduced the *Stena Superfast X*, the former *Dieppe Seaways* of DFDS Seaways and *SeaFrance Moliere* of SeaFrance, onto the Holyhead – Dublin route. Faster and bigger than the *Stena Nordica* she replaced, she essentially replaced the HSS *Stena Explorer* which had been withdrawn at the end of the summer season in 2014. In October 2015 the *Stena Explorer* was sold to *Karadeniz Holdings* of Turkey for use as office space at the Karmarine Shipyard in Yalova.

Seatruck Ferries introduced a third vessel onto their Liverpool – Dublin service in November 2015. Initially this was the former ESCO vessel *Clipper Ranger* but in March 2016 she was replaced by the larger *Seatruck Pace*, transferred from the Heysham – Dublin route. The *Clipper Ranger* was then moved to that route.

P&O Ferries ceased their Troon – Larne fast-ferry service at the end of the 2015 summer season. The charter of the vessel used, the *Express*, was ended and was taken up by the Swedish company, Gotlandsbåten.

IRELAND

In February 2015, The Department for Regional Development, Northern Ireland ordered a new ferry from Cammell Laird, Birkenhead for the service across the mouth of Strangford Loch. Similar to the 2001 built *Portaferry II*, the *Strangford II* will replace the 1969 built Strangford Ferry later in 2016. A similar vessel was ordered to replace the *Canna* on the service from Ballycastle to Rathlin Island.

When the Lough Foyle Ferry Company ceased their seasonal service from Greencastle to Magilligan in October 2015, they stated that they would not resume in Spring 2016. They sold their vessel, the *Foyle*

Venture, to a Frazer Ferries, a company seeking to establish a service across Carlingford Lough on the East coast. In July 2016, Frazer Ferries resumed the Greencastle to Magilligan service using the *Foyle Venture*.

The summer-only Lough Swilly Service between Buncrana and Rathmullan in County Donegal was also operated by the Lough Foyle Ferry Company, but did not operated during summer 2014 due to the withdrawal of subsidy. It was restored in 2015 by Arranmore Island Ferries, using the former CalMac ferry *Rhum*. In 2016 sister vessel *Coll* was operated.

SCOTLAND

Caledonian MacBrayne's newest unit, the *Loch Seaforth*, delivered in November 2014, eventually entered service in March 2015 using the old linkspan at Ullapool. A new linkspan was installed in April and May 2015 and during this time vehicle services were diverted to Uig, operated by the *Isle of Lewis*. The *Loch Seaforth* continued in passenger only mode. The chartered freight ship, the *Clipper Ranger*, continued in service until May. During summer 2015 both the *Loch Seaforth* and *Isle of Lewis* were operated on the route but this was not repeated in 2016.

Caledonian MacBrayne's second hybrid vessel, the *Lochinvar* was delivered almost a year after launch in May 2014. She was built to operate on the summer only Tarbert – Portavadie service and on other routes during the winter. In August, the vessel's builders, Ferguson Shipbuilders, went into administration. Fortunately, new owners purchased the yard and, as Ferguson Marine Engineering, in September 2015 secured the order for a third hybrid ferry to be operated by Caledonian MacBrayne. She is to be called the *Catriona*.

Two larger vessels subsequently were ordered from the same yard. The two 100m ships are expected operate on the Ardrossan – Brodick and Uig – Tarbert – Lochmaddy services. They are likely to supplement rather than replace the existing vessels.

Caledonian MacBraynes last 'Clyde streaker', the *Saturn*, which had been laid up since 2011, finally found a buyer in February 2015 in the form of Pentland Ferries of Orkney who renamed her the *Orcadia*.

In summer 2016 Caledonian MacBrayne moved the *Coruisk* from her traditional Mallaig – Armadale roster to operate as second ship on the Oban – Craignure route. Three vessels replaced her – the *Lochinvar*, the *Loch Bhrusda* and the *Lord of the Isles* (between trips to Lochboisdale on South Uist). However, the move proved controversial as it was found the smaller vessels could not operate in some tidal conditions leading to cancellations. At one stage, the company considered returning the *Coruisk* to her traditional route, but in the end it was decided to leave things as they were for the current season. The move of the *Lochinvar* to this route meant that the *Isle of Cumbrae* came out of retirement to operate on the Tarbert – Portavadie route.

All Caledonian MacBrayne and Argyll Ferries routes were put out to tender during 2015. There were two contenders – CalMac Ferries and Serco, who operate the Northlink service to Orkney and Shetland. After the Scottish elections in May 2016 it was announced that CalMac Ferries had secured the tender for the Caledonian MacBrayne routes.

In May 2015, the operators of the Cromarty – Nigg ferry announced that this summer only service would not resume as it was not possible to find a suitable places to moor the vessel, the *Cromarty Queen*, overnight. However in June 2016, the service was re-started by Highland Ferries, operators of the Fort William – Camusnagaul service, using the former Strathclyde Transport Renfrew – Yoker ferry *Renfrew Rose*, which they had purchased from Arranmore Fast Ferries of County Donegal.

Nick Widdows

Stena Adventurer *(Matthew Punter)*

Clansman *(John Hendy)*

Seven Sisters *(John Bryant)*

SECTION 1 – GB AND IRELAND – MAJOR PASSENGER OPERATORS
BRITTANY FERRIES

THE COMPANY *Brittany Ferries* is the trading name of *BAI SA*, a French private sector company and the operating arm of the *Brittany Ferries Group*. The UK operations are run by *BAI (UK) Ltd*, a UK private sector company, wholly owned by the *Brittany Ferries Group*.

MANAGEMENT Group Managing Director Christophe Mathieu, **Commercial Director, Passengers** Mike Bevens, **Commercial Director, Freight** Simon Wagstaff.

ADDRESS Millbay Docks, Plymouth, Devon PL1 3EW.

TELEPHONE Reservations *All Services* +44 (0)330 159 7000, **Freight – Administration & Enquiries** +44 (0)330 159 5000, **Reservations** +44 (0)330 159 5000.

INTERNET Passenger – Website www.brittanyferries.com *(English, French, Spanish, German)*, **Freight Website** www.brittanyferriesfreight.co.uk *(English)*

ROUTES OPERATED Conventional Ferries *All year* Plymouth – Roscoff (6 hrs (day), 7 hrs – 9 hrs (night); ***ARMORIQUE, PONT-AVEN***; up to 2 per day (Summer), 1 per day (Winter)), Poole – Cherbourg (4 hrs 15 mins; ***BARFLEUR***; 1 per day), Portsmouth – St Malo (8 hrs 45 mins (day), 10 hrs 45 mins (night); ***BRETAGNE***; *(1 per day)*, Portsmouth – Caen (Ouistreham) (6 hrs (day), 6 hrs – 8 hrs (night); ***NORMANDIE, MONT ST MICHEL***; 3 per day), Portsmouth – Le Havre (5 hrs 30 mins; ***BAIE DE SEINE, ETRETAT***, 1 per day), Portsmouth – Santander (Spain) (24 hrs; ***CAP FINISTERE, ETRETAT, PONT-AVEN***; up to 3 per week, Portsmouth – Bilbao (Spain) (24/32 hrs; ***BAIE DE SEINE, CAP FINISTERE***; up to 3 per week, **Summer only** Plymouth – Santander (Spain) (19 hrs 30 mins; ***PONT-AVEN***; 1 per week (April – October)), Cork – Roscoff (14 hrs; ***PONT-AVEN***; 1 per week (March – November)). **Fast Ferries Summer only** Portsmouth – Cherbourg (3 hrs; ***NORMANDIE EXPRESS***; up to 2 per day (April-September)). **Freight-only service** Poole – Bilbao (31 hrs; ***MN PELICAN***; 2 per week).

Note: The Portsmouth – Le Havre service and sailings to Spain operated by the BAIE DE SEINE and ETRETAT are branded 'économie'.

1	ARMORIQUE	29468 t	09	23.0k	167.0m	1500P	470C	65L	BA2	FR	9364980
2	BAIE DE SEINE	22382t	03	22.0k	199.4m	596P	316C	154T	A	FR	9212163
3	BARFLEUR	20133t	92	19.0k	158.0m	1212P	590C	112T	BA2	FR	9007130
4	BRETAGNE	24534t	89	19.5k	151.0m	1926P	580C	84T	BA	FR	8707329
5	CAP FINISTERE	32728t	01	28.0k	203.9m	1608P	1000C	140T	BA	FR	9198927
6	ETRETAT	26500t	08	23.5k	186.5m	800P	185C	120L	A	FR	9420423
7F	MN PELICAN	12076t	99	20.0k	154.5m	12P	-	115T	A2	FR	9170999
8	MONT ST MICHEL	35592t	02	21.2k	173.0m	2200P	880C	166T	BA2	FR	9238337
9	NORMANDIE	27541t	92	20.5k	161.0m	2120P	600C	126T	BA2	FR	9006253
10»	NORMANDIE EXPRESS	6581t	00	40.0k	97.2m	900P	260C	-	A	FR	8814134
11	PONT-AVEN	41748t	04	26.0k	184.3m	2400P	650C	85L	BA	FR	9268708

ARMORIQUE Built by STX Europe, Helsinki, Finland for *Brittany Ferries* to operate between Plymouth and Roscoff.

BAIE DE SEINE Built as the GOLFO DEI DELFINI by Stocznia Szczecinska, Szczecin, Poland for *Lloyd Sardegna* of Italy for service between Italy and Sardinia. However, due to late delivery the order was cancelled. In 2002 purchased by *DFDS Seaways*, and, during Winter 2002/03, passenger accommodation was enlarged and refitted, increasing passenger capacity from 308 to 596. In June 2003, renamed the DANA SIRENA, she replaced unmodified sister vessel, the DANA GLORIA on the Esbjerg – Harwich service. In February 2013 she was renamed the SIRENA SEAWAYS. At the end of September 2014 the route ceased and she moved to the Paldiski (Estonia) – Kapellskär route, replacing the PATRIA SEAWAYS. In December she was replaced by the LIVERPOOL SEAWAYS and laid up. During the early part of 2015 she performed relief work in the Baltic. In April 2015 she was chartered to *Brittany Ferries* for five years and renamed the BAIE DE SEINE. She entered service in May.

Barfleur *(John Bryant)*

Etretat *(John Bryant)*

MN Pelican *(George Holland)*

Pont Aven *(Darren Holdaway)*

BARFLEUR Built as the BARFLEUR by Kvaerner Masa-Yards, Helsinki for the *Truckline* (freight division of *Brittany Ferries*) Poole – Cherbourg service to replace two passenger vessels and to inaugurate a year-round passenger service. In 1999 the *Truckline* branding was dropped for passenger services and she was repainted into full *Brittany Ferries* livery. In 2005 operated partly Cherbourg – Poole and partly Cherbourg – Portsmouth but in 2006 returned to operating mainly to Poole. In February 2010, she was laid up. The conventional car ferry service ended the following month. In February 2011 she resumed service on the Poole – Cherbourg route. In September 2011 she was withdrawn again. In April 2012 chartered to *DFDS Seaways* to operate between Dover and Calais and renamed the DEAL SEAWAYS. In November 2012 returned to *Brittany Ferries* and renamed the BARFLEUR. Resumed the Poole – Cherbourg service in March 2013, replacing the COTENTIN but offering a service for both freight and passengers.

BRETAGNE Built by Chantiers de l'Atlantique, St Nazaire for the Plymouth – Santander and Cork – Roscoff services (with two sailings per week between Plymouth and Roscoff). In 1993 she was transferred to the Portsmouth – St Malo service. In 2004 also operated between Portsmouth and Cherbourg. In 2005 operated between Plymouth and Roscoff. In 2006 returned to the Portsmouth – St Malo route.

CAP FINISTERE Built as the SUPERFAST V by Howaldtswerke Deutsche Werft AG, Kiel, Germany for *Attica Enterprises* (now *Attica Group*) for use by *Superfast Ferries* of Greece. Initially operated between Patras and Ancona and in January 2007 switched to the Patras – Igoumenitsa – Bari route. In 2008 the route became Patras – Igoumenitsa – Ancona. In 2010 sold to *Brittany Ferries*, renamed the CAP FINISTERE and in March placed on the Portsmouth – Santander service, also operating some sailings between Portsmouth and Cherbourg. In 2011 began operating also between Portsmouth and Bilbao and only operated between Portsmouth and Cherbourg during the winter period. Now operates on Portsmouth – Santander and Portsmouth – Bilbao routes only.

ETRETAT Built as the NORMAN VOYAGER by CN Visentini, Porto Viro, Italy for *Epic Shipping* of the UK and chartered to *LD Lines*. Operated between Le Havre and Portsmouth and Le Havre and Rosslare. In September 2009 sub-chartered to *Celtic Link Ferries*. Initially operated between Cherbourg and Portsmouth and Cherbourg and Rosslare but the Portsmouth service was abandoned in November 2009. In October 2011 returned to *LD Lines* and placed on the St Nazaire – Gijon route. In November moved to the Portsmouth – Le Havre service and, following the establishment of the joint *LD Lines/DFDS* venture, the charter was transferred to *DFDS Seaways*. In April 2012 sold to *Stena RoRo*; she continued to be chartered to *DFDS*. In March 2014 chartered to *Brittany Ferries* and placed on the new 'économie' services between Portsmouth and Le Havre and Portsmouth and Santander. Renamed the ETRETAT.

MN PELICAN Built as the TRANS BOTNIA for *SeaTrans ANS* of Norway. Hull constructed by Santierul Naval, Galatz, Romania and vessel completed by Fosen Mekaniske Verksteder, Frengen, Norway. Chartered to *Transfennica* for service between Finland and Western Europe. In June 2006 sold to *Maritime Nantaise* of France. In January 2007 renamed the MN PELICAN. Placed on long term charter to the French MOD. In 2015 placed on the charter market. In January 2016 time chartered to *Brittany Ferries*.

MONT ST MICHEL Built by Van der Giessen-de Noord, Krimpen aan den IJssel, Rotterdam for *Brittany Ferries*. Used on the Portsmouth – Caen route.

NORMANDIE Built by Kvaerner Masa-Yards, Turku, Finland for *Brittany Ferries*. Used on the Portsmouth – Caen route.

NORMANDIE EXPRESS Incat Evolution 10 catamaran built as the INCAT TASMANIA. In November 2000 chartered to *TranzRail* of New Zealand and renamed THE LYNX. Placed on the Wellington – Picton service. In July 2003 replaced by 1997-built Incat 86m craft INCAT 046, given the marketing name 'The Lynx' and laid up. In Spring 2005 chartered to *Brittany Ferries* to operate on their Cherbourg – Portsmouth and Caen – Portsmouth services and renamed the NORMANDIE EXPRESS. In 2007 purchased by *Brittany Ferries*. In 2015 operated to Cherbourg and Le Havre but in 2016 only operated to Cherbourg.

PONT-AVEN Built by Jos L Meyer Werft, Papenburg, Germany for *Brittany Ferries* to operate on the Plymouth – Roscoff, Plymouth – Santander and Cork – Roscoff routes.

CONDOR FERRIES

THE COMPANY *Condor Ferries Ltd* is a Channel Islands private sector company owned by the *Condor Group*, Guernsey which is owned by *Macquarie European Infrastructure*.

MANAGEMENT Managing Director James Fulford, **Executive Director – Commercial** Alicia Andrews, **Marketing Manager** Justin Amey, **Sales Manager** Jonathan Godson.

ADDRESS Head Office New Jetty Offices, White Rock, St Peter Port, Guernsey GY1 2LL, **Sales and Marketing** Condor House, New Harbour Road South, Hamworthy, Poole BH15 4AJ.

TELEPHONE Administration *Guernsey* +44 (0)1481 728620, ***Poole*** +44 (0)1202 207207, **Passenger Reservations** +44 (0)845 609 1024, **Freight Reservations** +44 (0)1481 728521.

INTERNET Email *Passenger* reservations@condorferries.co.uk

Freight len.lepage@condorferries.co.uk **Website** www.condorferries.com *(English, French, German)*

ROUTES OPERATED *Conventional Passenger Ferry* Portsmouth to Guernsey (from 7 hrs) and Jersey (from 9 hrs) (*COMMODORE CLIPPER*; daily except Sun). **Fast Ferries** Poole – Guernsey (from 2 hrs 45 mins) and Jersey (from 4 hrs) (*CONDOR LIBERATION*; 1 per day), Guernsey (2 hrs) and Jersey (1 hr 20 mins) to St Malo (*CONDOR RAPIDE*; 1 per day). **Freight Ferry** Portsmouth – Guernsey – Jersey (10 hrs 30 min; *COMMODORE GOODWILL*; 1 per day), Guernsey – Jersey – St Malo (13 hrs; *COMMODORE GOODWILL*; 1 per week).

1	COMMODORE CLIPPER	14000t	99	18.0k	129.1m	500P	100C	92T	A	BS	9201750
2F	COMMODORE GOODWILL	11166t	96	17.3k	126.4m	12P	-	92T	A	BS	9117985
3»	CONDOR LIBERATION	6307t	10	39.0k	102.0m	873P	245C	12L	A	BS	9551363
4»	CONDOR RAPIDE	5007t	97	40.5k	86.6m	870P	200C	-	A	BS	9161560

COMMODORE CLIPPER Ro-pax vessel built by Van der Giessen-de Noord, Krimpen aan den IJssel, Rotterdam for *Commodore Ferries* to operate between Portsmouth and the Channel Islands. She replaced the ISLAND COMMODORE, a freight-only vessel. Her passenger capacity is normally restricted to 300 but is increased to 500 when the fast ferries are unable to operate.

COMMODORE GOODWILL Built by Koninklijke Scheldegroep BV, Vlissingen, The Netherlands for *Commodore Ferries*.

CONDOR LIBERATION Austal 102-metre Trimaran built speculatively by Austal Ships Pty, Fremantle, Australia as AUSTAL HULL 270. Laid up. In August 2014 sold to *Condor Ferries*. During autumn and early winter 2014/15 she was modified by Austal Ships in their shipyard at Balamban, Cebu, Philippines and in March 2015 renamed the CONDOR LIBERATION and placed on the Poole – Channel Islands service.

CONDOR RAPIDE Incat 86m catamaran built at Hobart, Tasmania, Australia as the INCAT 045. Chartered to *Transport Tasmania* of Australia and operated between Melbourne (Victoria) and Devonport (Tasmania). In 1999 she was chartered to the *Royal Australian Navy*, renamed the HMAS JERVIS BAY and took part in moving Australian troops from Darwin to Dili (East Timor) as part of the United Nations operation. She operated over 75 trips between the two points carrying personnel and equipment for the United Nations Transitional Administration in East Timor (UNTAET). The charter ended in May 2001 and she was renamed the INCAT 045 and laid up. In Spring 2003 she was chartered to *Traghetti Isole Sarde (TRIS)* of Italy, renamed the WINNER and operated between Genoa and Palau (Sardinia). In Autumn 2003 the charter ended, she resumed the name INCAT 045 and was laid up at Portland, Dorset. In 2004 chartered to *SpeedFerries* and renamed the SPEED ONE. In May 2008 purchased by *SpeedFerries*. In November 2008 the services ceased and the company went into administration. She was laid up at Tilbury. In May she was sold at auction to *Epic Shipping* of the UK and renamed the SEA LEOPARD. In April 2010 sold to *Condor Ferries* and renamed the CONDOR RAPIDE. Entered service in May 2010.

Commodore Goodwill *(John Bryant)*

Commodore Clipper *(Darren Holdaway)*

DAVID MACBRAYNE GROUP

THE COMPANY *David MacBrayne Limited* is a Scottish registered company, wholly owned by the Scottish Ministers. Its ferry operations are conducted through two subsidiary companies – *Argyll Ferries Ltd* and *CalMac Ferries Ltd* (trading as *Caledonian MacBrayne*). The majority of *CalMac Ferries* vessels are owned by *Caledonian Maritime Assets Limited*, a separate company which is also owned by the Scottish Ministers.

ARGYLL FERRIES

MANAGEMENT Managing Director Martin Dorchester, **Public Affairs Manager** David Cannon.

ADDRESS Ferry Terminal, Gourock PA19 1QP.

TELEPHONE Administration +44 (0)1475 650100, **Customer services** 0800 066 5000.

FAX Administration +44 (0)1475 650336,

INTERNET Email info@argyllferries.co.uk **Website** www.argyllferries.co.uk *(English)*

ROUTE OPERATED All-year passenger-only ferry Gourock – Dunoon (20 mins; *ALI CAT, ARGYLL FLYER, CORUISK of Caledonian MacBrayne (winter only)* 1 or 2 per hour.

1p	ALI CAT	74t	99	-	19.8m	250P	0C	0L	-	UK	
2p	ARGYLL FLYER	300t	01	19.5k	29.9m	227P	0C	0L	-	UK	9231016

ALI CAT Catamaran built for *Solent & Wight Line Cruises* of Ryde, Isle of Wight. She operated a passenger service from Cowes to Hamble and Warsash and cruises from Cowes. At times chartered to *Wightlink* to cover for their fast catamarans. In 2002 chartered to *Red Funnel Ferries* who had contracted with *Caledonian MacBrayne* to operate passenger-only services between Gourock and Dunoon in the morning and evening peaks. In June 2011 purchased by and operated by *Argyll Ferries*.

ARGYLL FLYER Built as the QUEEN OF ARAN II by OCEA, Les Sables d'Olonne, France for *Inis Mór Ferries*. In 2007 sold to *Aran Island Ferries* and renamed the BANRION CHONAMARA. In June 2011 sold to *Argyll Ferries*, renamed the ARGYLL FLYER and replaced the car ferry SATURN on the Gourock – Dunoon service.

CALEDONIAN MACBRAYNE

MANAGEMENT Managing Director Martin Dorchester, **Marketing and e.Commerce Manager** Cathy Craig, **Public Affairs Manager** David Cannon.

ADDRESS Ferry Terminal, Gourock PA19 1QP.

TELEPHONE Administration +44 (0)1475 650100, **Vehicle Reservations** +44 (0)800 066 5000.

FAX Administration +44 (0)1475 650336, **Vehicle Reservations** +44 (0)1475 635235.

INTERNET Email enquiries@calmac.co.uk **Website** www.calmac.co.uk *(English)*

ROUTES OPERATED All-year vehicle ferries (frequencies are for Summer – services are listed alphabetically, by mainland port or larger island port where service is between two islands), Ardmhor (Barra) – Eriskay (40 mins; *LOCH ALAINN*; up to 5 per day), Ardrossan – Brodick (Arran) (55 mins; *CALEDONIAN ISLES, ISLE OF ARRAN*; up to 6 per day), Colintraive – Rhubodach (Bute) (5 mins; *LOCH DUNVEGAN*; frequent service), Kennacraig – Port Askaig (Islay) (2 hrs 5 mins; *FINLAGGAN, HEBRIDEAN ISLES*; up to 4 per day), Kennacraig – Port Ellen (Islay) (2 hrs 20 mins; *FINLAGGAN, HEBRIDEAN ISLES*; service currently suspended due to harbour works), Largs – Cumbrae Slip (Cumbrae) (10 mins; *LOCH RIDDON, LOCH SHIRA,*; every 30 or 15 mins), Leverburgh (Harris) – Berneray (1 hr 10 mins; *LOCH PORTAIN*; 3-4 per day), Lochaline – Fishnish (Mull) (15 mins; *LOCH FYNE*; up to 14 per day), Mallaig – Armadale (Skye) (23 mins; *LOCHNEVIS* (Winter) *LOCHINVAR, LOCH BHRUSDA, LORD OF THE ISLES* (summer); up to 9 per day (2 in Winter)), Mallaig – Lochboisdale (South Uist) (3 hrs 30 mins; *LORD OF THE ISLES*; 1per day), Oban – Castlebay (Barra) (5 hrs); *ISLE OF LEWIS*; 1 per day), Oban – Coll – Tiree (2 hrs 45 min to Coll, 3 hrs 50 min to Tiree via Coll; *CLANSMAN*; 1 per day), Oban – Colonsay (2 hrs 15 mins; *CLANSMAN,* 5 per week), Oban – Craignure (Mull) (45 mins; *CORUISK, ISLE OF MULL*; up to 7 per day),

Isle of Mull *(John Hendy)*

Hebridean Isles *(Stuart Mackillop)*

Finlaggan *(Stuart Mackillop)*

Clansman *(Stuart Mackillop)*

Loch Bhrusda *(Stuart Mackillop)*

Loch Seaforth *(Stuart Mackillop)*

Oban – Lismore (50 mins;, **LOCH STRIVEN, RAASAY**; up to 5 per day), Sconser (Skye) – Raasay (15 mins; **HALLAIG**; up to 11 per day), Tarbert (Loch Fyne) – Portavadie (25 mins; **ISLE OF CUMBRAE, LOCHINVAR**; up to 12 per day), Tayinloan – Gigha (20 mins; **LOCH RANZA**; up to 10 per day), Tobermory (Mull) – Kilchoan (35 mins; **LOCH LINNHE**; up to 7 per day), Uig (Skye) – Lochmaddy (North Uist) (1 hr 45 mins; **HEBRIDES**; 1 or 2 per day), Uig (Skye) – Tarbert (Harris) (1 hr 40 mins; **HEBRIDES**; 1 or 2 per day), Ullapool – Stornoway (Lewis) (2 hrs 45 mins; **LOCH SEAFORTH**; up to 3 per day (one freight only)), Wemyss Bay – Rothesay (Bute) (35 mins; **ARGYLE, BUTE**; hourly).

All-year passenger and restricted vehicle ferries (frequencies are for Summer) Fionnphort (Mull) – Iona (5 mins; **LOCH BUIE**; frequent), Mallaig – Eigg – Muck – Rum – Canna – Mallaig (round trip 7 hrs (all islands); **LOCHNEVIS**; at least 1 sailing per day – most islands visited daily). **Note** Although these services are operated by vehicle ferries, special permission is required to take a vehicle and tourist cars are not normally conveyed.

Summer-only vehicle ferries Ardrossan – Campbeltown (2 hrs 30 mins; **ISLE OF ARRAN**; 3 per week), Claonaig – Lochranza (Arran) (30 mins; **LOCH TARBERT**; up to 9 per day), Kennacraig – Port Askaig – Colonsay – Oban (3 hrs 35 mins; **HEBRIDEAN ISLES**; 1 per week).

Winter-only vehicle ferry Tarbert (Loch Fyne) – Lochranza (Arran) (1 hr; **varies**; 1 per day), Note: A combined Oban – Lochboisdale/Barra service may operate during winter 2016/17.

1	ARGYLE	2643t	07	14.0k	69.0m	450P	60C	-	BAS	UK	9365178
2	BUTE	2612t	05	14.0k	69.0m	450P	60C	-	AS	UK	9319741
3	CALEDONIAN ISLES	5221t	93	15.0k	94.3m	1000P	120C	10L	BA	UK	9051284
4	CLANSMAN	5499t	98	16.5k	99.0m	638P	90C	6L	BA	UK	9158953
5	CORUISK	1599t	03	14.0k	65.0m	250P	40C	-	BA	UK	9274836
6	EIGG	69t	75	8.0k	24.3m	75P	6C	-	B	UK	
7	FINLAGGAN	5626t	11	16.5k	89.9m	550P	88C	-	BA	UK	9482902
8	HALLAIG	499t	13	9.0k	43.5m	150P	23C	2L	BA	UK	9652832
9	HEBRIDEAN ISLES	3040t	85	15.0k	85.1m	494P	68C	10L	BAS	UK	8404812
10	HEBRIDES	5506t	00	16.5k	99.0m	612P	110C	6L	BA	UK	9211975
11	ISLE OF ARRAN	3296t	84	15.0k	85.0m	446P	68C	8L	BA	UK	8219554
12	ISLE OF CUMBRAE	201t	77	8.5k	37.7m	139P	18C	-	BA	UK	7521625
13	ISLE OF LEWIS	6753t	95	18.0k	101.2m	680P	123C	10L	BA	UK	9085974
14	ISLE OF MULL	4719t	88	15.0k	90.1m	962P	80C	20L	BA	UK	8608339
15	LOCH ALAINN	396t	98	10.0k	43.0m	150P	24C	-	BA	UK	9147722
16	LOCH BHRUSDA	246t	96	8.0k	35.4m	150P	18C	-	BA	UK	9129483
17	LOCH BUIE	295t	92	9.0k	35.5m	250P	9C	-	BA	UK	9031375
18	LOCH DUNVEGAN	549t	91	9.0k	54.2m	200P	36C	-	BA	UK	9006409
19	LOCH FYNE	549t	91	9.0k	54.2m	200P	36C	-	BA	UK	9006411
20	LOCH LINNHE	206t	86	9.0k	35.5m	199P	12C	-	BA	UK	8512308
21	LOCH PORTAIN	950t	03	10.5k	50.0m	200P	32C	-	BA	UK	9274824
22	LOCH RANZA	206t	87	9.0k	35.7m	199P	12C	-	BA	UK	8519887
23	LOCH RIDDON	206t	86	9.0k	35.5m	199P	12C	-	BA	UK	8519875
24	LOCH SEAFORTH	8478t	14	19.2k	116.0m	700P	143C	20L	BA	UK	9665437
25	LOCH SHIRA	1024t	07	13.0k	43.0m	250P	24C	-	BA	UK	9376919
26	LOCH STRIVEN	206t	86	9.0k	35.7m	199P	12C	-	BA	UK	8512293
27	LOCH TARBERT	211t	92	9.0k	34.5m	149P	18C	-	BA	UK	9039389
28	LOCHINVAR	523t	14	9.0k	43.5m	150P	23C	2L	BA	UK	9652844
29	LOCHNEVIS	941t	00	13.0k	49.1m	190P	14C	-	A	UK	9209063
30	LORD OF THE ISLES	3504t	89	16.0k	84.6m	506P	56C	16L	BAS	UK	8710869
31	RAASAY	69t	76	8.0k	24.3m	75P	6C	-	B	UK	

Note In the following list, Gaelic names are shown in parenthesis.

ARGYLE *(EARRA-GHÀIDHEAL)*, BUTE *(EILEAN BHÒID)* Built by Stocznia Remontowa, Gdansk, Poland to operate on the Wemyss Bay – Rothesay route.

CALEDONIAN ISLES *(EILEANAN CHALEDONIA)* Built by Richards Shipyard, Lowestoft, UK for the Ardrossan – Brodick (Arran) service.

CLANSMAN *(FEAR-CINNIDH)* Built by Appledore Shipbuilders Ltd, Appledore, UK to replace the LORD OF THE ISLES on the Oban – Coll and Tiree and Oban – Castlebay and Lochboisdale services in the summer. She also serves as winter relief vessel on the Stornoway, Tarbert, Lochmaddy, Mull/Colonsay and Brodick routes.

CORUISK *(COIR' UISG')* Built by Appledore Shipbuilders Ltd, Appledore, UK to operate on the Mallaig – Armadale route during the summer. She operates on the Upper Clyde as a relief vessel during the winter. Between December 2013 and March 2014 operated for *Argyle Ferries* in lieu of the ALI CAT during peak periods and when that vessel could not sail due to adverse weather. In summer 2016 operated as second vessel on the Oban – Craignure service.

EIGG *(EILEAN EIGE)* Built by James Lamont & Co, Port Glasgow, UK. Since 1976 she has been employed mainly on the Oban – Lismore service. In 1996 she was transferred to the Tobermory (Mull) – Kilchoan route, very occasionally making sailings to the Small Isles (Canna, Eigg, Muck and Rum) for special cargoes. In 1999 her wheelhouse was raised to make it easier to see over taller lorries and she returned to the Oban – Lismore route. Now a spare vessel.

FINLAGGAN *(FIONN LAGAN)* Built by Stocznia Remontowa, Gdansk, Poland for the Kennacraig – Islay service.

HALLAIG *(HALLAIG)* Built by Ferguson Shipbuilders, Port Glasgow, UK to replace the LOCH STRIVEN on the Sconser – Raasay service. The vessel has both diesel and battery electric propulsion and can be 'plugged in' to a land supply on Raasay overnight.

HEBRIDEAN ISLES *(EILEANAN INNSE GALL)* Built by Cochrane Shipbuilders, Selby UK for the Uig – Tarbert/Lochmaddy service. She was used initially on the Ullapool – Stornoway and Oban – Craignure/Colonsay services pending installation of link-span facilities at Uig, Tarbert and Lochmaddy. She took up her regular role in May 1986. From May 1996 she no longer operated direct services in summer between Tarbert and Lochmaddy, this role being taken on by the new Harris – North Uist services of the LOCH BHRUSDA. In 2001 she was replaced by the HEBRIDES and transferred to the Islay service. In Autumn 2002 she operated between Scrabster and Stromness for *NorthLink Orkney and Shetland Ferries* before port modifications at Scrabster enabled the HAMNAVOE to enter service in Spring 2003. She then returned to the Islay service. She also relieved on the *NorthLink* Pentland Firth service between 2004 and 2007.

HEBRIDES *(INNSE GALL)* Built by Ferguson Shipbuilders Ltd, Port Glasgow, UK for the Uig – Tarbert and Uig – Lochmaddy services.

ISLE OF ARRAN *(EILEAN ARAINN)* Built by Ferguson Ailsa, Port Glasgow, UK for the Ardrossan – Brodick service. In 1993 transferred to the Kennacraig – Port Ellen/Port Askaig service, also undertaking the weekly Port Askaig – Colonsay – Oban summer service. From then until 1997/98 she also relieved on the Brodick, Coll/Tiree, Castlebay/Lochboisdale, Craignure and Tarbert/Lochmaddy routes in winter. In 2001 she was replaced by the HEBRIDEAN ISLES and became a reserve for the larger vessels. She has operated on the two-ship Islay service in summer since 2003; this service is now all-year-round. Following the delivery of the FINLAGGAN in May 2011 she became a spare vessel, and operates extra services between Ardrossan and Brodick and Ardrossan and Campbeltown during the peak summer period.

ISLE OF CUMBRAE *(EILEAN CHUMRAIGH)* Built by Ailsa Shipbuilding Ltd, Troon, UK for the Largs – Cumbrae Slip (Cumbrae) service. In 1986 she was replaced by the LOCH LINNHE and the LOCH STRIVEN and transferred to the Lochaline – Fishnish (Mull) service. She used to spend most of the winter as secondary vessel on the Kyle of Lochalsh – Kyleakin service; however, this ceased following the opening of the Skye Bridge in 1995. In 1997 she was transferred to the Colintraive – Rhubodach service. In Summer 1999 she was transferred to the Tarbert – Portavadie service. In May 2015 replaced by the new LOCHINVAR and laid up. In summer 2016 returned to the Tarbert – Portavadie service.

Lochinvar *(Stuart Mackillop)*

Loch Tarbert *(Miles Cowsill)*

Caledonian Isles *(Miles Cowsill)*

Isle of Arran *(Miles Cowsill)*

ISLE OF LEWIS *(EILEAN LEÒDHAIS)* Built by Ferguson Shipbuilders Ltd, Port Glasgow, UK for the Ullapool – Stornoway service. In February 2015 replaced by the new LOCH SEAFORTH. During peak summer period 2015 she operated an additional sailing between Ullapool and Stornoway. In summer 2016 operated between Oban and Castlebay.

ISLE OF MULL *(AN T-EILEAN MUILEACH)* Built by Appledore Ferguson, Port Glasgow, UK for the Oban – Craignure (Mull) service. She also operates some Oban – Colonsay sailings and until 1997/98 was the usual winter relief vessel on the Ullapool – Stornoway service. She has also deputised on the Oban – Castlebay/Lochboisdale and Oban – Coll/Tiree routes.

LOCH ALAINN *(LOCH ÀLAINN)* Built by Buckie Shipbuilders Ltd, Buckie, UK for the Lochaline – Fishnish service. Launched as the LOCH ALINE but renamed the LOCH ALAINN before entering service. After a brief period on the service for which she was built, she was transferred to the Colintraive – Rhubodach route. In 1998 she was transferred to the Largs – Cumbrae Slip service. In 2007 moved to the Ardmhor (Barra) – Eriskay service. She relieves the larger 'Loch' class vessels in the winter, with her own service covered by the LOCH BHRUSDA.

LOCH BHRUSDA *(LOCH BHRÙSTA)* Built by McTay Marine, Bromborough, Wirral, UK to inaugurate a new Otternish (North Uist) – Leverburgh (Harris) service. In 2001 the service became Berneray – Leverburgh. In 2003 she moved to the Eriskay – Barra service, previously operated by *Comhairle Nan Eilean Siar* vessels. In 2007 she became a spare vessel on the Clyde. In summer 2016 operated between Mallaig and Armadale. Note 'Bhrusda' is pronounced "Vroosta".

LOCH BUIE *(LOCH BUIDHE)* Built by J W Miller & Sons Ltd, St Monans, Fife, UK for the Fionnphort (Mull) – Iona service to replace the MORVERN (see *Arranmore Island Ferry Services*) and obviate the need for a relief vessel in the summer. Due to height restrictions, loading arrangements for vehicles taller than private cars are stern-only. Only islanders' cars and service vehicles (eg mail vans, police) are carried; no tourist vehicles are conveyed.

LOCH DUNVEGAN *(LOCH DÙNBHEAGAN)* Built by Ferguson Shipbuilders Ltd, Port Glasgow, UK for the Kyle of Lochalsh – Kyleakin service. On the opening of the Skye Bridge in October 1995 she was withdrawn from service and offered for sale. In Autumn 1997, she returned to service on the Lochaline – Fishnish route. In 1998 she was due to be transferred to the Colintraive – Rhubodach route but this was delayed because of problems in providing terminal facilities. She operated on the Clyde and between Mallaig and Armadale during the early summer and spent the rest of that summer laid up. In 1999 she was transferred to the Colintraive – Rhubodach route.

LOCH FYNE *(LOCH FINE)* Built by Ferguson Shipbuilders Ltd, Port Glasgow, UK for the Kyle of Lochalsh – Kyleakin service (see the LOCH DUNVEGAN). In Autumn 1997, she also served on the Lochaline – Fishnish route and was transferred to this route as regular vessel in 1998.

LOCH LINNHE *(AN LINNE DHUBH)* Built by Richard Dunston (Hessle) Ltd, Hessle, UK. Until 1997 she was used mainly on the Largs – Cumbrae Slip (Cumbrae) service and until Winter 1994/95 she was usually used on the Lochaline – Fishnish service during the winter. Since then she has relieved on various routes in winter. In Summer 1998 she operated mainly on the Tarbert – Portavadie route. In 1999 she was transferred to the Tobermory – Kilchoan service in summer.

LOCH PORTAIN *(LOCH PORTAIN)* Built by McTay Marine, Bromborough, Wirral, UK (hull constructed in Poland) to replace the LOCH BHRUSDA on the Berneray – Leverburgh service.

LOCH RANZA *(LOCH RAONASA)* Built by Richard Dunston (Hessle) Ltd, Hessle, UK for the Claonaig – Lochranza (Arran) seasonal service and used a relief vessel in the winter. In 1992 she was replaced by the LOCH TARBERT and transferred to the Tayinloan – Gigha service.

LOCH RIDDON *(LOCH RAODAIN)* Built by Richard Dunston (Hessle) Ltd, Hessle, UK. Until 1997 she was used almost exclusively on the Colintraive – Rhubodach service. In 1997, she was transferred to the Largs – Cumbrae Slip service. In January 2014 she became regular vessel on the Oban – Lismore service. However, after problems with using the slipways, she became the second vessel on the Largs – Cumbrae Slip service.

LOCH SEAFORTH *(LOCH SHIPHOIRT)* Built by Flensburger Schiffbau-Gesellschaft, Flensburg, Germany for the Stornoway – Ullapool service, replacing the ISLE OF LEWIS and freight vessel CLIPPER RANGER.

LOCH SHIRA *(LOCH SIORA)* Built by Ferguson Shipbuilders, Port Glasgow, UK for the Largs – Cumbrae Slip route.

LOCH STRIVEN *(LOCH SROIGHEANN)* Built by Richard Dunston (Hessle) Ltd, Hessle, UK. Used mainly on the Largs – Cumbrae Slip service until 1997. In Winter 1995/96 and 1996/97 she was used on the Tarbert – Portavadie and Claonaig – Lochranza routes. In 1997 she took over the Sconser – Raasay service. In winter 2014 replaced by the HALLAIG. In summer 2014 transferred to the Oban – Lismore route.

LOCH TARBERT *(LOCH AN TAIRBEIRT)* Built by J W Miller & Sons Ltd, St Monans, Fife, UK for the Claonaig – Lochranza service. She was the winter relief vessel on the Largs – Cumbrae Slip route between 1994/95 and 2007/08.

LOCHINVAR *(LOCH AN BARR)* As the HALLAIG. Operates on the Tarbert – Portavadie route. In summer 2016 transferred to Mallaig – Armadale.

LOCHNEVIS *(LOCH NIBHEIS)* Built by Ailsa Shipbuilding, Troon, UK to replace the LOCHMOR on the Mallaig – Small Isles service and the winter Mallaig – Armadale service. Although a vehicle ferry, cars are not normally carried to the Small Isles; the ro-ro facility is used for the carriage of agricultural machinery and livestock and it is possible to convey a vehicle on the ferry from which goods can be unloaded directly onto local transport rather than transhipping at Mallaig.

LORD OF THE ISLES *(RIGH NAN EILEAN)* Built by Appledore Ferguson, Port Glasgow, UK to replace the CLAYMORE on the Oban – Castlebay and Lochboisdale services and also the COLUMBA (1420t, 1964) on the Oban – Coll and Tiree service. She took over the Mallaig – Armadale and Mallaig – Outer Isles services in July 1998 but returned to her previous routes during the winter period. In Spring 2003 the Mallaig – Armadale service was taken over by the PIONEER standing in for the new CORUISK and she operated services from Oban to South Uist and Barra. In summer 2016 operated between Mallaig and Lochboisdale and also between Mallaig and Armadale.

RAASAY *(EILEAN RATHARSAIR)* Built by James Lamont & Co Ltd, Port Glasgow, UK for and used primarily on the Sconser (Skye) – Raasay service. In 1997 she was replaced by the LOCH STRIVEN, became a spare/relief vessel and inaugurated in October 2003 the winter service between Tobermory (Mull) and Kilchoan (Ardnamurchan). In summer 2016 operates as second vessel on Oban – Lismore route.

Under Construction

32	CATRIONA	499t	16	9.0k	43.5m	150P	23C	2L	BA	UK	9759862
33	NEWBUILDING 2	-	18	16.5k	102.0m	1000P	127C	16L	BA	UK	-
34	NEWBUILDING 3	-	18	16.5k	102.0m	1000P	127C	16L	BA	UK	-

CATRIONA Under construction by Ferguson Marine Engineering, Port Glasgow. Near sister vessel of the HALLAIG and LOCHINVAR. Route to be decided.

NEWBUILDING 2, NEWBUILDING 3 Under construction by Ferguson Marine Engineering, Port Glasgow. They are likely to supplement rather than replace existing vessels.

DFDS SEAWAYS

THE COMPANY *DFDS Seaways* is a business unit within *DFDS A/S*, a Danish private sector company. Services from Dover, Newhaven and Marseilles are operated by *DFDS Seaways France* which was inaugurated in March 2013 following the establishment of a *DFDS Seaways/LD Lines* joint venture in November 2012. It is 82% owned by *DFDS* and 18% by *Louis Dreyfus Armateurs*. The Newhaven – Dieppe route is branded as *Transmanche Ferries*, operating under a franchise awarded by *Syndicat Mixte de L'Activité Transmanche* in Dieppe.

MANAGEMENT President and CEO DFDS A/S Niels Smedegaard, **Executive Vice President Shipping Division** Peder Gellert Pedersen, **Managing Director, DFDS Seaways PLC** Sean Potter,

Delft Seaways *(John Bryant)*

Dover Seaways *(George Holland)*

Senior Vice President South Kell Robdrup, **Head of English Channel Business Area** Carsten Jensen, **Head of Passenger Business Area** Brian Thorsted Hansen.

ADDRESS (UK) DFDS A/S, Whitfield Court, White Cliffs Business Park Whitfield, Dover CT16 3PX.

TELEPHONE Administration +44 (0)1304 874001. **Passenger Reservations** 0871 574 7223, +44 (0)208 127 8303. **Freight Reservations** see website.

INTERNET Websites *Passenger* www.dfdsseaways.co.uk *(Chinese, Danish, Dutch, English, German, Italian, Japanese, Norwegian, Polish, Swedish)* ***Freight*** freight.dfdsseaways.com *(English)* ***Corporate*** www.dfds.com *(English)*

ROUTES OPERATED *Passenger ferries* Newcastle (North Shields) – IJmuiden (near Amsterdam, The Netherlands) (15 hrs; *KING SEAWAYS, PRINCESS SEAWAYS*; daily). **ROUTES OPERATED** Dover – Dunkerque (2 hrs; *DELFT SEAWAYS, DOVER SEAWAYS, DUNKERQUE SEAWAYS*, 12 per day), Dover – Calais (1 hr 30 mins; *CALAIS SEAWAYS, CÔTE DES FLANDRES, CÔTE DES DUNES*; 15 per day), Newhaven – Dieppe (4 hrs; *CÔTE D'ALBATRE, SEVEN SISTERS*; up to 3 per day, *Freight ferries* Zeebrugge (Belgium) – Rosyth (Scotland) (20 hrs; *FINLANDIA SEAWAYS*; 3 per week), Esbjerg – Immingham (18 hrs; *ARK DANIA, ARK GERMANIA*; 6 per week), Cuxhaven – Immingham (19 hrs; *HAFNIA SEAWAYS, SELANDIA SEAWAYS*; 4/5 per week), Gothenburg – Immingham (26 hrs (direct), *45 hrs (via Brevik (Fri)); *MAGNOLIA SEAWAYS, PETUNIA SEAWAYS, PRIMULA SEAWAYS*; 7 per week), Brevik – Immingham (25 hrs (direct), 42 hrs (via Gothenburg); *MAGNOLIA SEAWAYS, PETUNIA SEAWAYS, PRIMULA SEAWAYS*; 2 per week), Gothenburg – Brevik (Norway) – Ghent (Belgium) (Gothenburg 32 hrs, Brevik 32 hrs; *BEGONIA SEAWAYS, FIONIA SEAWAYS, FREESIA SEAWAYS*;; 5 per week), Vlaardingen – Immingham (14 hrs; *ANGLIA SEAWAYS, FICARIA SEAWAYS, JUTLANDIA SEAWAYS*; 8 per week), Vlaardingen – Felixstowe (7 hrs; *BRITANNIA SEAWAYS, SELANDIA SEAWAYS, SUECIA SEAWAYS*; 3 per day). Note: vessels are often switched between routes.

1F	ANGLIA SEAWAYS	13073t	00	18.5k	142.5m	12P	-	114T	A	DK	9186649
2F	ARK DANIA	33313t	14	20.0k	195.2m	12P	-	206T	A	DK	9609964
3F	ARK FUTURA	18725t	96	19.7k	183.3m	12P	-	164T	AS	DK	9129598
4F	ARK GERMANIA	33313t	14	20.0k	195.2m	12P	-	206T	A	DK	9609952
5F	BEGONIA SEAWAYS	37722t	04	22.5k	230.0m	12P	-	340T	AS	DK	9262089
6F	BRITANNIA SEAWAYS	24196t	00	21.1k	197.5m	12P	-	200T	AS	DK	9153032
7	CALAIS SEAWAYS	28833t	91	21.0k	163.6m	1850P	600C	100L	BA2	FR	8908466
8F	CORONA SEAWAYS	25609t	08	20.0k	184.8m	12P	-	250T	AS	UK	9357597
9	CÔTE D'ALBATRE	18425t	06	22.0k	112.0m	600P	300C	62L	BA	FR	9320128
10	CÔTE DES FLANDRES	33940t	05	25.0k	186.0m	1500P	700C	120L	BA2	FR	9305843
11	CÔTE DES DUNES	33796t	01	25.0k	186.0m	1500P	700C	120L	BA2	FR	9232527
12	DELFT SEAWAYS	35923t	06	25.5k	187.0m	780P	200C	120L	BA2	UK	9293088
13	DOVER SEAWAYS	35923t	06	25.8k	187.0m	780P	200C	120L	BA2	UK	9318345
14	DUNKERQUE SEAWAYS	35923t	05	25.8k	187.0m	780P	200C	120L	BA2	UK	9293076
15F	FICARIA SEAWAYS	37939t	04	22.5k	230.0m	12P	-	340T	AS	DK	9320568
16F	FINLANDIA SEAWAYS	11530t	00	20.0k	162.2m	12P	-	140T	A	LT	9198721
17F	FIONIA SEAWAYS	25609t	09	20.0k	184.8m	12P	-	250T	AS	UK	9395343
18F	FREESIA SEAWAYS	37722t	04	22.5k	230.0m	12P	-	340T	AS	DK	9274848
19F	HAFNIA SEAWAYS	25609t	08	20.0k	184.8m	12P	-	250T	AS	UK	9357602
20F	JUTLANDIA SEAWAYS	25609t	10	20.0k	184.8m	12P	–	250T	AS	UK	9395355
21	KING SEAWAYS	31788t	87	20.0k	161.6m	1400P	600C	104T	BA	DK	8502406
22F	MAGNOLIA SEAWAYS	32289t	03	22.5k	199.8m	12P	-	280T	AS	DK	9259496
23F	PETUNIA SEAWAYS	32289t	04	22.5k	199.8m	12P	-	280T	AS	DK	9259501
24F	PRIMULA SEAWAYS	37939t	04	22.5k	229.8m	12P	-	340T	AS	DK	9259513
25	PRINCESS SEAWAYS	31356t	86	18.5k	161.0m	1600P	600C	100T	BA	DK	8502391
26F	SELANDIA SEAWAYS	24196t	98	21.0k	197.5m	12P	-	206T	A	DK	9157284
27	SEVEN SISTERS	18425t	06	22.0k	112.0m	600P	300C	62L	BA	FR	9320130

SECTION 1 – GB & IRELAND PASSENGER OPERATIONS

Fionia Seaways *(George Holland)*

Selandia Seaways *(Rob de Visser)*

Calais Seaways *(Miles Cowsill)*

Côte des Flandres *(Miles Cowsill)*

| 28F | SUECIA SEAWAYS | 24196t | 99 | 21.0k | 197.5m | 12P | - | 206T | AS | DK | 9153020 |
| 29F | SUPER-FAST BALEARES | 30998t | 10 | 26.0k | 209.4m | 12P | - | 250T | A | ES | 9398527 |

ANGLIA SEAWAYS Built as the MAERSK ANGLIA by Guangzhou Shipyard International, Guangzhou, China for *Norfolkline*. Entered service as the GUANGZHOU 7130011 (unofficially the 'China II') but renamed shortly afterwards. Operated on the Scheveningen (from 2007 Vlaardingen) – Felixstowe service. In June 2009 moved to the Heysham – Dublin route. In August 2010 renamed the ANGLIA SEAWAYS. In January 2011 service withdrawn. In February 2011 chartered to *Seatruck Ferries* to inaugurate their new Heysham – Dublin service. In January 2012 returned to *DFDS Seaways* and placed on the Vlaardingen – Immingham route as an extra vessel. In April 2012 moved to the Zeebrugge – Rosyth service but proved too slow. In May chartered to *Seatruck Ferries* to operate between Heysham and Belfast. In August, this service ceased and she was switched to the Heysham – Dublin route and in September to the Heysham – Warrenpoint route. In April 2014 returned to *DFDS Seaways* and placed on Kiel – St Petersburg service. In July 2014 transferred to the Travemünde – Klaipėda route and in September to the Vlaardingen – Immingham service, providing additional capacity. In March 2015 placed on the charter market. In May 2015 returned to the Rotterdam – Felixstowe route.

ARK DANIA, ARK GERMANIA Built by P+S Werften GmbH, Stralsund, Germany. They are used for the German/Danish joint ARK Project providing NATO transport but are also available for *DFDS* use and charter when not required. They have a crane for loading containers on the weather deck. In December 2012 the order for these vessels was cancelled due to late delivery. Following negotiations with the shipyard it was agreed that they would be completed under a new contract which was signed in February 2013. Both vessels were delivered to *DFDS* in April 2014, the ARK GERMANIA almost complete, the ARK DANIA still incomplete. The latter vessel was towed to the Fayard shipyard, Odense, to be completed. The ARK GERMANIA entered service a few days after delivery, the ARK DANIA in November 2014.

ARK FUTURA Built as the DANA FUTURA by C N Visentini di Visentini Francesco & C, Donada, Italy for *DFDS*. In 2001 she was renamed the TOR FUTURA. Initially operated mainly between Esbjerg and Harwich, but latterly operated mainly between Esbjerg and Immingham. In 2004 chartered to *Toll Shipping* of Australia. Later time-chartered to the *Danish MoD* for 5.5 years. However, when not required for military service she has been chartered to other operators such as *P&O Ferries*, *Cobelfret Ferries* and *Van Uden Ro-Ro* and used on *DFDS Tor Line* services. In 2006 sold to *DFDS Lys Line Rederi A/S* of Norway, a *DFDS* subsidiary and chartered back. In April 2011 renamed the ARK FUTURA. Currently operating on the Marseilles – Tunis service.

BEGONIA SEAWAYS Built as the TOR BEGONIA by Flensburger Schiffbau-Gesellschaft, Flensburg, Germany for *DFDS Tor Line*. Operates on the Gothenburg – Immingham/Brevik route. In Summer 2009 lengthened by 30m by MWB Motorenwerke Bremerhaven AG, Germany. In July 2012 renamed the BEGONIA SEAWAYS.

BRITANNIA SEAWAYS Built as the TOR BRITANNIA by Fincantieri-Cantieri Navali Italiani SpA, Ancona, Italy for *DFDS Tor Line*. Operated on the Gothenburg – Immingham route until 2004 when she was transferred to the Esbjerg – Immingham route. In January 2010 chartered to *Norfolkline* to operate between Vlaardingen and Felixstowe. In May 2011 renamed the BRITANNIA SEAWAYS.

CALAIS SEAWAYS Built as the PRINS FILIP by NV Boelwerf SA, Temse, Belgium for *Regie voor Maritiem Transport (RMT)* of Belgium for the Ostend – Dover service. Although completed in 1991, she did not enter service until May 1992. In 1994 the British port became Ramsgate. Withdrawn in 1997 and laid up for sale. In 1998 she was sold to *Stena RoRo* and renamed the STENA ROYAL. In November 1998 she was chartered to *P&O Ferries* to operate as a freight-only vessel on the Dover – Zeebrugge route. In Spring 1999 it was decided to charter the vessel on a long-term basis and she was repainted into *P&O Stena Line* (later *P&O Ferries*) colours and renamed the P&OSL AQUITAINE. In Autumn 1999 she was modified to make her suitable to operate between Dover and Calais and was transferred to that route, becoming a passenger vessel again. In 2002 renamed the PO AQUITAINE and in 2003 the PRIDE OF AQUITAINE. In September 2005 sold to *LD Lines* and renamed the NORMAN SPIRIT. In October, inaugurated a Le Havre – Portsmouth service, replacing that previously operated by *P&O Ferries*. In November 2009 moved to the Dover – Boulogne route. In March 2010 chartered to *TransEuropa Ferries*, placed on the Ostend – Ramsgate service (as part of a joint venture) and renamed the OSTEND SPIRIT. In May 2011 returned to the Portsmouth – Le

Havre route and renamed the NORMAN SPIRIT. In November 2011 chartered to *DFDS Seaways* to add extra capacity to their Dover – Dunkerque route. In February 2012 transferred to the new Dover – Calais route, joint with *DFDS Seaways*. Ownership transferred to *DFDS Seaways* in late 2012. In March 2013 refurbished, repainted into *DFDS Seaways* colours and renamed the CALAIS SEAWAYS.

CORONA SEAWAYS Built as the TOR CORONA by Jinling Shipyard, Nanjing, China for *Macoma Shipping Ltd* of the UK and time-chartered to *DFDS Tor Line* for ten years. Used on the Fredericia – Copenhagen – Klaipėda service. In April 2012 renamed the CORONA SEAWAYS. In December 2015 transferred to the Vlaardingen – Immingham service.

CÔTE D'ALBATRE Built by Astilleros Barreras SA, Vigo, Spain for *Transmanche Ferries* to operate between Newhaven and Dieppe. In February 2009 she was moved to the Boulogne – Dover and Dieppe – Dover routes for *LD Lines*. In September 2009 moved to the Le Havre – Portsmouth route. The vessel has had periods laid up when not required on the Newhaven – Dieppe route.

CÔTE DES FLANDRES Built as the SEAFRANCE BERLIOZ by Chantiers de l'Atlantique, St Nazaire for *SeaFrance*. Launched in March 2005. In November 2011 laid up. In June 2012 sold to *Eurotransmanche*, a *Groupe Eurotunnel* company. In July 2012 renamed the BERLIOZ. In August 2012 chartered to *MyFerryLink* and resumed operation between Calais and Dover. In July 2015 chartered to *DFDS Seaways* and *MyFerryLink* operations ceased. After a prolonged occupation by former *MyFerryLink* workers, *DFDS Seaways* took possession in early September and, in November 2015, she was renamed the CÔTE DES FLANDRES. She re-entered service on the Dover – Calais route in February 2016.

CÔTE DES DUNES Built as the SEAFRANCE RODIN by Aker Finnyards, Rauma, Finland for *SeaFrance*. Launched in November 2001. In November 2011 laid up. In June 2012 sold to *Eurotransmanche*. In July 2012 renamed the RODIN. In August 2012 chartered to *MyFerryLink* and resumed operation between Calais and Dover. In July 2015 chartered to *DFDS Seaways* and *MyFerryLink* operations ceased. After a prolonged occupation by former *MyFerryLink* workers. *DFDS Seaways* took possession in early September and in November 2015 she was renamed the CÔTE DES DUNES. She re-entered service on the Dover – Calais route in February 2016.

DELFT SEAWAYS, DOVER SEAWAYS, DUNKERQUE SEAWAYS Built as the MAERSK DELFT, DOVER SEAWAYS and MAERSK DUNKERQUE by Samsung Heavy Industries, Koje (Geoje) Island, South Korea for *Norfolkline* to operate between Dover and Dunkerque. In July and August 2010 renamed the DELFT SEAWAYS, DOVER SEAWAYS and DUNKERQUE SEAWAYS. In November 2012 the DOVER SEAWAYS was moved to the Dover – Calais route.

FICARIA SEAWAYS Built as the TOR FICARIA by Flensburger Schiffbau-Gesellschaft, Flensburg, Germany for *DFDS Tor Line*. Operated on the Gothenburg – Immingham/Brevik service. In Summer 2009 lengthened by 30m by MWB Motorenwerke Bremerhaven AG, Germany. In July 2011 renamed the FICARIA SEAWAYS. In March 2015 placed on the Vlaardingen – Immingham service.

FINLANDIA SEAWAYS Launched as the FINNMAID but renamed the FINNREEL before delivery. Built by Jinling Shipyard, Nanjing, China for the *Macoma Shipping Group* and chartered to *Finnlines*. In 2008 sold to *DFDS Lisco* and in January 2009 delivered, chartered to *DFDS Tor Line* and renamed the TOR FINLANDIA. Operated on the Immingham – Rotterdam route until January 2011 when she was transferred to the Rosyth – Zeebrugge route. In May 2012 moved to the Cuxhaven – Immingham service but returned in July. In December 2012 renamed the FINLANDIA SEAWAYS. In October 2013 moved to the Kiel – St Petersburg service. In April 2014 returned to the Rosyth – Zeebrugge route.

FIONIA SEAWAYS Built as the TOR FIONIA by Jinling Shipyard, Nanjing, China for *Macoma Shipping Ltd* of the UK. Launched as the JINGLING 3. She was time-chartered to *DFDS Tor Line* for ten years (with an option on a further three). Delivered in May 2009 and initially replaced the TOR BEGONIA, TOR FICARIA and TOR FREESIA while they were being lengthened. In October 2011 renamed the FIONIA SEAWAYS. In March 2015 placed on the Gothenburg – Immingham service.

FREESIA SEAWAYS Built as the TOR FREESIA by Flensburger Schiffbau-Gesellschaft, Flensburg, Germany for *DFDS Tor Line*. Operates on the Gothenburg – Immingham/Brevik service. In Summer 2009 lengthened by 30m by MWB Motorenwerke Bremerhaven AG, Germany. In August 2012 renamed the FREESIA SEAWAYS.

HAFNIA SEAWAYS Built as the TOR HAFNIA by Jinling Shipyard, Nanjing, China for *Macoma Shipping Ltd* of the UK and time-chartered to *DFDS Tor Line* for ten years. Until 2013, mainly operated on the Immingham – Esbjerg route. In March 2011 renamed the HAFNIA SEAWAYS. In February 2013 transferred to the Vlaardingen – Immingham route. In January 2015 chartered to *Cobelfret Ferries* for four weeks. Currently operates on the Cuxhaven – Immingham service.

JUTLANDIA SEAWAYS Built as the TOR JUTLANDIA by Jinling Shipyard, Nanjing, China for *Macoma Shipping Ltd* of the UK and time-chartered to *DFDS Tor Line* for ten years. In July 2011 renamed the JUTLANDIA SEAWAYS. Currently operates on the Immingham – Esbjerg route. In late summer 2014 to be replaced by the ARK DANIA and moved to another route.

KING SEAWAYS Built as the NILS HOLGERSSON by Schichau Seebeckwerft AG, Bremerhaven, Germany for *Rederi AB Swedcarrier* of Sweden for their service between Trelleborg and Travemünde, joint with *TT-Line* of Germany (trading as *TT-Line*). In 1992 purchased by *Brittany Ferries* for entry into service in Spring 1993. After a major rebuild, she was renamed the VAL DE LOIRE and introduced onto the Plymouth – Roscoff, Plymouth – Santander and Cork – Roscoff routes. In 2004 transferred to the Portsmouth – St Malo and Portsmouth – Cherbourg services. In 2005 operated mainly Portsmouth – St Malo. In 2006 sold to *DFDS*, renamed the KING OF SCANDINAVIA and placed on the Newcastle – IJmuiden route. In January 2011 renamed the KING SEAWAYS.

MAGNOLIA SEAWAYS Built as the TOR MAGNOLIA by Flensburger Schiffbau-Gesellschaft, Flensburg, Germany for *DFDS Tor Line*. In July 2011 renamed the MAGNOLIA SEAWAYS. Currently operates on the Gothenburg – Ghent route.

PETUNIA SEAWAYS Built as the TOR PETUNIA by Flensburger Schiffbau-Gesellschaft, Flensburg, Germany for *DFDS Tor Line*. In July 2011 renamed the PETUNIA SEAWAYS. Currently operates on the Gothenburg – Ghent route.

PRIMULA SEAWAYS Built as the TOR PRIMULA by Flensburger Schiffbau-Gesellschaft, Flensburg, Germany for *DFDS Tor Line*. In July 2010 renamed the PRIMULA SEAWAYS. In July 2016 lengthened by 30m by MWB Motorenwerke Bremerhaven AG, Germany. Currently operates on the Gothenburg – Ghent route.

PRINCESS SEAWAYS Built by Schichau Seebeckwerft AG, Bremerhaven, Germany as the PETER PAN for *TT-Line* for the service between Travemünde and Trelleborg. In 1992 sold to *TT Line* of Australia (no connection) for use on their service between Port Melbourne (Victoria) and Devonport (Tasmania) and renamed the SPIRIT OF TASMANIA. In 2002 sold to *Nordsjøferger K/S* of Norway and renamed the SPIR. After modification work she was, in 2003, renamed the FJORD NORWAY and chartered to *Fjord Line*. Placed on the Bergen – Egersund – Hanstholm route. In 2005 placed on the Bergen – Stavanger – Newcastle route, but operated once a week to Hanstholm. In October 2006 sold to *DFDS* and renamed the PRINCESS OF NORWAY, remaining on the Newcastle – Norway service but no longer serving Hanstholm. In May 2007 moved to the Newcastle – IJmuiden route. In February 2011 renamed the PRINCESS SEAWAYS.

SELANDIA SEAWAYS Built as the TOR SELANDIA by Fincantieri-Cantieri Navali Italiani SpA, Ancona, Italy for *DFDS Tor Line*. Operated on the Gothenburg – Immingham route until 2004 when she was moved to the Gothenburg – Ghent route. In 2005 she moved to the Gothenburg – Harwich route. In July the UK terminal moved to Tilbury. In August 2010 renamed the SELANDIA SEAWAYS. Currently operates on the Rotterdam – Felixstowe route.

SEVEN SISTERS Built by Astilleros Barreras SA, Vigo, Spain for *Transmanche Ferries* to operate between Newhaven and Dieppe. In recent years generally held as a reserve vessel. In March 2014 transferred to the *DFDS Seaways* Portsmouth – Le Havre service. She continues to carry *Transmanche Ferries* branding. In 2015 returned to the Newhaven – Dieppe service as second vessel, continuing to operate for *DFDS Seaways*. The vessel has had periods laid up when not required on the Newhaven – Dieppe route.

Calais Seaways *(Miles Cowsill)*

Ark Futura *(John Bryant)*

Epsilon *(Matthew Punter)*

SUECIA SEAWAYS Built as the TOR SUECIA by Fincantieri-Cantieri Navali Italiani SpA, Ancona, Italy for *DFDS Tor Line*. Operated on the Gothenburg – Immingham route until 2004 when she was transferred to the Esbjerg – Immingham route. Later transferred to the Danish flag. In March 2010 chartered to *Norfolkline* to operate between Vlaardingen and Felixstowe and continued on the route when it was taken over by *DFDS*. In June 2011 renamed the SUECIA SEAWAYS.

SUPER-FAST BALEARES Built by Navantia SA Astilleros San Fernando, Puerto Real, Spain for *Acciona Trasmediterranea*. Operated between Cadiz and Grand Canaria, Canary Islands. In January 2016 chartered to *DFDS Seaways* and operated between Marseilles and Tunis. In April 2016 transferred to the Immingham – Gothenburg service.

Under Construction

| 30F | NEWBUILDING 1 | - | 17 | - | 209.6m | 12P | - | 262T | A2 | DK | - |
| 31F | NEWBUILDING 2 | - | 17 | - | 209.6m | 12P | - | 262T | A2 | DK | - |

NEWBUILDING 1, NEWBUILDING 2 under construction by Flensburger Schiffbau-Gesellschaft, Flensburg, Germany for the Siem Industries Inc (owners of FSG). They will be bareboat chartered to *DFDS Seaways* for five years with an option to purchase at the end of the charter period. They are expected to operate on North Sea routes. NEWBUILDING 1 will be delivered in May 2017 and NEWBUILDING 2 in September.

IRISH FERRIES

THE COMPANY *Irish Ferries* is a Republic of Ireland private sector company, part of the *Irish Continental Group*. It was originally mainly owned by the state-owned *Irish Shipping* and partly by *Lion Ferry AB* of Sweden. *Lion Ferry* participation ceased in 1977 and the company was sold into the private sector in 1987. Formerly state-owned *B&I Line* was taken over in 1991 and from 1995 all operations were marketed as *Irish Ferries*.

MANAGEMENT Irish Continental Group Chief Executive Office Eamonn Rothwell, **Irish Ferries Limited Managing Director** Andrew Sheen.

ADDRESS PO Box 19, Ferryport, Alexandra Road, Dublin 1, Republic of Ireland.

TELEPHONE Administration +353 (0)1 607 5700, **Reservations** *Ireland* +353 (0)818300 400, *Rosslare Harbour* +353 (0)53 913 3158, *Holyhead* +44 (0)8717 300200, *Pembroke Dock* +44 (0)8717 300500, *National* 44 (0)8717 300400, *24 hour information* +353 (0)818300 400 (Ireland) or 44 (0)8717 300400 (UK).

FAX Administration & Reservations *Dublin* +353 (0)1 607 5660, *Rosslare* +353 (0)53 913 3544.

INTERNET Email info@irishferries.com **Website** www.irishferries.com *(English, French, German, Italian)*

ROUTES OPERATED Conventional Ferries Dublin – Holyhead (3 hrs 15 mins; *EPSILON*; *ULYSSES*; 2-4 per day), Rosslare – Pembroke Dock (4 hrs; *ISLE OF INISHMORE*; 4 per day), Dublin – Cherbourg (17-19 hrs; *EPSILON*; 1 per week), Rosslare – Cherbourg (France) (17 hrs 30 mins; *OSCAR WILDE*; average of 3 per week), Rosslare – Roscoff (France) (16 hrs; *OSCAR WILDE*; 1 or 2 per week (seasonal)). **Fast Ferry** Dublin – Holyhead (1 hr 49 min; *JONATHAN SWIFT*; 2 per day) marketed as 'DUBLIN*Swift*'.

1	EPSILON	26375t	11	24.0k	177.5m	500P	500C	190T	A	IT	9539054
2	ISLE OF INISHMORE	34031t	97	21.3k	182.5m	2200P	802C	152T	BA2	CY	9142605
3»	JONATHAN SWIFT	5989t	99	37.0k	86.6m	800P	200C	-	BA	CY	9188881
4	KAITAKI	22365t	95	19.0k	181.6m	1650P	600C	130T	BA2	UK	9107942
5	OSCAR WILDE	31914t	87	22.0k	166.3m	1458P	580C	90T	BA	BS	8506311
6	ULYSSES	50938t	01	22.0k	209.0m	1875P	1342C	300T	BA2	CY	9214991
7»	WESTPAC EXPRESS	8403t	01	37.0k	101.0m	900P	182C	-	BA		9243227

EPSILON Built as the CARTOUR EPSILON by CN Visentini, Porto Viro, Italy. Chartered to *Caronte & Tourist SPA* of Italy. In November 2013 chartered to *Irish Ferries*. In February 2014 renamed the EPSILON.

ISLE OF INISHMORE Built by Van der Giessen-de Noord, Krimpen aan den IJssel, Rotterdam for *Irish Ferries* to operate on the Holyhead – Dublin service. In 2001 replaced by the ULYSSES and moved to the Rosslare – Pembroke Dock route. She also relieves on the Dublin – Holyhead route when the ULYSSES receives her annual overhaul.

JONATHAN SWIFT Austal Auto-Express 86 catamaran built by Austal Ships Pty, Fremantle, Australia for *Irish Ferries* for the Dublin – Holyhead route.

KAITAKI Built as the ISLE OF INNISFREE by Van der Giessen-de Noord, Krimpen aan den IJssel, Rotterdam for *Irish Ferries* to operate on the Holyhead – Dublin route. In 1997 transferred to the Rosslare – Pembroke Dock service; for a short period, before modifications at Pembroke Dock were completed, she operated between Rosslare and Fishguard. In Spring 2001 she was replaced by the ISLE OF INISHMORE and laid up. In July 2002 she was chartered to *P&O Portsmouth* for 5 years and renamed the PRIDE OF CHERBOURG. Entered service in October 2002. Withdrawn in October 2004. In January 2005, sub-chartered by *P&O* to *Stena RoRo*, renamed the STENA CHALLENGER and operated on the Karlskrona – Gdynia route. In June 2006 sub-chartered by *Stena RoRo* to *Toll Shipping* of New Zealand and renamed the CHALLENGER. In August 2006 she arrived in New Zealand and was placed on the Wellington – Picton route. In 2007 renamed the KAITAKI. . In 2009 charter extended until 2013 and in 2013 a new direct charter was agreed extending until June 2017.

OSCAR WILDE Built as the KRONPRINS HARALD by Oy Wärtsilä AB, Turku, Finland for *Jahre Line* of Norway for the Oslo – Kiel service. In 1991 ownership was transferred to *Color Line*. In early 2007 sold to *Irish Ferries* for delivery in September 2007. Chartered back to *Color Line* until that date. When delivered, renamed the OSCAR WILDE and in November placed on the Rosslare – Roscoff/Cherbourg routes.

ULYSSES Built by Aker Finnyards, Rauma, Finland for *Irish Ferries* for the Dublin – Holyhead service.

WESTPAC EXPRESS Austal Auto-Express catamaran built by Austal Ships Pty, Fremantle, Australia. Chartered through a number of third party companied to the *US Marine Corps* as a support vessel. In 2015 returned to *Austal Ships*. In May 2016 sold to the *Irish Continental Group*. Chartered to *Sealift Inc* of the USA and continues to be operated for the *US Marine Corps*.

Under Construction

| 8 | NEWBUILDING | 50000t | 18 | 22.5k | 194.8m- | 1850P | 1216C | 165L | BA2 | - | - |

NEWBUILDING Under construction by Flensburger Schiffbau-Gesellschaft, Flensburg, Germany. She will probably replace the chartered EPSILON when delivered in May 2018.

ISLE OF MAN STEAM PACKET COMPANY

THE COMPANY *The Isle of Man Steam Packet Company Limited* is an Isle of Man-registered company.

MANAGEMENT Chief Executive Officer Mark Woodward.

ADDRESS Imperial Buildings, Douglas, Isle of Man IM1 2BY.

TELEPHONE Administration +44 (0)1624 645645, **Reservations** +44 (0)1624 661661

FAX Administration +44 (0)1624 645627.

INTERNET Email iom.reservations@steam-packet.com **Website** www.steam-packet.com *(English)*

ROUTES OPERATED Conventional Ferries *All year* Douglas (Isle of Man) – Heysham (3 hrs 30 mins; **BEN-MY-CHREE**; up to 2 per day), **November-March** Douglas – Liverpool (Birkenhead) (4 hrs 15 mins; **BEN-MY-CHREE**; 2 per week). **Fast Ferries *March-October*** Douglas – Liverpool (2 hrs 40 mins; **MANANNAN**; up to 2 per day), Douglas – Belfast (2 hrs 55 mins; **MANANNAN**; up to 2 per week), Douglas – Dublin (2 hrs 55 mins; **MANANNAN**; up to 2 per week), Douglas – Heysham (2 hrs; **MANANNAN**; occasional), **Freight Ferry** Douglas – Heysham (3 hrs 30 mins; **ARROW**; as required)

| 1F | ARROW | 7606t | 98 | 15.0k | 122.3m | 12P | - | 84T | A | IM | 9119414 |
| 2 | BEN-MY-CHREE | 12747t | 98 | 18.0k | 124.9m | 630P | 275C | 90T | A | IM | 9170705 |

Isle of Inishmore *(George Holland)*

Manannan *(Stan Basnett)*

| 3» | MANANNAN | 5743t | 98 | 43.0k | 96.0m | 820P | 200C | - | A | IM | 9176072 |

ARROW Built as the VARBOLA by Astilleros de Huelva SA, Huelva, Spain for the *Estonian Shipping Company*. On completion, chartered to *Dart Line* and placed on the Dartford – Vlissingen route. In 1999 she was renamed the DART 6. At the end of August 1999, the charter was terminated and she was renamed the VARBOLA. She undertook a number of short-term charters, including *Merchant Ferries*. In 2000 long-term chartered to *Merchant Ferries* to operate between Heysham and Dublin. In 2003 the charter ended and she was chartered to *Dart Line* to replace the DART 9; she was placed initially on the Dartford – Vlissingen route but later transferred to the Dartford – Dunkerque route. Later sub-chartered to *NorseMerchant Ferries* and placed on the Heysham – Dublin route. In 2004 the charter transferred to *NorseMerchant Ferries*. In 2005 sold to *Elmira Shipping* of Greece and renamed the RR ARROW. In October 2007 sold to *Seatruck Ferries* but the charter to *Norfolkline* continued. Renamed the ARROW. In June 2009 returned to *Seatruck Ferries*. In April 2014 long term chartered to *IOMSP*. When not required she is sub-chartered to other operators.

BEN-MY-CHREE Built by Van der Giessen-de Noord, Krimpen aan den IJssel, Rotterdam for the *IOMSP Co* and operates between Douglas and Heysham. Additional passenger accommodation was added at her spring 2004 refit. In 2005 her passenger certificate was increased from 500 to 630. She operates some sailings between Douglas and Liverpool (Birkenhead) in the winter.

MANANNAN Incat 96m catamaran built at Hobart, Tasmania. Initially chartered to *Transport Tasmania* of Australia and operated between Port Melbourne (Victoria) and Georgetown (Tasmania). In 1999 chartered to *Fast Cat Ferries* of New Zealand and operated between Wellington (North Island) and Picton (South Island) under the marketing name 'Top Cat'. In 2000 she was laid up. In 2001 she was chartered to the *US Navy* and renamed the USS JOINT VENTURE (HSV-X1). In 2008 the charter was terminated and she was renamed the INCAT 050. Later purchased by *IOMSP*. Following conversion back to civilian use she was renamed the MANANNAN and entered service in May 2009.

NORTHLINK FERRIES

THE COMPANY *NorthLink Ferries* is a UK based company, wholly owned *Serco Group plc*. The service is operated on behalf of Scottish Ministers.

MANAGEMENT Managing Director Stuart Garrett, **Customer Service Director** Peter Hutchinson.

ADDRESS Ferry Terminal, Ferry Road, Stromness, Orkney KW16 3BH.

TELEPHONE Customer Services 0845 6000 449, (International +44 (0)1856 885500), **Freight Reservations** 0845 6060 449.

FAX Administration +44 (0)1856 851795.

INTERNET Email info@northlinkferries.co.uk **Website** www.northlinkferries.co.uk *(English)*

ROUTES OPERATED *Passenger Ferries* Scrabster – Stromness (Orkney) (1 hr 30 min; *HAMNAVOE*; up to 3 per day), Aberdeen – Lerwick (Shetland) (direct) (12 hrs; *HJALTLAND, HROSSEY*; 3 northbound/4 southbound per week), Aberdeen – Kirkwall, Hatston New Pier (Orkney) (5 hrs 45 mins) – Lerwick (14 hrs; *HJALTLAND, HROSSEY*; 4 northbound/3 southbound per week). *Freight Ferries* Aberdeen – Kirkwall (Orkney) (12 hrs; *HELLIAR, HILDASAY*; 4 per week), Aberdeen – Lerwick (Shetland) (*HELLIAR, HILDASAY*; 4 per week).

1	HAMNAVOE	8780t	02	19.3k	112.0m	600P	95C	20L	BA	UK	9246061
2F	HELLIAR	7800t	98	17.0k	122.3m	12P	-	86T	A	IM	9119397
3F	HILDASAY	7606t	99	17.0k	122.3m	12P	-	84T	A	IM	9119426
4	HJALTLAND	11720t	02	24.0k	125.0m	600P	150C	30L	BA	UK	9244958
5	HROSSEY	11720t	02	24.0k	125.0m	600P	150C	30L	BA	UK	9244960

HAMNAVOE Built by Aker Finnyards, Rauma, Finland for *NorthLink Orkney and Shetland Ferries Ltd* to operate on the Scrabster – Stromness route. Did not enter service until Spring 2003 due to late completion of work at Scrabster to accommodate the ship. *Caledonian MacBrayne's* HEBRIDEAN ISLES covered between October 2002 and Spring 2003.

HELLIAR Built as the LEHOLA by Astilleros de Huelva SA, Huelva, Spain for the *Estonian Shipping Company*. Initially used on *ESCO* Baltic services. In 1998 chartered to *Czar Peter Line* to operate between Moerdijk (The Netherlands) and Kronstadt (Russia). In 1999 chartered to *Delom* of France to operate between Marseilles and Sete and Tunis. In 2000 she returned to *ESCO*, operating between Kiel and Tallinn. In 2003 chartered to *Scandlines AG* and transferred to subsidiary *Scandlines Estonia AS*. Operated Rostock – Helsinki – Muuga initially and later Rostock – Helsinki. Service finished at the end of 2004 and in 2005 she was chartered to *P&O Ferries* to operate between Hull and Rotterdam and Hull and Zeebrugge. In 2005 sold to *Elmira Shipping* of Greece. Later renamed the RR TRIUMPH. In 2006 transferred to *P&O Irish Sea* to operate between Liverpool and Dublin. In 2007 chartered to *Balearia* of Spain and operated from Barcelona. In December 2007 purchased by *Seatruck Ferries* and renamed the TRIUMPH. In Spring 2008 she was sub-chartered to *Condor Ferries* to cover for the refit period of the COMMODORE GOODWILL. In June 2008 placed on the Liverpool – Dublin route and in July renamed the CLIPPER RACER. In February 2009 replaced by the new CLIPPER PACE. In April 2009 again chartered to *Balearia*. In January 2011 chartered to *NorthLink Ferries* and renamed the HELLIAR.

HILDASAY Built as the LEILI by Astilleros de Huelva SA, Huelva, Spain for the *Estonian Shipping Company*. Used on Baltic services. In 2002 chartered to *Crowley Maritime* of the USA and renamed the PORT EVERGLADES EXPRESS. In 2004 resumed the name LEILI and chartered to *NorseMerchant Ferries* to operate between Birkenhead and Dublin. In July 2005 moved to the Heysham – Belfast route and at the same time sold to *Elmira Shipping* of Greece and renamed the RR SHIELD. In 2007 sold to *Attica Group* of Greece and renamed the SHIELD. In January 2008 sold to *Seatruck Ferries* but continued to be chartered to *Norfolkline*. In June 2009 returned to *Seatruck Ferries*. In January 2009 chartered to *NorthLink Orkney and Shetland Ferries* and renamed the HILDASAY.

HJALTLAND, HROSSEY Built by Aker Finnyards, Rauma, Finland for *NorthLink Orkney and Shetland Ferries* to operate on the Aberdeen – Kirkwall – Lerwick route when services started in 2002.

ORKNEY FERRIES

THE COMPANY *Orkney Ferries Ltd* (previously the *Orkney Islands Shipping Company*) is a British company, owned by *Orkney Islands Council*.

MANAGEMENT Ferry Services Manager Fraser Murray.

ADDRESS Shore Street, Kirkwall, Orkney KW15 1LG.

TELEPHONE Administration +44 (0)1856 872044, **Reservations** +44 (0)1856 872044.

FAX Administration & Reservations +44 (0)1856 872921.

INTERNET Email info@orkneyferries.co.uk **Website** www.orkneyferries.co.uk *(English)*

ROUTES OPERATED Kirkwall (Mainland) to Eday (1 hr 15 mins), Rapness (Westray) (1 hr 25 mins), Sanday (1 hr 25 mins), Stronsay (1 hr 35 mins), Papa Westray (1 hr 50 mins), North Ronaldsay (2 hrs 30 mins) ('North Isles service') (timings are direct from Kirkwall – sailings via other islands take longer; *EARL SIGURD, EARL THORFINN, VARAGEN*; 1/2 per day except Papa Westray which is twice weekly and North Ronaldsay which is weekly), Pierowall (Westray) – Papa Westray (25 mins; *GOLDEN MARIANA*; up to six per day (Summer service – passenger-only)), Kirkwall – Shapinsay (25 mins; *SHAPINSAY*; 6 per day), Houton (Mainland) to Lyness (Hoy) (35 mins; *HOY HEAD*; 5 per day), and Flotta (35 mins; *HOY HEAD*; 4 per day) ('South Isles service') (timings are direct from Houton – sailings via other islands take longer), Tingwall (Mainland) to Rousay (20 mins; *EYNHALLOW*; 6 per day), Egilsay (30 mins; *EYNHALLOW*; 5 per day) and Wyre (20 mins; *EYNHALLOW*; 5 per day) (timings are direct from Tingwall – sailings via other islands take longer), Stromness (Mainland) to Moaness (Hoy) (25 mins; *GRAEMSAY*; 2/3 per day) and Graemsay (25 mins; *GRAEMSAY*; 2/3 per day) (passenger/cargo service – cars not normally conveyed).

1	EARL SIGURD	771t	90	12.5k	45.0m	190P	26C	-	BA	UK	8902711
2	EARL THORFINN	771t	90	12.5k	45.0m	190P	26C	-	BA	UK	8902723
3	EYNHALLOW	104t	87	10.5k	28.8m	95P	11C	-	BA	UK	8960880
4p	GOLDEN MARIANA	33t	73	9.5k	15.2m	40P	0C	-	-	UK	

Arrow *(Miles Cowsill)*

Hamnavoe *(Miles Cowsill)*

Varagen *(Miles Cowsill)*

Earl Sigurd *(Miles Cowsill)*

5	GRAEMSAY	90t	96	10.0k	20.6m	73P	2C	-	C	UK	
6	HOY HEAD	358t	94	11.0k	53.5m	125P	24C	3L	BA	UK	9081722
7	SHAPINSAY	199t	89	10.0k	32.6m	91P	16C	-	BA	UK	8814184
8	THORSVOE	385t	91	10.6k	35.0m	122P	16C	-	BA	UK	9014743
9	VARAGEN	928t	88	14.5k	49.9m	144P	33C	5L	BA	UK	8818154

EARL SIGURD, EARL THORFINN Built by McTay Marine, Bromborough, Wirral, UK to inaugurate ro-ro working on the 'North Isles service'.

EYNHALLOW Built by David Abels Boat Builders, Bristol, UK to inaugurate ro-ro services from Tingwall (Mainland) to Rousay, Egilsay and Wyre. In 1991 she was lengthened by 5 metres, to increase car capacity.

GOLDEN MARIANA Built by Bideford Shipyard Ltd, Bideford, UK for *A J G England* of Padstow as a dual-purpose passenger and fishing vessel. In 1975 sold to *M MacKenzie* of Ullapool, then to *Pentland Ferries*, *Wide Firth Ferry* in 1982, and *Orkney Islands Council* in 1986. Passenger-only vessel. Generally operates summer-only feeder service between Pierowall (Westray) and Papa Westray.

GRAEMSAY Built by Ailsa Shipbuilding, Troon UK to operate between Stromness (Mainland), Moaness (Hoy) and Graemsay. Designed to offer an all-year-round service to these islands, primarily for passengers and cargo. Between October 2009 and January 2010 lengthened by 4.4 metres.

HOY HEAD Built by Appledore Shipbuilders Ltd, Appledore, UK to replace the THORSVOE on the 'South Isles service'. During winter 2012/13 extended by 14 metres at Cammell Laird Shiprepairers & Shipbuilders, Birkenhead, England.

SHAPINSAY Built by Yorkshire Drydock Ltd, Hull, UK for the service from Kirkwall (Mainland) to Shapinsay. In April 2011 lengthened by 6 metres at the Macduff Shipyards, Macduff, Scotland to increase car capacity from 12 to 16 and re-engined.

THORSVOE Built by Campbeltown Shipyard, Campbeltown, UK for the 'South Isles service'. In 1994 replaced by the new HOY HEAD and became the main reserve vessel for the fleet.

VARAGEN Built by Cochrane Shipbuilders, Selby, UK for *Orkney Ferries*, a private company established to start a new route between Gills Bay (Caithness, Scotland) and Burwick (South Ronaldsay, Orkney). However, due to problems with the terminals it was not possible to maintain regular services. In 1991, the company was taken over by *Orkney Islands Shipping Company* and the VARAGEN became part of their fleet, sharing the 'North Isles service' with the EARL SIGURD and the EARL THORFINN and replacing the freight vessel ISLANDER (494t, 1969).

P&O FERRIES

THE COMPANY *P&O Ferries Holdings Ltd* is a private sector company, a subsidiary of *Dubai World*, owned by the Government of Dubai. In Autumn 2002 *P&O North Sea Ferries*, P&O Irish Sea, *P&O Portsmouth* and *P&O Stena Line* (*Stena Line* involvement having ceased) were merged into a single operation.

MANAGEMENT Chief Executive Officer Helen Deeble, **Fleet Director** John Garner, **Finance Director** Karl Howarth, **Human Resources Director** Lesley Cotton, **Ports Director** Sue Mackenzie, **Chief Commercial Officer** Janette Bell, **Company Secretary** Susan Kitchin.

ADDRESSES *Head Office and Dover Services* Channel House, Channel View Road, Dover, Kent CT17 9TJ, *Hull* King George Dock, Hedon Road, Hull HU9 5QA, *Larne* P&O Irish Sea, Larne Harbour, Larne, Co Antrim BT40 1AW *Rotterdam* Beneluxhaven, Rotterdam (Europoort), Postbus 1123, 3180 Rozenburg, Netherlands, *Zeebrugge* Leopold II Dam 13, Havendam, 8380 Zeebrugge, Belgium.

TELEPHONE Administration *UK* +44 (0)1304 863000, **Passenger Reservations** *UK* 08716 64 64 64, *France* +33 (0)825 12 01 56, *Belgium* +32 (0)70 70 77 71, *The Netherlands* +31 (0)20 20 08333, *Spain* +34 (0)902 02 04 61, *Luxembourg* +34 (0)20 80 82 94. **Freight Reservations** *UK* 0870 6000 868, *Republic of Ireland* +353 (0)1 855 0522.

SECTION 1 – GB & IRELAND PASSENGER OPERATIONS

FAX Passenger Reservations *UK East and South Coast* +44 (0)1304 863464, *West Coast* 44 (0)02828 872195, *The Netherlands* +31 (0)118 1225 5215, *Belgium* +32 (0)50 54 71 12, **Freight Reservations** *Cairnryan* +44 (0)1581 200282, *Larne* +44 (0)28 2827 2477..

INTERNET Email customer.services@poferries.com **Website** www.poferries.com *(English, French, Dutch, German)* www.poirishsea.com *(English)* www.poferriesfreight.com *(English, French, German)*

ROUTES OPERATED Passenger Dover – Calais (1 hr 15 mins – 1 hr 30 mins; *PRIDE OF BURGUNDY, PRIDE OF CANTERBURY, PRIDE OF KENT, SPIRIT OF BRITAIN, SPIRIT OF FRANCE*; up to 25 per day), Hull – Zeebrugge (Belgium) (from 12 hrs 30 mins; *PRIDE OF BRUGES, PRIDE OF YORK*; 1 per day), Hull – Rotterdam (Beneluxhaven, Europoort) (The Netherlands) (from 10 hrs; *PRIDE OF HULL, PRIDE OF ROTTERDAM*; 1 per day), Cairnryan – Larne (1 hr 45 min; *EUROPEAN CAUSEWAY, EUROPEAN HIGHLANDER*; 7 per day), Liverpool – Dublin (8 hrs; *EUROPEAN ENDEAVOUR, NORBANK, NORBAY*; up to 3 per day (some sailings are freight only). **Freight-only** Dover – Calais (1 hr 30 mins; *EUROPEAN SEAWAY*; 2/3 per day (plus services on passenger ferries)), Tilbury – Zeebrugge (8 hrs; *NORSKY, NORSTREAM*; 10 per week), Middlesbrough (Teesport) – Rotterdam (Beneluxhaven, Europoort) (16 hrs; *ESTRADEN*; 3 per week), Middlesbrough (Teesport) – Zeebrugge (15 hrs 30 mins; *BORE SONG, MISTRAL*; 6 per week).

1	BORE SONG	25235t	11	18.5k	195.0m	12P	-	210T	A2	FI	9443566
2F	ESTRADEN	18205t	99	19.0k	162.7m	12P	130C	170T	A	FI	9181077
3	EUROPEAN CAUSEWAY	20646t	00	22.7k	159.5m	410P	315C	84T	BA2	BS	9208394
4	EUROPEAN ENDEAVOUR	22152t	00	22.5k	180.0m	366P	-	120L	BA2	BS	9181106
5	EUROPEAN HIGHLANDER	21128t	02	22.6k	162.7m	410P	315C	84T	BA2	BS	9244116
6F+	EUROPEAN SEAWAY	22986t	91	21.0k	179.7m	200P	-	120L	BA2	UK	9007283
7F	MISTRAL	10471t	98	22.0k	153.5m	12P	-	112T	A	FI	9183788
8	NORBANK	17464t	93	22.5k	166.7m	114P	-	125T	A	NL	9056583
9	NORBAY	17464t	92	21.5k	166.7m	114P	-	125T	A	BM	9056595
10F	NORSKY	19992t	99	20.0k	180.0m	12P	-	194T	A	FI	9186182
11F	NORSTREAM	19992t	99	20.0k	180.0m	12P	-	194T	A	FI	9186194
12	PRIDE OF BRUGES	31598t	87	18.5k	179.0m	1050P	310C	185T	A	NL	8503797
13	PRIDE OF BURGUNDY	28138t	92	21.0k	179.7m	1420P	465C	120L	BA2	UK	9015254
14	PRIDE OF CANTERBURY	30635t	91	21.0k	179.7m	2000P	537C	120L	BA2	UK	9007295
15	PRIDE OF HULL	59925t	01	22.0k	215.4m	1360P	205C	263T	AS	BS	9208629
16	PRIDE OF KENT	30635t	92	21.0k	179.7m	2000P	537C	120L	BA2	UK	9015266
17	PRIDE OF ROTTERDAM	59925t	00	22.0k	215.4m	1360P	205C	263T	AS	NL	9208617
18	PRIDE OF YORK	31785t	87	18.5k	179.0m	1050P	310C	185T	A	BS	8501957
19	SPIRIT OF BRITAIN	47592t	11	22.0k-	212.0m	2000P	194C	180L	BA2	UK	9524231
20	SPIRIT OF FRANCE	47592t	12	22.0k-	212.0m	2000P	194C	180L	BA2	UK	9533816

BORE SONG Built by Flensburger Schiffbau-Gesellschaft, Flensburg, Germany for *Bore Shipowners (Rettig Group Bore)* of Finland. In July 2011 chartered to *Mann Lines* to cover for the ESTRADEN'S refit. In September 2011 chartered to *P&O Ferries* and placed on the Middlesbrough – Zeebrugge route.

ESTRADEN Built as the ESTRADEN by Aker Finnyards, Rauma, Finland for *Rederi Ab Engship* (later *Bore Shipowners)* of Finland and chartered to *ArgoMann*. Later in 1999 renamed the AMAZON. In 2001 the charter was taken over by *Mann Lines* and in August she resumed the name ESTRADEN. In 2006 *Rederi AB Engship* was taken over by *Rettig Group Bore* and she remained on charter to *Mann Lines*. In January 2015 chartered to *P&O Ferries* to replace the WILHELMINE of *Cobelfret Ferries* on the Rotterdam – Middlesbrough (Teesport) service.

EUROPEAN CAUSEWAY Built by Mitsubishi Heavy Industries, Shimonoseki, Japan for *P&O Irish Sea* for the Cairnryan – Larne service.

EUROPEAN ENDEAVOUR Built as the MIDNIGHT MERCHANT by Astilleros Españoles SA, Seville, Spain for *Cenargo* (then owners of *NorseMerchant Ferries)*. On delivery, chartered to *Norfolkline* to operate as second

Eynhallow *(Miles Cowsill)*

Spirit of Britain *(Miles Cowsill)*

vessel on the Dover – Dunkerque (Ouest) service. In 2002 modified to allow two-deck loading. In 2006 chartered to *Acciona Trasmediterranea* of Spain and renamed the EL GRECO. Used on Mediterranean and Canary Island services. In 2007 sold to *P&O Ferries* and renamed the EUROPEAN ENDEAVOUR. Operated on the Dover – Calais route and as a re-fit relief vessel on Irish Sea routes. In May 2010 laid up. In February 2011 moved to the Liverpool – Dublin route.

EUROPEAN HIGHLANDER Built by Mitsubishi Heavy Industries, Shimonoseki, Japan for *P&O Irish Sea* for the Cairnryan – Larne service.

EUROPEAN SEAWAY Built by Schichau Seebeckwerft AG, Bremerhaven, Germany for *P&O European Ferries* for the Dover – Zeebrugge freight service. In 2000 a regular twice-daily freight-only Dover-Calais service was established, using this vessel which continued to operate to Zeebrugge at night. In 2001 car passengers (not foot or coach passengers) began to be conveyed on the Dover – Zeebrugge service. In 2003 the Zeebrugge service ended and she operated only between Dover and Calais in a freight-only mode. In 2004 withdrawn and laid up. In January 2005 returned to the Dover – Calais route. In July 2012 chartered to GLID, a joint venture between Centrica Renewable Energy Limited and EIG, for use by technicians working on the North Sea Lynn and Inner Dowsing wind farm array four miles off Skegness. In October 2012 returned to the Dover – Calais service. In April 2013 laid up at Tilbury. In August 2014 chartered as a wind farm accommodation and support vessel near the North German coast. In April 2015 returned to layup at Tilbury. In August 2015 returned to service on the Dover – Calais route.

MISTRAL Built by J J Sietas KG, Hamburg, Germany for *Godby Shipping AB* of Finland. Chartered to *Transfennica*. In 2003 chartered to *UPM-Kymmene Oy* of Finland and operated between Rauma and Santander. In 2005 chartered to *Finnlines*. Until the end of 2007 used on a Helsinki – Hamina – Zeebrugge service only available northbound for general traffic. From January 2008 operated on *UPM-Kymmene Seaways'* service from Hamina to Lübeck, Amsterdam and Tilbury. In June 2013 charter ended. During the ensuing period she undertook several short charters. In October 2014 chartered to *P&O Ferries* as second ship on the Zeebrugge – Middlesbrough (Teesport) service; she has also operated between Tilbury and Zeebrugge.

NORBANK Built by Van der Giessen-de Noord, Krimpen aan den IJssel, Rotterdam, The Netherlands for *North Sea Ferries* for the Hull – Rotterdam service. She was originally built for and chartered to *Nedlloyd* but the charter was taken over by *P&O* in 1996 and she was bought by *P&O* in 2003. She retains Dutch crew and registry. In May 2001 moved to the Felixstowe – Europoort route. In January 2002 transferred to *P&O Irish Sea* and operated on the Liverpool – Dublin route.

NORBAY Built by Van der Giessen-de Noord, Krimpen aan den IJssel, Rotterdam, The Netherlands for *North Sea Ferries* for the Hull – Rotterdam service. Owned by *P&O*. In January 2002 transferred to *P&O Irish Sea* and operated on the Liverpool – Dublin route.

NORSKY, NORSTREAM Built by Aker Finnyards, Rauma, Finland for *Bore Line* of Finland and chartered to *P&O North Sea Ferries*. They generally operated on the Teesport – Zeebrugge service. In September 2011, the NORSTREAM was moved to the Tilbury – Zeebrugge route. In January 2013, the NORSKY was also moved to the Tilbury – Zeebrugge route.

PRIDE OF BRUGES Built as the NORSUN by NKK, Tsurumi, Japan for the Hull – Rotterdam service of *North Sea Ferries*. She was owned by *Nedlloyd* and was sold to *P&O* in 1996 but retains Dutch crew and registry. In May 2001 replaced by the PRIDE OF ROTTERDAM and in July 2001, after a major refurbishment, she was transferred to the Hull – Zeebrugge service, replacing the NORSTAR (26919t, 1974). In 2003 renamed the PRIDE OF BRUGES.

PRIDE OF BURGUNDY Built by Schichau Seebeckwerft AG, Bremerhaven, Germany for *P&O European Ferries* for the Dover – Calais service. When construction started she was due to be a sister vessel to the EUROPEAN SEAWAY (see Section 3) called the EUROPEAN CAUSEWAY and operate on the Zeebrugge freight route. However, it was decided that she should be completed as a passenger/freight vessel (the design allowed for conversion) and she was launched as the PRIDE OF BURGUNDY. In 1998, transferred to *P&O Stena Line* and renamed the P&OSL BURGUNDY. In 2002 renamed the PO BURGUNDY and in 2003 renamed the PRIDE OF BURGUNDY. In 2004 she operated mainly in freight-only mode. In 2005 returned to full passenger service.

Pride of York *(Miles Cowsill)*

European Seaway *(Miles Cowsill)*

Pride of Kent *(Miles Cowsill)*

Norbank *(George Holland)*

PRIDE OF CANTERBURY Built as the EUROPEAN PATHWAY by Schichau Seebeckwerft AG, Bremerhaven, Germany for *P&O European Ferries* for the Dover – Zeebrugge freight service. In 1998 transferred to *P&O Stena Line*. In 2001 car/foot passengers were again conveyed on the route. In 2002/03 rebuilt as a full passenger vessel and renamed the PRIDE OF CANTERBURY; now operates between Dover and Calais.

PRIDE OF HULL Built by Fincantieri-Cantieri Navali Italiani SpA, Venice, Italy for *P&O North Sea Ferries* to replace (with the PRIDE OF ROTTERDAM) the NORSEA and NORSUN plus the freight vessels NORBAY and NORBANK on the Hull – Rotterdam service.

PRIDE OF KENT Built as the EUROPEAN HIGHWAY by Schichau Seebeckwerft AG, Bremerhaven, Germany for *P&O European Ferries* for the Dover – Zeebrugge freight service. In 1998 transferred to *P&O Stena Line*. In Summer 1999 she operated full-time between Dover and Calais. She returned to the Dover – Zeebrugge route in the autumn when the P&OSL AQUITAINE was transferred to the Dover – Calais service. In 2001 car/foot passengers were again conveyed on the route. In 2002/03 rebuilt as a full passenger vessel and renamed the PRIDE OF KENT; now operates between Dover and Calais.

PRIDE OF ROTTERDAM Built by Fincantieri-Cantieri Navali Italiani SpA, Venice, Italy. Keel laid as the PRIDE OF HULL but launched as the PRIDE OF ROTTERDAM. Owned by Dutch interests until 2006 when she was sold to *P&O Ferries*. Further details as the PRIDE OF HULL.

PRIDE OF YORK Built as the NORSEA by Govan Shipbuilders Ltd, Glasgow, UK for the Hull – Rotterdam service of *North Sea Ferries* (jointly owned by *P&O* and *The Royal Nedlloyd Group* of The Netherlands until 1996). In December 2001 she was replaced by the new PRIDE OF HULL and, after a two-month refurbishment, in 2002 transferred to the Hull – Zeebrugge service, replacing the NORLAND (26290t, 1974). In 2003 renamed the PRIDE OF YORK.

SPIRIT OF BRITAIN, SPIRIT OF FRANCE Built by STX Europe, Rauma, Finland for the Dover – Calais service. Car capacity relates to dedicated car deck only; additional cars can be accommodated on the freight decks as necessary.

PENTLAND FERRIES

THE COMPANY *Pentland Ferries* is a UK private sector company.

MANAGEMENT Managing Director Andrew Banks, **Designated Person Ashore** Kathryn Banks.

ADDRESS Pier Road, St Margaret's Hope, South Ronaldsay, Orkney KW17 2SW.

TELEPHONE Administration & Reservations +44 (0)1856 831226.

FAX Administration & Reservations +44 (0)1856 831697.

INTERNET Email sales@pentlandferries.co.uk **Website** www.pentlandferries.co.uk *(English)*

ROUTE OPERATED Gills Bay (Caithness) – St Margaret's Hope (South Ronaldsay, Orkney) (1 hour; *PENTALINA*; up to 4 per day).

| 1 | ORCADIA | 899t | 78 | 13.0k | 69.5m | - | 40C | - | AS | UK | 7615490 |
| 2 | PENTALINA | 2382t | 08 | 17.1k | 59.0m | 345P | 70C | 9L | A | UK | 9437969 |

ORCADIA Built as the SATURN by Ailsa Shipbuilding, Troon for *Caledonian MacBrayne* and initially used on the Wemyss Bay – Rothesay services. Between 1986 and 2005 she usually rotated on this service and services from Gourock; until 2000 this, in summer, included Clyde cruising but this was not repeated in 2001. In the summers 2005 – 2010, she operated additional peak summer sailings between Ardrossan and Brodick with a maximum capacity of 250 passengers. In October 2010 she took over the Gourock – Dunoon service. In June 2011 replaced by *Argyll Ferries* passenger ferries. During Summer 2011 she operated additional sailings between Ardrossan and Brodick. In September returned to the Gourock – Dunoon route to provide additional capacity for the Cowal Games. She was then laid up. In February 2015 sold to *Pentland Ferries* and renamed the ORCADIA.

PENTALINA Catamaran built by FBMA Marine, Cebu, Philippines for *Pentland Ferries*.

European Endeavour *(Gordon Hislip)*

European Highlander *(Gordon Hislip)*

Orcadia *(Miles Cowsill)*

Pentalina *(Miles Cowsill)*

Red Osprey *(Andrew Cooke)*

Red Jet 6 *(Darren Holdaway)*

Red Falcon *(Andrew Cooke)*

RED FUNNEL FERRIES

THE COMPANY Red Funnel Ferries is the trading name of the Southampton, Isle of Wight and South of England Royal Mail Steam Packet Company Limited, a British private sector company. The company was acquired by JP Morgan International Capital Corporation in 2000; it was purchased by the management in 2004 and in 2007 it was sold to *Infracapital Partners LP* – the infrastructure fund of the *Prudential Group*.

MANAGEMENT Managing Director Kevin George, **Commercial Director** Colin Hetherington.

ADDRESS 12 Bugle Street, Southampton SO14 2JY.

TELEPHONE Administration +44 (0)23 8024 8500, **Reservations *UK*** 0844 844 9988, ***Elsewhere*** +44 (0)23 8001 9192.

FAX Administration & Reservations *UK* +44 (0)23 8024 8501.

INTERNET Email post@redfunnel.co.uk **Website** www.redfunnel.co.uk *(English)*

ROUTES OPERATED Conventional Ferries Southampton – East Cowes (55 mins; *RED EAGLE, RED FALCON, RED OSPREY*; hourly). **Fast Passenger Ferries** Southampton – Cowes (22 mins; *RED JET 3, RED JET 4, RED JET 6*; every hour or half hour).

1	RED EAGLE	3953t	96	13.0k	93.2m	895P	200C	18L	BA	UK	9117337
2	RED FALCON	3953t	94	13.0k	93.2m	895P	200C	18L	BA	UK	9064047
3»p	RED JET 3	213t	98	33.0k	32.9m	190P	0C	0L	-	UK	9182758
4»p	RED JET 4	342t	03	35.0k	39.8m	277P	0C	0L	-	UK	9295854
5»p	RED JET 6	-	16	35.0k	40.0m	275P	0C	0L	-	UK	9788083
6	RED OSPREY	3953t	94	13.0k	93.2m	895P	200C	18L	BA	UK	9064059

RED EAGLE Built by Ferguson Shipbuilders, Port Glasgow, UK for the Southampton – East Cowes service. During Winter 2004/05 stretched by 10 metres and height raised by 3 metres at Gdansk, Poland.

RED FALCON Built by Ferguson Shipbuilders, Port Glasgow, UK for the Southampton – East Cowes service. In 2004 stretched by 10 metres and height raised by 3 metres at Gdansk, Poland. 'In spring 2014 she received a £2m upgrade'.

RED JET 3 FBM Marine catamaran built at Isle of Wight, UK.

RED JET 4 North West Bay Ships Pty Ltd catamaran built in Hobart, Tasmania, Australia.

RED JET 6 Built by Shemara Refit LLP, Venture Quays, Cowes, Isle of Wight, UK.

RED OSPREY Built by Ferguson Shipbuilders, Port Glasgow, UK for the Southampton – East Cowes service. In 2003 stretched by 10 metres and height raised by 3 metres at Gdansk, Poland. In spring 2015 she received a £2m upgrade (as RED FALCON in 2015).

SHETLAND ISLANDS COUNCIL

THE COMPANY *Shetland Islands Council* is a British local government authority.

MANAGEMENT Ferry Services Manager Jim Mouatt, **Marine Superintendent** Kevin Main.

ADDRESS Port Administration Building, Sella Ness, Mossbank, Shetland ZE2 9QR.

TELEPHONE Administration +44 (0)1806 244234, 244266, **Reservations *Yell Sound & Bluemull*** +44 (0)1595 745804, ***Fair Isle*** +44 (0)1595 760363, ***Whalsay*** +44(0)1595 745804, ***Skerries*** +44 (0)1595 745804, ***Papa Stour*** +44 (0)1595 745804.

TELEPHONE Administration +44 (0)1806 244234, 244266, **Reservations *Yell Sound & Bluemull*** +44 (0)1595 745804, ***Fair Isle*** +44 (0)1595 760363, ***Whalsay*** +44(0)1595 745804, ***Skerries*** +44 (0)1595 745804, ***Papa Stour*** +44 (0)1595 745804.

FAX +44 (0)1806 244232.

INTERNET Email ferries@sic.shetland.gov.uk **Website:** www.shetland.gov.uk/ferries *(English)*

ROUTES OPERATED Yell Sound Service Toft (Mainland) – Ulsta (Yell) (20 mins; *DAGALIEN, DAGGRI*; up to 26 per day), **Bluemull Sound Service** (Gutcher (Yell) – Belmont (Unst) (10 mins; *BIGGA, FIVLA, GEIRA*; up to 28 per day), Gutcher – Hamars Ness (Fetlar) (25 mins; *BIGGA, FIVLA, GEIRA*; up to 8 per day), **Bressay** Lerwick (Mainland) – Maryfield (Bressay) (5 mins; *LEIRNA*; up to 23 per day), **Whalsay** Laxo/Vidlin (Mainland) – Symbister (Whalsay) (30-45 mins; *HENDRA, LINGA*; up to 18 per day), **Skerries** Vidlin (Mainland) – Out Skerries (1 hr 30 mins; *FILLA*; up to 10 per week), Out Skerries – Lerwick (3 hours; *FILLA*; 2 per week), **Fair Isle** (Grutness (Mainland) – Fair Isle (3 hrs; *GOOD SHEPHERD IV*; 2 per week), **Papa Stour** West Burrafirth (Mainland) – Papa Stour (40 mins; *SNOLDA*; up to 7 per week).

1	BIGGA	274t	91	11.0k	33.5m	96P	21C	4L	BA	UK	9000821
2	DAGALIEN	1861t	04	12.0k	61m	145P	30C	4L	BA	UK	9291626
3	DAGGRI	1861t	04	12.0k	61m	145P	30C	4L	BA	UK	9291614
4	FILLA	356t	03	12.0k	35.5m	30P	10C	2L	BA	UK	9269192
5	FIVLA	230t	85	11.0k	29.9m	95P	15C	4L	BA	UK	8410237
6	GEIRA	226t	88	10.8k	29.9m	95P	15C	4L	BA	UK	8712489
7	GOOD SHEPHERD IV	76t	86	10.0k	18.3m	12P	1C	0L	C	UK	
8	HENDRA	248	82	11.0k	33.8m	100P	18C	4L	BA	UK	8200254
9	LEIRNA	420t	92	9.0k	35.1m	100P	20C	4L	BA	UK	9050199
10	LINGA	658t	01	11.0k	35.8m	100P	16C	2L	BA	UK	9242170
11	SNOLDA	130t	83	9.0k	24.4m	12P	6C	1L	A	UK	8302090

BIGGA Built by JW Miller & Sons Ltd, St Monans, Fife, UK. Used on the Toft – Ulsta service. In 2005 moved to the Bluemull Sound service.

DAGALIEN, DAGGRI Built by Stocznia Polnócna, Gdansk, Poland to replace the BIGGA and HENDRA on Toft – Ulsta service.

FILLA Built by Stocznia Polnócna, Gdansk, Poland for the Lerwick /Vidlin – Out Skerries service. She looks like an oil rig supply vessel and is capable of transporting fresh water for replenishing the tanks on the Skerries in case of drought.

FIVLA Built by Ailsa Shipbuilding, Troon, UK. Now a spare vessel, though often used on the Bluemull service.

GEIRA Built by Richard Dunston (Hessle), Hessle, UK. Formerly used on the Laxo – Symbister route. Replaced by the HENDRA in 2005 and moved to the Bluemull Sound service.

GOOD SHEPHERD IV Built by JW Miller & Sons Ltd, St Monans, Fife, UK. Used on the service between Grutness (Mainland) and Fair Isle. Vehicles conveyed by special arrangement and generally consist of agricultural vehicles. She is pulled up on the marine slip on Fair Isle at the conclusion of each voyage.

HENDRA Built by McTay Marine, Bromborough, Wirral, UK for the Laxo – Symbister service. In 2002 transferred to the Toft – Ulsta service. In 2004 replaced by new vessels DAGGRI and DAGALIEN and moved to the Bluemull Sound service. In May 2005 returned to the Laxo – Symbister service as second vessel.

LEIRNA Built by Ferguson Shipbuilders, Port Glasgow, UK. Used on the Lerwick – Maryfield (Bressay) service.

LINGA Built by Stocznia Polnócna, Gdansk, Poland. Used on the Laxo – Symbister service.

SNOLDA Built as the FILLA by Sigbjorn Iversen, Flekkefjord, Norway. Used on the Lerwick (Mainland) – Out Skerries and Vidlin (Mainland) – Out Skerries services. At other times she operated freight and charter services around the Shetland Archipelago. She resembles a miniature oil rig supply vessel. Passenger capacity was originally 20 from 1st April to 31st October inclusive but is now 12 all year. In 2003 renamed the SNOLDA; replaced by the new FILLA and, in 2004, transferred to the West Burrafirth – Papa Stour route.

Leirna *(Miles Cowsill)*

Hendra *(Miles Cowsill)*

STENA LINE

MANAGEMENT Route Manager North Sea Annika Hult, **Route Manager Irish Sea North** Paul Grant, **Route Manager Irish Sea South** Ian Davies.

ADDRESS UK Stena House, Station Approach, Holyhead, Anglesey LL65 1DQ, **The Netherlands** PO Box 2, 3150 AA, Hook of Holland, The Netherlands.

TELEPHONE Administration UK +44 (0)1407) 606631, **The Netherlands** +31 (0)174 389333, **Reservations UK** 0844 7707070 (from UK only), **The Netherlands** +31 (0)174 315811.

FAX Administration & Reservations UK +44 (0)1407 606811, **The Netherlands** +31 (0)174 387045, **Telex** 31272.

INTERNET Email info@stenaline.com **Website** www.stenaline.co.uk *(English)*

ROUTES OPERATED Conventional Ferries Cairnryan – Belfast (2 hrs 15 mins; *STENA SUPERFAST VII*, *STENA SUPERFAST VII*; up to 6 per day, Port of Liverpool (Twelve Quays River Terminal, Birkenhead) – Belfast (8 hrs; *STENA PERFORMER (freight only)*, *STENA LAGAN, STENA MERSEY*; 1 per day (Mon), 2 per day (Sun, Tue-Sat)), Holyhead – Dublin (3 hrs 15 mins; *STENA ADVENTURER, STENA SUPERFAST X*; 4 per day), Fishguard – Rosslare (3 hrs 30 mins; *STENA EUROPE*; 2 per day), Rosslare – Cherbourg (17 – 20 hrs; *STENA HORIZON*; 3 per week), Harwich – Hook of Holland (The Netherlands) (7 hrs 30 mins; *STENA BRITANNICA, STENA HOLLANDICA*; 2 per day), **Freight Ferries** Heysham – Belfast (7 hrs; *STENA HIBERNIA, STENA PRECISION*; 2 per day), Harwich – Rotterdam (8 hrs; *CAPUCINE, SEVERINE*; 11 per week), Killingholme – Hook of Holland (11 hrs; *STENA TRANSIT, STENA TRANSPORTER*; 1 per day), Killingholme – Rotterdam (13 hrs; *STENA SCOTIA*; 3 per week).

1F	CAPUCINE	16342t	11	16.0k	150.0m	12P	-	140T	A	UK	9539066
2F	SEVERINE	16342t	12	16.0k	150.0m	12P	-	140T	A	NL	9539078
3	STENA ADVENTURER	43532t	03	22.0k	210.8m	1500P	-	210L	BA2	UK	9235529
4	STENA BRITANNICA	63600t	10	22.0k	240.0m	1200P	-	300T	BA2	UK	9419175
5	STENA EUROPE	24828t	81	20.5k	149.0m	2076P	456C	60T	BA	UK	7901760
6F	STENA HIBERNIA	13017t	96	18.6k	142.5m	12P	-	114T	A	NL	9121637
7	STENA HOLLANDICA	63600t	10	22.5k	240.0m	1200P	-	300T	BA2	NL	9419163
8	STENA HORIZON	26500t	06	23.5k	186.5m	720P	160C	135L	A	IT	9332559
9	STENA LAGAN	27510t	05	23.5k	186.5m	720P	160C	135T	A	UK	9329849
10	STENA MERSEY	27510t	05	23.5k	186.5m	720P	160C	135T	A	UK	9329851
11F	STENA PERFORMER	19722t	12	21.0k	142.0m	12P	-	151T	A	IM	9506227
12F	STENA PRECISION	19722t	12	21.0k	142.0m	12P	-	151T	A	IM	9506239
13F	STENA SCOTIA	13017t	96	18.6k	142.5m	12P	-	114T	A	NL	9121625
14	STENA SUPERFAST VII	30285t	01	22.0k	203.3m	1200P	660C	110L	BA2	UK	9198941
15	STENA SUPERFAST VIII	30285t	01	22.0k	203.3m	1200P	660C	110L	BA2	UK	9198953
16	STENA SUPERFAST X	30285t	02	22.0k	203.3m	1200P	660C	110L	BA2	UK	9211511
17F+	STENA TRANSIT	34700t	11	22.2k	212.0m	300P	-	290T	A2	NL	9469388
18F+	STENA TRANSPORTER	34700t	11	22.2k	212.0m	300P	-	290T	A2	NL	9469376

CAPUCINE, SEVERINE Built by the Kyokuyo Shipyard, Shimonoseki, Japan for *CLdN*. Initially operated on their Ipswich – Rotterdam service. This service was suspended in August 2012. In September, they were chartered to *Stena Line* and placed on the Harwich – Rotterdam service.

STENA ADVENTURER Ro-pax vessel built by Hyundai Heavy Industries, Ulsan, South Korea, for *Stena RoRo* and chartered to *Stena Line* to operate between Holyhead and Dublin.

STENA BRITANNICA Built by Waden Yards in Wismar and Warnemünde, Germany, for *Stena Rederi* (bow sections constructed at Warnemünde and stern and final assembly at Wismar). Replaced the 2003 built STENA BRITANNICA on the Harwich – Hook of Holland service.

Stena Europe *(Henk van der Lugt)*

Stena Superfast VII *(Darren Holdaway)*

Stena Britannica *(Rob de Visser)*

Stena Transporter *(Rob de Visser)*

Stena Horizon *(Gordon Hislip)*

Capucine *(Miles Cowsill)*

Stena Superfast X *(George Holland)*

STENA EUROPE Built as the KRONPRINSESSAN VICTORIA by Götaverken Arendal AB, Gothenburg, Sweden for *Göteborg-Frederikshavn Linjen* of Sweden (trading as *Sessan Linjen*) for their Gothenburg – Frederikshavn service. Shortly after delivery, the company was taken over by *Stena Line* and services were marketed as *Stena-Sessan Line* for a period. In 1982 she was converted to an overnight ferry by changing one vehicle deck into two additional decks of cabins and she was switched to the Gothenburg – Kiel route (with, during the summer, daytime runs from Gothenburg to Frederikshavn and Kiel to Korsør (Denmark)). In 1989 she was transferred to the Oslo – Frederikshavn route and renamed the STENA SAGA. In 1994, transferred to *Stena Line BV*, renamed the STENA EUROPE and operated between Hook of Holland and Harwich. She was withdrawn in June 1997, transferred to the *Lion Ferry* (a *Stena Line* subsidiary) Karlskrona – Gdynia service and renamed the LION EUROPE. In 1998 she was transferred back to *Stena Line* (remaining on the same route) and renamed the STENA EUROPE. In early 2002 the cabins installed in 1982 were removed and other modifications made and she was transferred to the Fishguard – Rosslare route.

STENA HIBERNIA Built as the MAERSK IMPORTER by Miho Shipyard, Shimizu, Japan for *Norfolkline*. Used on the Scheveningen (from 2007 Vlaardingen) – Felixstowe service. In October 2009 moved to the Heysham-Belfast service. In July 2010 renamed the HIBERNIA SEAWAYS. In July 2011 renamed the STENA HIBERNIA. In September 2012 transferred to *Stena RoRo*. In November chartered to *Stena Line* and placed on the Birkenhead – Belfast service. In September 2015 moved to the Heysham – Belfast route.

STENA HOLLANDICA Built by Nordic Yards in Wismar and Warnemünde, Germany, for *Stena Rederi* (bow sections constructed at Warnemünde and stern and final assembly at Wismar) to replace the previous STENA HOLLANDICA on the Harwich – Hook of Holland service. Entered service May 2010.

STENA HORIZON Built as the CARTOUR BETA by CN Visentini, Porto Viro, Italy for Levantina Trasporti of Italy. Chartered to *Caronte & Tourist* of Italy and operated between Messina and Salerno (Sicily). In October 2011 chartered to *Celtic Link Ferries*, renamed the CELTIC HORIZON and placed on the Rosslare – Cherbourg route. In March 2014 service and charter taken over by *Stena Line*. Renamed the STENA HORIZON.

STENA LAGAN, STENA MERSEY Built as the LAGAN VIKING and MERSEY VIKING by CN Visentini, Donada, Italy for *Levantina Trasporti* of Italy. Chartered to *NorseMerchant Ferries* and placed on the Birkenhead – Belfast route. In 2008 sold to *Norfolkline*, then resold to *Epic Shipping* and chartered back. In August 2010, following *Norfolkline's* purchase by *DFDS Seaways*, they were renamed the LAGAN SEAWAYS and MERSEY SEAWAYS respectively. Between January and July 2011 they were operated by *Stena Line Irish Sea Ferries*, a 'stand-alone' company pending consideration of a take-over by *Stena Line* by the UK and Irish competition authorities. In July 2011 the take-over was confirmed and in August 2011 they were renamed the STENA LAGAN and STENA MERSEY. In April 2012 they were sold to *Stena RoRo* and chartered back by *Stena Line*.

STENA PERFORMER Built as the SEATRUCK PERFORMANCE by Flensburger Schiffbau-Gesellschaft, Flensburg, Germany for *Seatruck Ferries*. In September 2012 chartered to *Stena Line* to operate between Heysham and Belfast and renamed the STENA PERFORMER. In September 2015 moved to the Birkenhead – Belfast route.

STENA PRECISION Built as the SEATRUCK PRECISION by Flensburger Schiffbau-Gesellschaft, Flensburg, Germany for *Seatruck Ferries*. In September 2012 chartered to *Stena Line* to operate between Heysham and Belfast and renamed the STENA PRECISION.

STENA SCOTIA Built as the MAERSK EXPORTER by Miho Shipyard, Shimizu, Japan for *Norfolkline*. Used on the Scheveningen (from 2007 Vlaardingen) – Felixstowe service until March 2009 when she was moved to the Heysham – Belfast route. In July 2010 renamed the SCOTIA SEAWAYS. In July 2011 renamed the STENA SCOTIA. In September 2013 transferred to *Stena RoRo* and placed on the charter market. In September 2014 chartered to *Stena Line* and inaugurated a new service between Rotterdam and Killingholme

STENA SUPERFAST VII, STENA SUPERFAST VIII Built as the SUPERFAST VII and SUPERFAST VIII by Howaldtswerke Deutsche Werft AG, Kiel, Germany for *Attica Enterprises* (now *Attica Group*) for use by *Superfast Ferries* between Rostock and Hanko. In 2006 sold to *Tallink*. The Finnish terminal was transferred to Helsinki and daily return trips between Helsinki and Tallinn were introduced. These ceased in September 2008. The operation was ceased for the winter season in December 2009 and 2010. Service resumed at the end of April 2010 and 2011. In August 2011 chartered to *Stena Line* for three years (with an option to extend by one year) and renamed the STENA SUPERFAST VII, STENA SUPERFAST VIII. In November 2011, after a major refit, they were placed on a service between Cairnryan and Belfast (replacing the Stranraer – Belfast service).

STENA SUPERFAST X Built as the SUPERFAST X by Howaldtswerke Deutsche Werft AG, Kiel, Germany for *Attica Enterprises* (now *Attica Group*) for use by *Superfast Ferries*. In May 2002 she and the SUPERFAST IX (see ATLANTIC VISION, *Tallink*, Section 6) began operating between Rosyth (Scotland) and Zeebrugge. In 2004 fitted with additional cabins and conference/seating areas. In 2007 sold to *Veolia Transportation* and renamed the JEAN NICOLI. Chartered to *CoTuNav* of Tunisia and operated between France/Italy and Tunisia. Later chartered to *ANEK Lines* of Greece and operated on the Patras – Corfu – Igoumenitsa – Venice route. In July 2008 chartered to *SeaFrance* and renamed the SEAFRANCE MOLIERE. After modifications she was placed on the Dover – Calais route. In November 2011 laid up. In January 2012 offered for sale or charter. In July 2012 sold to *Scapino Shipping Ltd* of Monaco and renamed the MOLIERE. In October 2012 chartered to the *DFDS/LD Lines* joint venture and, in November, renamed the DIEPPE SEAWAYS and introduced onto the Dover – Calais service. In May 2014 sold to *Stena Line North Sea Ltd*. In December 2014 charter ended. Refurbished and, in March 2015, chartered to *Stena Line*, renamed the STENA SUPERFAST X and placed on the Holyhead – Dublin route.

STENA TRANSIT, STENA TRANSPORTER Built by Samsung Heavy Industries, Koje, South Korea. Used on the Hook of Holland – Killingholme service.

Under construction

Four new ferries are on order. As use is not yet known; they are shown in Section 7.

WESTERN FERRIES

THE COMPANY *Western Ferries (Clyde) Ltd* is a British private sector company.

MANAGEMENT Managing Director Gordon Ross.

ADDRESS Hunter's Quay, Dunoon, Argyll PA23 8HJ.

TELEPHONE Administration +44 (0)1369 704452, **Reservations** Not applicable.

INTERNET Email enquiries@western-ferries.co.uk **Website** www.western-ferries.co.uk *(English)*

ROUTE OPERATED McInroy's Point (Gourock) – Hunter's Quay (Dunoon) (20 mins; *SOUND OF SCARBA, SOUND OF SEIL, SOUND OF SHUNA, SOUND OF SOAY*; every 20 mins (15 mins in peaks)).

1	SOUND OF SCARBA	489t	01	11.0k	49.95m	220P	40C	4/5L	BA	UK	9237424
2	SOUND OF SEIL	497t	13	11.0k	49.95m	220P	40C	4/5L	BA	UK	9665217
3	SOUND OF SHUNA	489t	03	11.0k	49.95m	220P	40C	4/5L	BA	UK	9289441
4	SOUND OF SOAY	497t	13	11.0k	49.95m	220P	40C	4/5L	BA	UK	9665229

SOUND OF SCARBA, SOUND OF SHUNA Built by Ferguson Shipbuilders, Port Glasgow, UK for *Western Ferries*.

SOUND OF SEIL, SOUND OF SOAY Built by Cammell Laird Shiprepairers & Shipbuilders, Birkenhead, UK for *Western Ferries*.

Sound of Scarba *(Miles Cowsill)*

WIGHTLINK

THE COMPANY *Wightlink* is a British private sector company, owned by the *Balfour Beatty Infrastructure Partners LLP*. The routes and vessels were previously part of *Sealink (British Rail)* but were excluded from the purchase of most of the *Sealink* operations by *Stena Line AB* in 1990. They remained in *Sea Containers'* ownership until purchased by *CINVen* Ltd, a venture capital company in 1995. The company was the subject of a management buy-out financed by the *Royal Bank of Scotland* in 2001 and was sold to the *Macquarie Group* of Australia in 2005. It was purchased by *Balfour Beatty Infrastructure Partners LLP* in February 2015.

MANAGEMENT Interim Chief Executive John Burrows, **Head of Marketing** Mark Persad, **Commercial Director** Clive Tilley.

ADDRESS Gunwharf Road, Portsmouth PO1 2LA.

TELEPHONE Administration and Reservations +44 (0)333 999 7333.

INTERNET Email bookings@wightlink.co.uk **Website** www.wightlink.co.uk *(English, Dutch, French, German)*

ROUTES OPERATED Conventional Ferries Lymington – Yarmouth (Isle of Wight) (approx 35 mins; *WIGHT LIGHT, WIGHT SKY*, hourly), Portsmouth – Fishbourne (Isle of Wight) (approx 35 mins; *ST. CECILIA, ST. CLARE, ST. FAITH, WIGHT SUN*; half-hourly or hourly depending on time of day). **Fast Passenger Ferries** Portsmouth – Ryde (Isle of Wight) (passenger-only) (under 20 mins; *WIGHT RYDER I, WIGHT RYDER II*; 2 per hour).

1	ST. CECILIA	2968t	86	12.0k	77.0m	771P	142C	12L	BA	UK	8518546
2	ST. CLARE	5359t	01	13.0k	86.0m	878P	186C	-	BA2	UK	9236949
3	ST. FAITH	3009t	89	12.5k	77.0m	771P	142C	12L	BA	UK	8907228
4	WIGHT LIGHT	2546t	08	11.0k	62.4m	360P	65C	-	BA	UK	9446972
5»p	WIGHT RYDER I	520t	09	20.0k	40.9m	260P	0C	-	-	UK	9512537
6»p	WIGHT RYDER II	520t	09	20.0k	40.9m	260P	0C	-	-	UK	9512549
7	WIGHT SKY	2456t	08	11.0k	62.4m	360P	65C	-	BA	UK	9446984
8	WIGHT SUN	2546t	09	11.0k	62.4m	360P	65C	-	BA	UK	9490416

ST. CECILIA, ST FAITH Built by Cochrane Shipbuilders, Selby, UK for *Sealink British Ferries* for the Portsmouth – Fishbourne service.

ST. CLARE Built by Stocznia Remontowa, Gdansk, Poland for the Portsmouth – Fishbourne service. She is a double-ended ferry with a central bridge. During winter 2015/16 modified for double deck loading.

WIGHT LIGHT, WIGHT SKY, WIGHT SUN Built by Brodogradilište Kraljevica, Croatia for the Lymington – Yarmouth route. One of these ships now operates on the Portsmouth – Fishbourne route.

WIGHT RYDER I, WIGHT RYDER II Catamarans built by FBMA Marine, Balamban, Cebu, Philippines. Operate on the Portsmouth – Ryde service.

Note: When one of the 'Wight Riders' is unavailable a replacement vessel is usually chartered. This is generally the SOLENT CAT of *Solent & Wightline Cruises* – 74t, 2000, 13k, 20.1m, 250 passengers, catamaran.

Under Construction

9	NEWBUILDING	-	18	-	89.7m	1200P	178C	-	BA2	UK	-

NEWBUILDING Under construction by the Cemre Shipyard, Yalova, Turkey. She will be hybrid diesel/battery electric vessel.

Wight Sun *(Andrew Cooke)*

St Cecilia *(George Holland)*

Glenachulish *(John Hendy)*

SECTION 2 – MINOR FERRY OPERATORS

ARGYLL AND BUTE COUNCIL

THE COMPANY *Argyll and Bute Council* is a British local government authority.

Head of Economic Development and Strategic Transportation Jim Smith,

Marine Operations Manager Stewart Clark.

ADDRESS 1A Manse Brae, Lochgilphead, Argyll PA31 8RD.

TELEPHONE Administration +44 (0)1546 604673.

FAX Administration +44 (0)1546 604738.

INTERNET Email stewart.clark@argyll-bute.gov.uk **Website** www.argyll-bute.gov.uk/transport-and-streets/ferry-travel

ROUTES OPERATED Vehicle ferries Seil – Luing (5 mins; *BELNAHUA*; approx half-hourly), Port Askaig (Islay) – Feolin (Jura) (5 mins; *EILEAN DHIURA*; approx half-hourly). **Passenger-only ferries** Port Appin – Lismore (10 mins; *THE LISMORE*; approx hourly), Ellenabeich – Easdale (5 mins; *EASDALE*; approx quarter-hourly).

1	BELNAHUA	35t	72	8.0k	17.1m	40P	5C	1L	BA	UK
2p	EASDALE	-	93	6.5k	6.4m	11P	0C	0L	-	UK
3	EILEAN DHIURA	86t	98	9.0k	25.6m	50P	13C	1L	BA	UK
4p	THE LISMORE	12t	88	8.0k	9.7m	20P	0C	0L	-	UK

BELNAHUA Built by Campbeltown Shipyard, Campbeltown, UK for *Argyll County Council* for the Seil – Luing service. In 1975, following local government reorganisation, transferred to *Strathclyde Regional Council*. In 1996, transferred to *Argyll and Bute Council*.

EASDALE Built for *Strathclyde Regional Council* for the Ellenabeich – Easdale passenger-only service. In 1996, following local government reorganisation, transferred to *Argyll and Bute Council*.

EILEAN DHIURA Built by McTay Marine, Bromborough, Wirral, UK for *Argyll and Bute Council* to replace the *Western Ferries (Argyll)* SOUND OF GIGHA on the Islay – Jura route. *ASP Ship Management* manage and operate this vessel on behalf of *Argyll and Bute Council*.

THE LISMORE Built for *Strathclyde Regional Council* for the Port Appin – Lismore passenger-only service. In 1996, following local government reorganisation, transferred to *Argyll and Bute Council*.

ARRANMORE FAST FERRIES

THE COMPANY *Arranmore Fast Ferries* is a Republic of Ireland private sector company.

MANAGEMENT Managing Director Seamus Boyle.

ADDRESS Leabgarrow, Arranmore, County Donegal, Republic of Ireland.

TELEPHONE Administration & Reservations +353 (0)87 3171810**.**

INTERNET Email: info.fastferry@gmail.com **Website** www.arranmorefastferry.com *(English).* App can be downloaded from Twitter – @Arranmore Ferry

ROUTE OPERATED Burtonport (County Donegal) – Leabgarrow (Arranmore Island) (20 mins; *MORVERN*; up to 8 per day).

1	MORVERN	83t	73	8.0k	26.6m	96P	10C	-	B	IR
2p	OCEAN WARRIOR	18t	89	18.0k	14.3m	12P	0C	-	-	IR

MORVERN Built by James Lamont & Co Ltd, Port Glasgow, UK for *Caledonian MacBrayne*. After service on a number of routes she was, after 1979, the main vessel on the Fionnphort (Mull) – Iona service. In 1992 she was replaced by the LOCH BUIE and became a spare vessel. In 1995 sold to *Arranmore Island Ferry Services*. In 2001 sold to *Bere Island Ferries*. In February 2010 refurbished by Bere Island Boatyard and sold to *Arranmore Charters*. Extended in June 2012.

OCEAN WARRIOR Built by FBM Marine, Cowes, Isle of Wight as an RNLI Tyne class lifeboat ALEXANDER COUTANACHE (No1157) and operated at St Helier, Channel Islands until June 2009 when she became a relief vessel. Bought by *Arranmore Fast Ferries* in December 2014 and renamed the OCEAN WARRIOR.

ARRANMORE ISLAND FERRY SERVICES

THE COMPANY *Arranmore Island Ferry Services (Bád Farrantoireacht Arainn Mhór)* is a Republic of Ireland company, supported by *Roinn na Gaeltachta (The Gaeltacht Authority)*, a semi-state-owned body responsible for tourism and development in the Irish-speaking areas of The Republic of Ireland.

MANAGEMENT Managing Director Dominic Sweeney.

ADDRESS Cara na nOilean, Burtonport Pier, Letterkenny, Co. Donegal, Republic of Ireland.

TELEPHONE Administration & Reservations *Arranmore Island Service* +353 (0)7495 20532, +353 (0)7495 42233, *Lough Swilly Service* +353 (0)87 2112331.

INTERNET Email arranmoreferry@gmail.com **Websites** www.arranmoreferry.com swillyferry.com *(English)*

ROUTES OPERATED *Arranmore Island Service* Burtonport (County Donegal) – Leabgarrow (Arranmore Island) (15 mins; **COLL, RHUM**; up to 10 per day (Summer), 8 per day (Winter)), *Lough Swilly Service (summer only)* Buncrana (County Donegal) – Rathmullan (County Donegal) (20 mins; **COLL**; up to 8 per day).

1	COLL	69t	74	8.0k	25.3m	96P	6C	-	B	IR
2	RHUM	69t	73	8.0k	25.3m	96P	6C	-	B	IR

COLL Built by James Lamont & Co Ltd, Port Glasgow, UK for *Caledonian MacBrayne*. For several years she was employed mainly in a relief capacity. In 1986 she took over the Tobermory (Mull) – Kilchoan service from a passenger-only vessel; the conveyance of vehicles was not inaugurated until 1991. In 1996 she was transferred to the Oban – Lismore route. In 1998 she was sold to *Arranmore Island Ferry Services*.

RHUM Built by James Lamont & Co Ltd, Port Glasgow, UK for *Caledonian MacBrayne*. Until 1987, she was used primarily on the Claonaig – Lochranza (Arran) service. After that time she served on various routes. In 1994 she inaugurated a new service between Tarbert (Loch Fyne) and Portavadie. In 1997 she operated between Kyles Scalpay and Scalpay until the opening of the new bridge on 16th December 1997. In 1998 she was sold to *Arranmore Island Ferry Services*.

BERE ISLAND FERRIES

THE COMPANY *Bere Island Ferries Ltd* is a Republic of Ireland private sector company.

MANAGEMENT Operator Colum Harrington.

ADDRESS Ferry Lodge, West End, Bere Island, Beara, County Cork, Republic of Ireland.

TELEPHONE Administration +353 (0)27 75009, **Reservations** Not applicable, **Mobile** +353 (0)86 2423140.

FAX Administration +353 (0)27 75000, **Reservations** Not applicable.

INTERNET Email biferry@eircom.net **Website** www.bereislandferries.com *(English)*

1F	KIRSTY M	109t	66	10.5k	23.7m	0P	-	1L	B	IR
2	OILEAN NA H-OIGE	69t	80	7.0k	18.6m	75P	4C	-	B	IR
3	SANCTA MARIA	67t	83	7.0k	18.6m	75P	4C	-	B	IR

Belnahua (*Brian Maxted*)

Rhum *Nick Widdows)*

SECTION 2 – MINOR FERRY OPERATORS

KIRSTY M Landing craft (Klasse 521) built as the LCM 12 SPROTTE by Rheinwerft Walsum, Walsum, Germany for the German Navy. In 1993 withdrawn and sold to a German firm and converted to a civilian ferry. She was later sold to *Mainstream Salmon Farm (Aquascot Seafarms Ltd)*, Orkney, renamed the KIRSTY M and used as a work boat. In December 2009 sold to *Bere Island Ferries* and converted back to ferry operation. She is used in a freight-only mode and doesn't have a licence to carry passengers.

OILEAN NA H-OIGE Built as the EILEAN NA H-OIGE by Lewis Offshore Ltd, Stornoway, UK for *Western Isles Islands Council* (from 1st April 1996 the *Western Isles Council* and from 1st January 1998 *Comhairle Nan Eilean Siar*) for their Ludaig (South Uist) – Eriskay service. From 2000 operated from a temporary slipway at the Eriskay causeway. This route ceased in July 2001 following the full opening of the causeway and she was laid up. In 2002 she was moved to the Eriskay – Barra service. In 2003 replaced by the LOCH BHRUSDA of *Caledonian MacBrayne* and laid up. Later sold to *Bere Island Ferries* and renamed the OILEAN NA H-OIGE (same name – "The Island of Youth" – in Irish rather than Scots Gaelic).

SANCTA MARIA Built as the EILEAN BHEARNARAIGH by George Brown & Company, Greenock, UK for *Western Isles Islands Council* for their Otternish (North Uist) – Berneray service. From 1996 until 1999 she was operated by *Caledonian MacBrayne* in conjunction with the LOCH BHRUSDA on the service between Otternish and Berneray and during the winter she was laid up. Following the opening of a causeway between North Uist and Berneray in early 1999, the ferry service ceased and she became reserve vessel for the Eriskay route. This route ceased in July 2001 following the opening of a causeway and she was laid up. In 2002 operated between Eriskay and Barra as reserve vessel. In 2003 sold to *Transalpine Redemptorists Inc*, a community of monks who live on Papa Stronsay, Orkney. Used for conveying supplies to the island – not a public service. In 2008 sold to *Bere Island Ferries*. Entered service in May 2009.

BK MARINE

THE COMPANY *BK Marine* is a UK company.

MANAGEMENT Managing Director Donald Gordon Fraser Ross.

ADDRESS Herrislea House Hotel, Veensgarth, Tingwall, Shetland ZE2 9SB.

TELEPHONE Administration & Reservations +44 (0)1595 840208.

INTERNET Website www.bkmarine.co.uk *(English)*

ROUTE OPERATED *All year* Foula – Walls (Mainland) (2 hours; ***NEW ADVANCE***; 2 per week (Winter), 3 per week (Summer)), ***Summer only*** Foula – Scalloway (3 hrs 30 mins; ***NEW ADVANCE***; alternate Thursdays).

1	NEW ADVANCE	25t	96	8.7k	9.8m	12P	1C	0L	C	UK

NEW ADVANCE Built by Richardson's, Stromness, Orkney, UK for *Shetland Islands Council* for the Foula service. Although built at Penryn, Cornwall, she was completed at Stromness. She has a Cygnus Marine GM38 hull and is based on the island where she can be lifted out of the water. Vehicle capacity is to take residents' vehicles to the island – not for tourist vehicles. In 2004 it was announced that the vessel and service would be transferred to the *Foula Community*. However, it was then found that under EU rules the route needed to be offered for competitive tender. In July 2006 the contract was awarded to *Atlantic Ferries Ltd* who began operations in October 2006. In August 2011 replaced by *BK Marine*.

CLARE ISLAND FERRY COMPANY

THE COMPANY *Clare Island Ferry Company* is owned and operated by the O'Grady family, natives of Clare Island, Republic of Ireland, who have been operating the Clare Island Mail Boat Ferry service since 1880.

MANAGEMENT Managing Director Chris O'Grady.

ADDRESS Clare Island Ferry Co Ltd, Clare Island, Co Mayo, Republic Of Ireland.

TELEPHONE/FAX *May-September* +353 (0)98 23737 ***Winter*** +353 (0)98 25212, +353 (0)86 8515003.

INTERNET Email clareislandferry@anu.ie **Website** www.clareislandferry.com *(English)*

ROUTE OPERATED Roonagh (Co Mayo) – Clare Island (15 mins; *CLEW BAY QUEEN, PIRATE QUEEN*; **Winter** 1 to 2 trips per day, **Summer** up to 5 per day, Roonagh – Inishturk (50 mins; *CLEW BAY QUEEN, PIRATE QUEEN*; **Winter** 1 per day **Summer** up to 2 per day. Tourist vehicles are not normally carried.

1	CLEW BAY QUEEN	64t	72	10.0k	21.9m	96P	6C	-	B	IR	
2p	PIRATE QUEEN	73t	96	10.5k	19.8m	96P	0C	-	-	IR	

CLEW BAY QUEEN Built as the KILBRANNAN by James Lamont & Co Ltd, Port Glasgow, UK for *Caledonian MacBrayne*. Used on a variety of routes until 1977, she was then transferred to the Scalpay (Harris) – Kyles Scalpay service. In 1990 she was replaced by the CANNA and, in turn, replaced the CANNA in her reserve/relief role. In 1992 sold to *Arranmore Island Ferry Services* and renamed the ÁRAINN MHÓR. She was subsequently sold to *Údarás na Gaeltachta* and leased back to *Arranmore Island Ferry Services*. In 2008 she was sold to *Clare Island Ferry Company* and renamed the CLEW BAY QUEEN. She operates a passenger and heavy freight service to both Clare Island and Inishturk all year round. In winter passenger capacity is reduced to 47 with 3 crew. Fitted with crane for loading and unloading cargo.

PIRATE QUEEN Built by Arklow Marine Services in 1996 for *Clare Island Ferry Company*. She operates a daily passenger and light cargo service to Clare Island and Inishturk all year round. In winter passenger capacity is reduced to 47 with 3 crew. Fitted with crane for loading and unloading cargo.

CROSS RIVER FERRIES

THE COMPANY *Cross River Ferries Ltd* is a Republic of Ireland company, part of the *Doyle Shipping Group*.

MANAGEMENT Operations Manager Eoin O'Sullivan.

ADDRESS Westlands House, Rushbrooke, Cobh, County Cork, Republic of Ireland.

TELEPHONE Administration +353 (0)21 42 02 900 **Reservations** Not applicable.

INTERNET Website www.scottcobh.ie/pages/ferry.html *(English)*

ROUTE OPERATED Carrigaloe (near Cobh, on Great Island) – Glenbrook (Co Cork) (4 mins; *CARRIGALOE, GLENBROOK*; frequent service 07.00 – 00.15 (one or two vessels used according to demand)).

1	CARRIGALOE	225t	70	8.0k	49.1m	200P	27C	-	BA	IR	7028386
2	GLENBROOK	225t	71	8.0k	49.1m	200P	27C	-	BA	IR	7101607

CARRIGALOE Built as the KYLEAKIN by Newport Shipbuilding and Engineering Company, Newport (Gwent), UK for the *Caledonian Steam Packet Company* (later *Caledonian MacBrayne*) for the Kyle of Lochalsh – Kyleakin service. In 1991 sold to *Marine Transport Services Ltd* and renamed the CARRIGALOE. She entered service in March 1993. In Summer 2002 chartered to the *Lough Foyle Ferry Company*, returning in Spring 2003.

GLENBROOK Built as the LOCHALSH by Newport Shipbuilding and Engineering Company, Newport (Gwent), UK for the *Caledonian Steam Packet Company* (later *Caledonian MacBrayne*) for the Kyle of Lochalsh – Kyleakin service. In 1991 sold to *Marine Transport Services Ltd* and renamed the GLENBROOK. She entered service in March 1993.

FRAZER FERRIES

THE COMPANY *Frazer Ferries Ltd*, is a Republic of Ireland company. In June 2016 it took over Passage East Ferries and Lough Foyle Ferry Service. It plans to open a service between Greenore, Co Louth, Republic of Ireland and Greencastle, Co Down in 2017.

MANAGEMENT Director John Driscol, **Manager Passage East** Gary O Hanlon, **Manager Lough Foyle** *Not known*.

ADDRESSES Registered Office Riverfront, Howley's Quay, Limerick, Republic of Ireland. **Passage East Ferry** Barrack Street, Passage East, Co Waterford, Republic of Ireland. **Lough Foyle Ferry** The Pier, Greencastle, Co Donegal, Republic of Ireland.

TELEPHONE Lough Foyle Ferry +353 (0)74 93 8190, **Passage East Ferry** +353 (0)51 382480.

INTERNET Lough Foyle Ferry Email info@loughfoyleferry.com **Website** www.loughfoyleferry.com *(English)*

Passage East Ferry Email passageferry@yahoo.ie **Website** www.passageferry.ie *(English)*

Carlingford Ferry Website www.carlingfordferries.ie (registered but not yet active).

ROUTE OPERATED Lough Foyle Ferry *March-October* Greencastle (Inishowen, Co Donegal, Republic of Ireland) – Magilligan (Co Londonderry, Northern Ireland) (10 mins; *FOYLE VENTURE*; hourly), **Passage East Ferry** Passage East (County Waterford) – Ballyhack (County Wexford) (7 mins; *FBD TINTERN*; frequent service), **Carlingford Ferry** Greenore, Co Louth, Republic of Ireland and Greencastle, Co Down, Northern Ireland (service to start 2017).

| 1 | FBD TINTERN | 236t | 71 | 9.0k | 54.8m | 130P | 30C | - | BA | IR | |
| 2 | FOYLE VENURE | 324t | 78 | 10.0k | 47.9m | 300P | 44C | - | BA | IR | 7800033 |

FBD TINTERN Built as the STADT LINZ by Schiffswerft Oberwinter, Oberwinter/Rhein, Germany for *Rheinfähre Linz – Remagen GmbH* of Germany and operated on the Rhine between Linz and Remagen. In 1990 renamed the ST JOHANNES. In 1997 sold to *Fähren Bremen-Stedingen GmbH*, renamed the VEGESACK and operated across the Weser between Lemwerder and Vegesack. In 2003 she became a reserve vessel and in 2004 was renamed the STEDINGEN. Later sold to *Schraven BV* of The Netherlands and refurbished. In Autumn 2005 sold to *Passage East Ferry* and renamed the FBD TINTERN.

FOYLE VENTURE Built as the SHANNON WILLOW by Scott & Sons (Bowling) Ltd, Bowling, Glasgow, UK for *Shannon Ferry Ltd*. In 2000 replaced by the SHANNON BREEZE and laid up for sale. In 2003 sold to the *Lough Foyle Ferry Company Ltd* and renamed the FOYLE VENTURE. In November 2015 sold to *Frazer Ferries*. In July 2016 re-opened the *Lough Foyle Ferry*.

THE HIGHLAND COUNCIL

THE COMPANY *The Highland Council* (previously *Highland Regional Council*) is a Scottish Local Authority.

MANAGEMENT Area Community Services Manager Cameron Kemp, **Ferry Foremen** Allan McCowan and Donald Dixon.

ADDRESS *Area Office* Lochybridge Depot, Carr's Corner Industrial Estate, Fort William PH33 6TQ, *Ferry Office* Ferry Cottage, Ardgour, Fort William PH33 7AA.

TELEPHONE Administration *Area Office* +44 (0)1397 709000, *Corran* +44 (0)1855 841243.

INTERNET   Email   communityservices@highland.gov.uk   **Website** www.highland.gov.uk/info/1526/public_and_community_transport/111/public_transport/3 *(English)*

ROUTES OPERATED Vehicle Ferries Corran – Ardgour (5 mins; *CORRAN, MAID OF GLENCOUL*; half-hourly).

| 1 | CORRAN | 351t | 01 | 10.0k | 42.0m | 150P | 30C | 2L | BA | UK | 9225990 |
| 2 | MAID OF GLENCOUL | 166t | 75 | 8.0k | 32.0m | 116P | 16C | 1L | BA | UK | 7521613 |

CORRAN Built by George Prior Engineering Ltd, Hull, UK for *The Highland Council* to replace the MAID OF GLENCOUL as main vessel.

MAID OF GLENCOUL Built by William McCrindle Ltd, Shipbuilders, Ardrossan, UK for *Highland Regional Council* for the service between Kylesku and Kylestrome. In 1984 the ferry service was replaced by a bridge and she was transferred to the Corran – Ardgour service. In April 1996, ownership transferred to *The Highland Council*. In 2001 she became the reserve vessel.

The *Highland Council* also supports both services operated by *Highland Ferries*.

Morvern *Nick Widdows)*

Scillonian III *(John Hendy)*

HIGHLAND FERRIES

THE COMPANY *Highland Ferries* is a UK private sector operation. Services are operated under contract to *The Highland Council*.

MANAGEMENT Operator Dougie Robertson.

TELEPHONE Administration +44(0)7468 417137 **Reservations** Not applicable.

INTERNET Email southuist24@hotmail.co.uk

Facebook www.facebook.com/CamusnagaulFerry

1p	CAILIN AN AISEAG	-	80	7.5k	9.8m	26P	0C	0L	-	UK	
2	RENFREW ROSE	65t	84	7.6k-	17.5m	12P	3C	0L	B	UK	

ROUTES OPERATED Vehicle Ferry *1st June – 30th September* Cromarty – Nigg (Ross-shire) (10 mins; *RENFREW ROSE*; half-hourly), **Passenger-only Ferry** Fort William – Camusnagaul (10 mins; *CAILIN AN AISEAG*; up to 5 per day).

CAILIN AN AISEAG Built by Buckie Shipbuilders Ltd, Buckie, UK for *Highland Regional Council* and used on the Fort William – Camusnagaul passenger-only service. In 2006 the service transferred to *Geoff Ward* under contract with a different vessel. In 2013 the CAILIN AN AISEAG resumed service with *Highland Ferries*.

RENFREW ROSE Built by MacCrindle Shipbuilding Ltd, Ardrossan for *Strathclyde PTE* (later *Strathclyde Partnership for Transport*). Built as a small car ferry but operated passenger only between Renfrew and Yoker (apart from occasionally carrying ambulances in earlier days before they became too heavy). In March 2010 laid up. In June 2012 sold to *Arranmore Fast Ferries* for use as a passenger/car ferry. In June 2016 sold to *Highland Ferries* to reopen the Cromarty – Nigg service.

ISLES OF SCILLY STEAMSHIP COMPANY

THE COMPANY *Isles of Scilly Steamship Company* is a British private sector company.

MANAGEMENT Chief Executive Robert Goldsmith, **Marketing & Communications Manager** Sharon Sandercock.

ADDRESS *Scilly* PO Box 10, Hugh Town, St Mary's, Isles of Scilly TR21 0LJ, ***Penzance*** Steamship House, Quay Street, Penzance, Cornwall, TR18 4BZ.

TELEPHONE Administration & Reservations +44 (0) 1736 334220.

INTERNET Email sales@islesofscilly-travel.co.uk **Website** www.islesofscilly-travel.co.uk *(English)*

ROUTES OPERATED *Passenger services:* Penzance – St Mary's (Isles of Scilly) (2 hrs 40 mins; ***SCILLONIAN III***; 1 per day), St Mary's – Tresco/St Martin's/St Agnes/Bryher; ***LYONESSE LADY, SWIFT LADY (inter-island boats)***; irregular), ***Freight service***: GRY MARITHA; Freight from Penzance Monday, Wednesday and Fridays (weather dependant, all year round).

1F	GRY MARITHA	590t	81	10.5k	40.3m	6P	5C	1L	C	UK	8008462
2	LYONESSE LADY	40t	91	9.0k	15.5m	4P	1C	0L	AC	UK	
3F	MALI ROSE	768t	92	-	50.2m	6P	10C	1L	SC	NO	9065144
4	SCILLONIAN III	1346t	77	15.5k	67.7m	485P	5C	-	C	UK	7527796
5F	SWIFT LADY	-	04	30.0k	8.4m	0P	0C	0L	-	UK	

GRY MARITHA Built by Moen Slip AS, Kolvereid, Norway for *Gjofor* of Norway. In design she is a coaster rather than a ferry. In 1990 she was sold to the *Isles of Scilly Steamship Company*. She operates a freight and passenger service all year (conveying most goods to and from the Islands). During the winter she provides the only sea service to the islands, the SCILLONIAN III being laid up.

LYONESSE LADY Built Lochaber Marine Ltd of Corpach, Fort William, Scotland, for inter-island ferry work.

MALI ROSE Pallet and deck cargo carrier built by Halsnøy Verft, Halsnøy, Norway. Passed through various hands until June 2016 when she was sold to *Isles of Scilly Steamship Company* to replace the GRY MARITHA.

SCILLONIAN III Built by Appledore Shipbuilders Ltd, Appledore, UK for the Penzance – St Mary's service. She operates from late March to November and is laid up in the winter. She is the last major conventional passenger/cargo ferry built for UK waters and probably Western Europe. Extensively refurbished during Winter 1998/99 and 2012/13. She can carry cars in her hold and on deck, as well as general cargo/perishables, boats, trailer tents and passenger luggage.

SWIFT LADY Stormforce 8.4 RIB (Rigid Inflatable Boat) built by Redbay Boats of Cushendall, Co Antrim, Northern Ireland for inter-island ferry work conveying mail and as back-up to the LYONESSE LADY.

KERRERA FERRY

THE COMPANY *Kerrera Ferry Ltd* is a UK company.

MANAGEMENT Managing Director Duncan MacEachen.

ADDRESS The Ferry, Isle of Kerrera, by Oban PA34 4SX.

TELEPHONE Administration +44 (0)1631 563665.

INTERNET Email kerreraferry@hotmail.com **Website** www.kerrera-ferry.co.uk *(English)*

ROUTE OPERATED Gallanach (Argyll) – Kerrera (5 mins; *GYLEN LADY*; on demand 10.30 – 12.30 and 14.00 – 18.00, Easter – October, other times by arrangement).

1	GYLEN LADY	9t	99	8.0k	10.0m	12P	1C	-	B	UK

GYLEN LADY Built by Corpach Boatyard, Corpach, UK to inaugurate a vehicle ferry service to the Isle of Kerrera, replacing an open passenger boat.

MURPHY'S FERRY SERVICE

THE COMPANY *Murphy's Ferry Service* is privately operated.

MANAGEMENT Operator Brendan Murphy.

ADDRESS Lawrence Cove, Bere Island, Co Cork, Republic of Ireland.

TELEPHONE Administration +353 (0)87 2386095.

FAX Administration +353 (0)27 75988.

INTERNET Email edel@bereislandlodge.com **Website** www.murphysferry.com *(English)*

ROUTE OPERATED Castletownbere (Pontoon – 3 miles to east of town centre) – Bere Island (Lawrence Cove, near Rerrin) (20 mins; *IKOM K*; up to 8 per day).

1	IKOM K	55t	99	10.0k	16.0m	60P	4C	1L	B	IR

IKOM K Built by Arklow Marine Services, Arklow, Republic of Ireland for *Murphy's Ferry Service*.

RATHLIN ISLAND FERRY

THE COMPANY *Rathlin Island Ferry Ltd* is a UK private sector company owned by Ciarán and Mary O'Driscoll of County Cork, Republic of Ireland.

MANAGEMENT Managing Director Ciarán O'Driscoll.

ADDRESS Ballycastle Ferry Terminal, 18 Bayview Road, Ballycastle, County Antrim BT54 6BT.

TELEPHONE Administration & Reservations +44 (0)28 2076 9299.

INTERNET Email info@rathlinballycastleferry.com **Website** www.rathlinballycastleferry.com *(English)*

SECTION 2 – MINOR FERRY OPERATORS

ROUTE OPERATED Vehicle Ferry Ballycastle – Rathlin Island (45 min; **CANNA**; up to 4 per day). **Passenger-only Fast Ferry** (20 min; **RATHLIN EXPRESS**; up to 6 per day). The service is operated on behalf of the *Northern Ireland Department of Regional Development*.

1	CANNA	69t	76	8.0k	24.3m	140P	6C	1L	B	UK
2»p	RATHLIN EXPRESS	31t	09	18.0k	17.7m	98P	0C	0L	-	UK

CANNA Built by James Lamont & Co Ltd, Port Glasgow, UK for *Caledonian MacBrayne*. She was the regular vessel on the Lochaline – Fishnish (Mull) service. In 1986 she was replaced by the ISLE OF CUMBRAE and until 1990 she served in a relief capacity in the north, often assisting on the Iona service. In 1990 she was placed on the Kyles Scalpay (Harris) – Scalpay service (replaced by a bridge in Autumn 1997). In Spring 1997 *Caledonian MacBrayne* was contracted to operate the Ballycastle – Rathlin Island route and she was transferred to this service. In June 2008 she was chartered by *Caledonian Maritime Assets Limited* to *Rathlin Island Ferry Ltd* who took over the operation of the service.

RATHLIN EXPRESS Built by Arklow Marine Services, Arklow, Republic of Ireland for *Rathlin Island Ferry Ltd*.

Under Construction

3	SPIRIT OF RATHLIN	-	17	-	25.0m	140P	5C	-	B	UK

SPIRIT OF RATHLIN Under construction by Arklow Marine Services, Arklow, Irish Republic for *DRD (Northern Ireland)*, UK to replace the CANNA. To be chartered to *Rathlin Island Ferry Ltd*.

SHANNON FERRY

THE COMPANY *Shannon Ferry Group Ltd* is a Republic of Ireland private company owned by eighteen shareholders on both sides of the Shannon Estuary.

MANAGEMENT Managing Director Eugene Maher.

ADDRESS Ferry Terminal, Killimer, County Clare, Republic of Ireland.

TELEPHONE Administration +353 (0)65 9053124, **Reservations** Phone bookings not available; Online booking available at www.shannonferries.com

FAX Administration +353 (0)65 9053125, **Reservations** Fax bookings not available; Online booking available at www.shannonferries.com

INTERNET Email enquiries@shannonferries.com **Website** www.shannonferries.com *(English)*

ROUTE OPERATED Killimer (County Clare) – Tarbert (County Kerry) (20 mins; **SHANNON BREEZE, SHANNON DOLPHIN**; hourly (half-hourly during June, July, August and September)).

1	SHANNON BREEZE	611t	00	10.0k	80.8m	350P	60C	-	BA	IR	9224910
2	SHANNON DOLPHIN	501t	95	10.0k	71.9m	350P	52C	-	BA	IR	9114933

SHANNON BREEZE, SHANNON DOLPHIN Built by Appledore Shipbuilders, Appledore, UK for *Shannon Ferry Group Ltd*.

SHERKIN ISLAND FERRY

THE COMPANY The *Sherkin Island Ferry* is privately operated in the Republic of Ireland

MANAGEMENT Operator: Vincent O'Driscoll.

TELEPHONE Administration +44 (0)7881 634726.

INTERNET Email info@sherkinferry.com **Website** www.sherkinferry.com *(English)*

ROUTE OPERATED Passenger only Baltimore (Co Cork) – Sherkin Island (10 minutes; **MYSTIC WATERS**; up to 10 per day). **Note:** No vehicle service advertised.

01p	MYSTIC WATERS	100t	72		19.8m	99P	0C	0L	-	IR	8943038
02	YOKER SWAN	65t	84		21.9m	50P	3C	0L	B	IR	-

MYSTIC WATERS Built by Ryton Marine Ltd, Wallsend, UK as the FREDA CUNNINGHAM for *Tyne & Wear PTE*. Withdrawn in 1993 and sold to *Tyne Towage Ltd*, Newcastle and renamed the ANYA DEV. Later sold and renamed the LADY LAURA. In 2006 sold to *Sherkin Island Ferry* and renamed the MYSTIC WATERS.

YOKER SWAN Built by MacCrindle Shipbuilding Ltd, Ardrossan for *Strathclyde PTE* (later *Strathclyde Partnership for Transport*). Built as a small car ferry but operated passenger only between Renfrew and Yoker (apart from carrying ambulances in earlier days before they became too heavy). In March 2010 laid up. Later sold to *Sherkin Island Ferry* for use as a passenger/car ferry. She is used as required to convey vehicles and freight to and from the island. No public service is advertised.

SKYE FERRY

THE COMPANY The *Skye Ferry* is owned by the *Isle of Skye Ferry Community Interest Company*, a company limited by guarantee.

MANAGEMENT Ferry Development Manager Jo Crawford.

ADDRESS 6 Coulindune, Glenelg, Kyle, Ross-shire, IV40 8JU.

TELEPHONE Administration +44 (0)7881 634726.

INTERNET Email info@skyeferry.co.uk **Website** skyeferry.co.uk *(English)*

ROUTE OPERATED *Easter – October only* Glenelg – Kylerhea (Skye) (10 mins; **GLENACHULISH**; frequent service).

| 1 | GLENACHULISH | 44t | 69 | 9.0k | 20.0m | 12P | 6C | - | BSt | UK | |

GLENACHULISH Built by Ailsa Shipbuilding Company, Troon, UK for the *Ballachulish Ferry Company* for the service between North Ballachulish and South Ballachulish, across the mouth of Loch Leven. In 1975 the ferry was replaced by a bridge and she was sold to *Highland Regional Council* and used on a relief basis on the North Kessock – South Kessock and Kylesku – Kylestrome routes. In 1983 she was sold to *Murdo MacKenzie*, who had operated the Glenelg – Skye route as ferryman since 1959. The vessel was eventually bought by *Roddy MacLeod* and the service resumed in September 1990. The *Isle of Skye Ferry Community Interest Company* reached agreement with *Mr MacLeod* that he would operate the ferry in 2006. In 2007 she was sold to the Company. During winter 2012 she was chartered to *The Highland Council* to operate between North and South Strome following a road closure due to a rock fall. She is the last turntable ferry in operation.

STRANGFORD LOUGH FERRY SERVICE

THE COMPANY The *Strangford Lough Ferry Service* is operated by the *DRD Transport NI*, a Northern Ireland Government Department (formerly operated by *Department of the Environment (Northern Ireland)* and later in 2016 to become *Department for Infrastructure (DfI) NI).*

MANAGEMENT Ferry Manager Tim Tew.

ADDRESS Strangford Lough Ferry Service, The Slip, Strangford, Co Down BT30 7NE.

TELEPHONE Administration +44 0300 200 7898, **Reservations** Not applicable.

INTERNET Website www.nidirect.gov.uk/strangford-ferry-timetable *(English)*

ROUTE OPERATED Strangford – Portaferry (County Down) (10 mins; **PORTAFERRY II, STRANGFORD FERRY**; half-hourly).

| 1 | PORTAFERRY II | 312t | 01 | 12.0k | 38.2m | 260P | 28C | - | BA | UK | 9237436 |
| 2 | STRANGFORD FERRY | 186t | 69 | 10.0k | 32.9m | 263P | 20C | - | BA | UK | 6926311 |

PORTAFERRY II Built by McTay Marine, Bromborough, Wirral, UK for *DRD (Northern Ireland).*

STRANGFORD FERRY Built by Verolme Dockyard Ltd, Cork, Republic of Ireland for *Down County Council*. Subsequently transferred to the *DOE (Northern Ireland)* and then the *DRD (Northern Ireland)*. Following delivery of the PORTAFERRY II, she became reserve ferry.

Under Construction

| 3 | STRANGFORD II | 312t | 16 | 12.0k | 38.2m | 260P | 28C | - | BA | UK |

STRANGFORD II Under construction by Cammell Laird, Birkenhead for *DRD (Northern Ireland)*, UK to replace the STRANGFORD FERRY.

C TOMS & SON LTD

THE COMPANY *C Toms & Son Ltd* is a British private sector company.

MANAGEMENT Managing Director Allen Toms.

ADDRESS East Street, Polruan, Fowey, Cornwall PL23 1PB.

TELEPHONE Administration +44 (0)1726 870232.

INTERNET Email enquiries@ctomsandson.co.uk **Website** www.ctomsandson.co.uk *(English)*

ROUTE OPERATED *Car Ferry* Fowey – Bodinnick (Cornwall) (5 mins; *GELLAN*, *JENACK*; frequent), *Passenger Ferry* Fowey – Polruan (Cornwall) (5 mins; *KALEY*, *LADY DIANA*, *LADY JEAN*, *TAMSIN*, *THREE COUSINS*; frequent).

1	GELLAN	50t	03	4.5k	36.0m	50P	10C	-	BA	UK
2	JENACK	60t	00	4.5k	36.0m	50P	15C	-	BA	UK
3p	KALEY	7.6t	03	-	9.5m	48P	0C	-	-	UK
4p	LADY DI	-	81	-	8.2m	36P	0C	-	-	UK
5p	LADY JEAN	-	-	-	-	12P	0C	-	-	UK
6p	THREE COUSINS	-	14	-	-	12P	0C	-	-	UK

GELLAN, JENACK Built by C Toms & Sons Ltd, Fowey, UK.

KALEY, LADY DIANA, LADY JEAN, THREE COUSINS Built by C Toms & Sons Ltd, Fowey, UK.

VALENTIA ISLAND CAR FERRY

THE COMPANY *Valentia Island Car Ferry* is the trading name of *Valentia Island Ferries Ltd*, a Republic of Ireland private sector company.

MANAGEMENT Manager Richard Foran.

ADDRESS Valentia Island, County Kerry, Republic of Ireland.

TELEPHONE Administration +353 (0)66 76141, **Reservations** Not applicable.

FAX Administration +353 (0)66 76377, **Reservations** Not applicable.

INTERNET Email reforan@indigo.ie **Website** www.facebook.com (search for Valentia Island Car Ferry *(English)*

ROUTE OPERATED Reenard (Co Kerry) – Knightstown (Valentia Island) (5 minutes; *GOD MET ONS III*; frequent service, 1st April – 30th September).

| 1 | GOD MET ONS III | 95t | 63 | - | 43.0m | 95P | 18C | - | BA | IR |

GOD MET ONS III Built by BV Scheepswerven Vh HH Bodewes, Millingen, The Netherlands for *FMHE Res* of The Netherlands for a service across the River Maas between Cuijk and Middelaar. In 1987 a new bridge was opened and the service ceased. She was latterly used on contract work in the Elbe and then laid up. In 1996 acquired by *Valentia Island Ferries* and inaugurated a car ferry service to the island. **Note** This island never had a car ferry service before. A bridge was opened at the south end of the island in 1970; before that a passenger/cargo service operated between Reenard Point and Knightstown.

WOOLWICH FREE FERRY

THE COMPANY The *Woolwich Free Ferry* is operated by *Briggs Marine*, a British private sector company on behalf of *Transport for London*.

MANAGEMENT Ferry Manager Jeremy McCarthy.

ADDRESS New Ferry Approach, Woolwich, London SE18 6DX.

TELEPHONE Administration +44 (0)20 8853 9400, **Reservations** Not applicable.

FAX Administration +44 (0)20 8316 6096, **Reservations** Not applicable.

INTERNET Website www.tfl.gov.uk/modes/river/woolwich-ferry *(English)*

ROUTE OPERATED Woolwich – North Woolwich (free ferry) (5 mins; ***ERNEST BEVIN, JAMES NEWMAN, JOHN BURNS***; every 10 mins (weekdays – two ferries in operation), every 15 mins (weekends – one ferry in operation)). **Note** One ferry is always in reserve/under maintenance.

1	ERNEST BEVIN	1194t	63	8.0k	56.7m	310P	32C	6L	BA	UK	5426998
2	JAMES NEWMAN	1194t	63	8.0k	56.7m	310P	32C	6L	BA	UK	5411905
3	JOHN BURNS	1194t	63	8.0k	56.7m	310P	32C	6L	BA	UK	5416010

ERNEST BEVIN, JAMES NEWMAN, JOHN BURNS Built by Robb Caledon Shipbuilders Ltd, Dundee, UK for the *London County Council* who operated the service when the vessels were new. In 1965 ownership was transferred to the *Greater London Council*. Following the abolition of the *GLC* in April 1986, ownership was transferred to the *Department of Transport* and in 2001 to *Transport for London*. The *London Borough of Greenwich* operated the service on their behalf. In 2008 the operation of the service was transferred to Serco. An alternative loading is 6 x 18m articulated lorries and 14 cars; lorries of this length are too high for the nearby northbound Blackwall Tunnel.

John Burns and James Newman *(Ferry Publications Library)*

SECTION 2 – MINOR FERRY OPERATORS

Cemil Bayulgen and Valentine *(Nick Widdows)*

SECTION 3 – GB & IRELAND – FREIGHT ONLY FERRIES
CLDN/COBELFRET FERRIES

THE COMPANIES *Compagnie Luxembourgouise de Navigation SA (CLdN)* is a Luxemburg company. *Cobelfret Ferries NV* is a Belgian private sector company, a subsidiary of *Cobelfret NV*. The two companies operate as a single network with a single fleet.

MANAGEMENT CLdN Ro-Ro SA (Luxembourg) Caroline Dubois, **Cobelfret Waterways SA (Vlissingen)** Geert Bogaerts, **CLdN ro-ro Agencies Ltd (UK)** Karla Fairway.

ADDRESSES *Luxembourg* CLdN ro-ro SA, 3-7 rue Schiller, 2519 Luxembourg, Luxembourg, *UK – Purfleet* CCLdN ro-ro Agencies Ltd, Long Reach House, London Road, Purfleet, Essex RM19 1RP UK, *UK – Killingholme* C.RO Ports Killingholme Ltd, Clough Lane, North Killingholme, Immingham DN40 3JS, UK, *Irish Republic* CLdN ro-ro Agencies AB, Port Centre, 2nd Floor, Alexandra Road, Dublin Port, Dublin 1 Republic of Ireland.

TELEPHONE *Luxembourg* +352 (0)26 44 66 1, *UK (Purfleet, Ipswich & Killingholme)* +44 (0)1708 865522, *Irish Republic* +353 (0)1 856 1608.

FAX Administration & Reservations *UK (Purfleet & Killingholme)* +44 (0)1708 866418, *Luxembourg* +352(0)26 44 66 299, *Irish Republic* +353 (0)1 704 0164.

INTERNET Email postbox@cldn.com **Websites** www.cldn.com www.cobelfret.com *(English)*

ROUTES OPERATED *Cobelfret Ferries Services* Zeebrugge – Purfleet (9 hrs; *ADELINE, WILHELMINE, CELESTINE CLASS, MAZARINE CLASS*; 2/3 per day), Zeebrugge – Killingholme (13 hrs; *PAULINE; YASMINE*; 6 per week), *CLdN Services* Rotterdam – Purfleet (14 hrs 30 mins; *CEMIL BAYULGEN, MAZARINE CLASS*); 6 per week), Rotterdam – Killingholme (14 hrs; *OPALINE CLASS* and *MAZARINE CLASS*; 6 per week), Zeebrugge – Esbjerg (24hrs; *CELESTINE CLASS*; 1 per week), Zeebrugge – Dublin (36 hrs; *MAZARINE CLASS* and *OPALINE CLASS*; 4 per week), Rotterdam – Dublin (38 hrs; *CELESTINE CLASS, MAZARINE CLASS, OPALINE CLASS*; 3 per week), Purfleet – Rotterdam – Leixoes (Portugal) – Purfleet (69-79 hrs; *CATHERINE, VARIES*; 2 per week), Zeebrugge – Gothenburg (32-33 hrs; *CELESTINE CLASS, SOMERSET*; 5 per week (1 weekly calls at Hirtshals in both directions), (CELESTINE CLASS = CELESTINE, CELANDINE, CLEMENTINE, MELUSINE, VALENTINE and VICTORINE, MAZARINE CLASS = MAZARINE, PALATINE, PEREGRINE and VESPERTINE; OPALINE CLASS = AMANDINE and OPALINE. *CLdN Container service* Rotterdam – Dublin (43/47 hrs;); *ARX* ; 1 per week).

Contract Services for Ford Motor Company Vlissingen – Dagenham (11 hrs; *CELESTINE, CYMBELINE, UNDINE*; 2 per day).

1	ADELINE	21020t	12	15.8k	150.0m	12P	-	170T	A	MT	9539092
2	AMANDINE	33960t	11	18.5k	195.4m	12P	-	270T	A	LU	9424871
3	CATHERINE	21287t	02	18.0k	182.2m	12P	-	200T	A2	BE	9209453
4	CELANDINE	23987t	00	17.9k	162.5m	12P	630C	157T	A	BE	9183984
5	CELESTINE	23986t	96	17.8k	162.5m	12P	630C	157T	A	BE	9125372
6	CEMIL BAYULGEN	29004t	10	17.8k	193.3m	12P	-	270T	A	TR	9422134
7	CLEMENTINE	23986t	97	17.8k	162.5m	12P	630C	157T	A	BE	9125384
8	CYMBELINE	11866t	92	17.0k	147.4m	8P	350C	100T	A2	LU	9007764
9	MASSIMO MURA	23235t	03	17.1k	193.0m	12P	-	180T	A	IT	9234094
10	MAZARINE	25593t	09	18.5k	195.4m	12P	-	180T	A	LU	9376696
11	MELUSINE	23987t	99	17.8k	162.5m	12P	630C	157T	A	BE	9166637
12	OPALINE	33960t	10	18.5k	195.4m	12P	-	270T	A	MT	9424869
13	PALATINE	25593t	09	18.5k	195.4m	12P	-	180T	A	LU	9376701
14	PAULINE	49166t	06	21.7k	200.0m	12P	656C	258T	A	LU	9324473
15	PEREGRINE	25235t	10	18.5k	195.4m	12P	-	180T	A	MT	9376725
16	SOMERSET	21005t	00	18.0k	183.4m	12P	-	180T	A	BE	9188221
17	UNDINE	11854t	91	15.0k	147.4m	8P	350C	100T	A2	LU	9006112

Melusine *(Nick Widdows)*

Mazarine *(Nick Widdows)*

Valentine *(Nick Widdows)*

Cymbeline *(Nick Widdows)*

18	VALENTINE	23987t	99	18.0k	162.5m	12P	630C	157T	A	BE	9166625
19	VESPERTINE	25235t	10	18.5k	195.4m	12P	-	180T	A	LU	9376713
20	VICTORINE	23987t	00	17.8k	162.5m	12P	630C	157T	A	BE	9184029
21	WILHELMINE	21020t	12	15.8k	150.0m	12P	-	170T	A	LU	9539080
22	YASMINE	49166t	07	21.7k	200.0m	12P	656C	258T	A	LU	9337353

ADELINE Built by the Kyokuyo Shipyard, Shimonoseki, Japan. After competition, a additional deck and sponsons were retro-fitted at the Chengxi Shipyard, Jiangyin, China.

AMANDINE Built by Flensburger Schiffbau-Gesellschaft, Flensburg, Germany. Operates mainly between Rotterdam and Killingholme and Rotterdam/Zeebrugge and Dublin.

CATHERINE Built as the ROMIRA by Zhonghua Shipyard, Zhonghua, China for *Dag Engström Rederi* of Sweden. For six months engaged on a number of short-term charters, including *Cobelfret Ferries* who used her on both the Rotterdam – Immingham and Zeebrugge – Purfleet routes. In September 2002 purchased by *Cobelfret Ferries* and, in November 2002, renamed the CATHERINE and placed on the Rotterdam – Immingham service. In Spring 2003 chartered to the *US Defense Department* to convey materials to the Persian Gulf. Returned in late summer and operated thereafter on the Rotterdam – Immingham service. In January 2009 chartered to *CoTuNav* of Tunisia. In February 2010 returned to *Cobelfret* service and operated on the Rotterdam – Purfleet service. In March 2010 again chartered to *CoTuNav*. In March 2011 chartered to *RMR Shipping* to operate between Western Europe and Antwerp, Eemshaven, Harwich and Dublin to Lagos (Nigeria). In May 2011 returned to *Cobelfret Ferries* and used on the Zeebrugge – Gothenburg service until January 2013 when she began operating on the Purfleet route during the week and the Gothenburg route at weekend (one round trip). From April 2013 operated full-time on the Purfleet service. In March 2014 transferred to the Rotterdam – Leixoes route.

CELANDINE, VALENTINE, VICTORINE Built by Kawasaki Heavy Industries, Sakaide, Japan for *Cobelfret*. The CELANDINE was originally to be called the CATHERINE and the VICTORINE the CELANDINE. The names were changed before delivery. Generally used on the Zeebrugge – Purfleet route. In May 2011 the CELANDINE was chartered to *RMR Shipping*. Returned in November 2013.

CELESTINE Built by Kawasaki Heavy Industries, Sakaide, Japan as the CELESTINE. In 1996 chartered to the *British MoD* and renamed the SEA CRUSADER. She was originally expected to return to *Cobelfret Ferries* in early 2003 and resume the name CELESTINE; however, the charter was extended because of the Iraq war. Returned in September 2003 and placed on the Zeebrugge – Immingham service. In November 2006 moved to the Zeebrugge – Purfleet route. In November 2008 moved to the Ostend – Dartford service. In April 2009 the route became Ostend – Purfleet. In April 2010 chartered to *RMR Shipping*. In May 2014 returned to *Cobelfret Ferries* and in May 2016 transferred to the Dagenham – Vlissingen service.

CEMIL BAYULGEN Built by Flensburger Schiffbau-Gesellschaft, Flensburg, Germany for UN Ro-Ro of Turkey for service between Turkey and Italy. In June 2015 chartered to *CLdN*.

CLEMENTINE Built by Kawasaki Heavy Industries, Sakaide, Japan for *Cobelfret Ferries*. Mainly used on the Zeebrugge – Immingham service. In 2007 moved to the Zeebrugge – Purfleet route. In March 2013 chartered to *RMR Shipping*. In July 2013 chartered to *DFDS Seaways* and placed on the Immingham – Cuxhaven service. In November 2014 returned to *Cobelfret Ferries*. In January 2015 she retuned to charter with *DFDS Seaways* for four weeks.

CYMBELINE, UNDINE Built by Dalian Shipyard, Dalian, China for *Cobelfret Ferries*. Currently mainly used on the Dagenham – Vlissingen route. They were occasionally used on a weekend Southampton – Vlissingen service but this ceased in 2012 following the closure of the Southampton Ford Transit factory. Occasional weekend trips are made to Middlesbrough (Teesport).

MASSIMO MURA Built as the BEACHY HEAD by Flensburger Schiffbau-Gesellschaft, Flensburg, Germany for *AWSR Shipping*. On delivery, chartered to *Transfennica* and operated between Hanko (Finland) and Lübeck (Germany). In July 2006 chartered to *Stora Enso* and placed on the Kotka – Gothenburg route. In late August transferred to the Antwerp – Gothenburg service. In 2007 chartered to *Transfennica*. In January 2009 chartered to *Finnlines* and normally used on the Helsinki – Aarhus route. In January 2012 chartered

SECTION 3 – FREIGHT ONLY FERRIES

to *North Sea RoRo*. In March 2013 the service ceased and she was chartered to *DFDS Seaways*. In April 2014 sold to *C Bulk NV* of Belgium, an associated company of *CLdN/Cobelfret Ferries* and renamed the WILLIAMSBORG. In July she was chartered to *Nordana Line A/S* of Denmark operating from Mediterranean ports to the USA and Latin America. In January 2016 chartered to *Grimaldi Lines* of Italy and renamed the MASSIMO MURA.

MAZARINE, PALATINE, PEREGRINE, VESPERTINE Built by Flensburger Schiffbau-Gesellschaft, Flensburg, Germany.

MELUSINE Built by Kawasaki Heavy Industries, Sakaide, Japan for *Cobelfret*. Similar to the CLEMENTINE.

OPALINE Built by Flensburger Schiffbau-Gesellschaft, Flensburg, Germany. Operates mainly between Rotterdam and Killingholme and Rotterdam and Dublin.

PAULINE, YASMINE Built by Flensburger Schiffbau-Gesellschaft, Flensburg, Germany to operate on the Zeebrugge – Killingholme route.

SOMERSET Built as the SPAARNEBORG by Flender Werft AG, Lübeck, Germany for *Wagenborg* of The Netherlands and time-chartered to *Stora-Enso* to operate between Zeebrugge and Gothenburg in conjunction with *Cobelfret Ferries*. She also operated between Tilbury and Gothenburg during 2010. In August 2011 chartered to the *Canadian MoD* to operate between Montreal and Cyprus in connection with the Libyan 'no fly zone'. On return in November she was laid up in Zeebrugge and in January 2012 moved to Gothenburg. In August 2012 chartered to *LD Lines* to operate between Marseilles and Tunis. In March 2013 returned to the *Stora Enso/ Cobelfret Ferries* Zeebrugge – Gothenburg service. In November 2014 the arrangement between *Stora Enso* and *Cobelfret Ferries* ended and she was chartered to *SOL Continent Line* who took over the operation of the service, operating between Finland, Germany, Belgium and the UK. In January 2015 sold to *CLdN* and renamed the SOMERSET. Generally operates between Zeebrugge and Gothenburg.

WILHELMINE Built by the Kyokuyo Shipyard, Shimonoseki, Japan for *CLdN*. After completion, a additional deck and sponsons were retro-fitted at the Chengxi Shipyard, Jiangyin, China. Initially used on the Zeebrugge – Purfleet service. In January 2013 chartered to *P&O Ferries* to operate between Tilbury and Zeebrugge. After three weeks moved to the Middlesbrough – Rotterdam service. In November 2014 the charter ended and she was placed on the Zeebrugge – Purfleet service. She returned to *P&O Ferries* for five weeks during the refit period in January and February 2015 and again operated Middlesbrough – Rotterdam.

Under construction

22	NEWBUILDING 1	-	17	-	235.0m	12P	8000C	580T	A2	-	
23	NEWBUILDING 2	-	17	-	235.0m	12P	8000C	580T	A2	-	
24	NEWBUILDING 3	-	18	17.6k	211.0m	12P	-	400T	A2	-	-
25	NEWBUILDING 4	-	18	17.6k	211.0m	12P	-	400T	A2	-	-

NEWBUILDING 1, NEWBUILDING 2 Under construction by Hyundai Mipo Dockyard, Ulsan, South Korea. They are convertible to LPG propulsion and designed to be useable on deep sea ro-ro services as well as *CLdN's* current short sea routes.

NEWBUILDING 3, NEWBUILDING 4 Under construction by Uljanik Shipyard, Pula, Croatia. To operate on North Sea routes. There is an option of four more vessels.

CLdN also operates the container ship ARX (6901t, 2005, 707 TEU, IMO 9328625, Maltese flag (ex LUPUS 1 2005, ex C2C LUPUS 2007, ex C2C ASTRALIS 2010).

CLdN also own the CAPUCINE and SEVERINE, on charter to *Stena Line*.

FINNLINES

THE COMPANY *Finnlines PLC* is a Finnish private sector company. Services to the UK are marketed by *Finnlines UK Ltd*, a British private sector company. From 1st January 2001, *Finncarriers* was merged into the parent company, trading as *Finnlines Cargo Service*.

MANAGEMENT President & CEO Emanuele Grimaldi, **Head of Group Marketing North Sea ro-ro** Staffan Herlin.

ADDRESS *Finland* PO Box 197, 00181 Helsinki, Finland, **_UK_** Finnlines UK Ltd, Finhumber House, Queen Elizabeth Dock, Hedon Road, HULL HU9 5PB.

TELEPHONE Administration & Reservations *Finland* +358 (0)10 343 50, **_UK_** +44 (0)1482 377 655.

FAX *Administration Finland* +358 (0)10 343 5200, **_UK_** +44 (0)1482 787 229.

INTERNET *Email Finland* info.fi@finnlines.com **_UK_** info.uk@finnlines.com **_Website_** www.finnlines.com (English, Finnish, German, Polish, Swedish)

ROUTES OPERATED Irregular service from St Petersburg, Helsinki, Rauma and Kotka to Hull, Immingham, Amsterdam, Antwerp and Bilbao. For details see website. In view of the fact that ships are liable to be transferred between routes, the following is a list of all Finnlines Cargo Service ro-ro vessels, including those which currently do not serve the UK. Ro-pax vessels on Baltic services are listed in Section 6.

1	FINNBREEZE	28002t	11	20.0k	184.8m	12P	600C	200T	A	FI	9468889
2	FINNCARRIER	12251t	98	20.0k	154.5m	12P	-	124T	A2	FI	9132002
3	FINNHAWK	11530t	01	20.0k	162.2m	12P	-	140T	A	FI	9207895
4	FINNKRAFT	11530t	00	20.0k	162.2m	12P	-	140T	A	FI	9207883
5	FINNMASTER	12251t	98	20.0k	154.5m	12P	-	124T	A2	FI	9132014
6	FINNMERCHANT	23235t	03	21.0k	193.0m	12P	-	180T	A	FI	9234082
7	FINNMILL	25732t	02	20.0k	184.8m	12P	-	190T	A	FI	9212656
8	FINNPULP	25732t	02	20.0k	184.8m	12P	-	190T	A	FI	9212644
9	FINNSEA	28002t	11	21.0k	184.8m	12P	600C	200T	A	FI	9468891
10	FINNSKY	28002t	12	21.0k	184.8m	12P	600C	200T	A	FI	9468906
11	FINNSUN	28002t	12	21.0k	184.8m	12P	600C	200T	A	FI	9468918
12	FINNTIDE	28002t	12	21.0k	184.8m	12P	600C	200T	A	LU	9468920
13	FINNWAVE	28002t	12	21.0k	184.8m	12P	600C	200T	A	FI	9468932

FINNBREEZE, FINNSEA, FINNSKY, FINNSUN, FINNTIDE, FINNWAVE Built by Jinling Shipyard, Nanjing, China for *Finnlines*.

FINNCARRIER Built as the UNITED CARRIER by Fosen Mekaniske Verksteder A/S, Rissa, Norway for *United Shipping* (a subsidiary of *Birka Shipping*) of Finland and chartered to *Transfennica*. During 2000 she was used on their Kemi – Oulu – Antwerp – Felixstowe service. In 2001 the route was transferred to *Finnlines* and the vessel used sub-chartered to them (charter later transferred to *Finnlines*). In 2002 *United Shipping* was renamed *Birka Cargo* and the ship was renamed the BIRKA CARRIER. In 2006 the service ceased. In 2008 the charter was extended a further four years. In January 2013 chartered to *Transfennica*. In June 2013 she was renamed the CARRIER. In January 2015 sold to *Finnlines* but not delivered until the end of the year, when the charter ended. In January 2016 renamed the FINNCARRIER.

FINNHAWK Built by Jinling Shipyard, Nanjing, China for the *Macoma Shipping Group* and chartered to *Finnlines*. In April 2008 purchased by *Finnlines*. Currently operates used on service between Finland and The Netherlands, Belgium, the UK and Spain.

FINNKRAFT Built by Jinling Shipyard, Nanjing, China for the *Macoma Shipping Group* and chartered to *Finncarriers*. In April 2008 purchased by *Finnlines*. Currently operates on services between Finland and Germany.

FINNMASTER Built as the UNITED TRADER by Fosen Mekaniske Verksteder A/S, Rissa, Norway for *United Shipping* (a subsidiary of *Birka Shipping*) of Finland and chartered to *Transfennica*. During 2000 used on

Finnmill *(Henk van der Lugt)*

Finnmerchant *(John Bryant)*

their Kemi – Oulu – Antwerp – Felixstowe service. In 2001 the route was transferred to *Finnlines* and the vessels used sub-chartered to them (charter later transferred to *Finnlines*). In 2002 *United Shipping* was renamed *Birka Cargo* and she was renamed the BIRKA TRADER. In 2006 the service ceased and she was transferred to other *Finnlines* routes. In 2008 the charter was extended a further four years. In January 2013 chartered to *Transfennica*. In July 2013 renamed the TRADER. In January 2015 sold to *Finnlines* but not delivered until the end of the year, when the charter ended. In January 2016 renamed the FINNMASTER.

FINNMERCHANT Built as the LONGSTONE by Flensburger Schiffbau-Gesellschaft, Flensburg, Germany for *AWSR Shipping* (later Foreland Shipping). Chartered to *Transfennica* and operated between Hanko (Finland) and Lübeck (Germany). In January 2009 chartered to *Finnlines* and placed on the Helsinki – Aarhus route. In January 2012 chartered to *North Sea RoRo*. In March 2013 the operation ceased and the charter was taken over by *DFDS Seaways* and she was placed on the Immingham – Cuxhaven route. In May took over the Zeebrugge – Rosyth route. In October 2013 sold to *C Bulk NV* of Belgium, an associated company of *CLdN/Cobelfret Ferries*. In April 2014 charter to *DFDS* ended and she was chartered to an Australian operator. In November 2014 renamed the DORSET. In December 2014 the charter ended and she returned to *CLdN*. In early January 2015 placed on the Zeebrugge – Purfleet service. Later in the month sold to *Finnlines* and renamed the FINNMERCHANT.

FINNMILL, FINNPULP Built by Jinling Shipyard, Nanjing, China for the *Macoma Shipping Group* and chartered to *Finnlines*. In 2008 purchased by *Finnlines*. During Winter 2008/09 extra ramps were added at STX Europe Helsinki shipyard to enable ro-ro traffic to be conveyed on the weather deck.

MANN LINES

THE COMPANY *Mann Lines* are owned by *Mann & Son (London) Ltd* of Great Britain. They replaced in 2001 *ArgoMann Ferry Service*, a joint venture between *Argo Reederei* of Germany and *Mann & Son*.

MANAGEMENT Managing Director Bill Binks, **Commercial Manager** David Brooks.

ADDRESS Mann & Son (London) Ltd, The Naval House, Kings Quay Street, Harwich CO12 3JJ.

TELEPHONE Administration & Reservations UK +44 (0)1255 245200, *Germany* +49 (0)421 1638500, *Finland* +358 (0)2 275 0000, *Estonia* +372 (0)679 1450.

FAX Administration & Reservations UK +44 (0)1255 245219, *Germany* +49 (0)421 1638520, *Finland* +358 (0)2 253 5905, *Estonia* +372 (0)679 1455.

INTERNET Email enquiry@manngroup.co.uk **Website** www.mannlines.com *(English, Finnish, Estonian, German, Russian)*

ROUTES OPERATED Harwich (Navyard) – Cuxhaven – Paldiski – Turku – Bremerhaven (Germany) – Harwich *(STENA FORETELLER*; weekly).

| 1 | STENA FORETELLER | 24688t | 02 | 22.0k | 195.3m | 12P | - | 210T | A2 | SE | 9214666 |

STENA FORETELLER Built as the STENA FORETELLER by Dalian Shipyard Co Ltd, Dalian, China for *Stena RoRo*. Initially chartered to *Cetam* of France to operate between Marseilles and Tunis and renamed the CETAM MASSILIA. In November 2003 the charter ended and she resumed her original name. A number of short-term commercial and military charters followed until June 2006 when she was chartered to *StoraEnso* paper group to operate between Gothenburg and Finnish ports. In September 2009 she was chartered to *Rederi AB Transatlantic* who took over responsibility to operate all *StoraEnso's* Baltic services. In February 2012 she was chartered to *Transfennica*. In January 2015 chartered to *Mann Lines*.

SEA-CARGO

THE COMPANY *Sea-Cargo AS* of Norway is a subsidiary of *SeaTrans DS* of Norway.

MANAGEMENT Managing Director Ole Saevild, **Director Business Development** Erik A Paulsen, **General Manager (Immingham)** Mark Brighton, **General Manager (Aberdeen)** Ian Shewan.

ADDRESS Norway Wernersholmvegen 5, 5232 Paradis, Norway, *Immingham* Sea-Cargo UK, West Riverside Road, Immingham Dock, Immingham DN40 2NT, *Aberdeen* Sea-Cargo Aberdeen Ltd, Matthews Quay, Aberdeen Harbour, Aberdeen, AB11 5PG.

TELEPHONE Administration & Bookings Bergen +47 55 10 84 84, *Immingham* +44 (0)1469 577119, *Aberdeen* +44 (0)1224 596481.

FAX Administration & Reservations Bergen +47 85 02 82 16, *Immingham* 44 (0)1469 577708, *Aberdeen* +44 (0)1224 582360.

INTERNET Email mail@sea-cargo.no **Website** www.sea-cargo.no *(English)*

ROUTES OPERATED *Sea-Cargo* operate a network of services from West Norway to Amsterdam, Aberdeen, Immingham and Esbjerg. The schedule varies from week to week and is shown on the company website. The SC ASTREA and NORRLAND are generally used on the twice-weekly Immingham – Tanager, Haugesund, Bergen and Odda service and the SEA-CARGO EXPRESS on the weekly Aberdeen – Tanager, Haugesund, Bergen, Florø, Aalesund, Kristiansund, Trondheim and Molde service.

1	NORRLAND	5562t	90	14.5k	107.5m	0P	-	28T	A	AG	8818764
2	SC AHTELA	8610t	91	14.8k	139.5m	12P	-	92T	AS	MT	8911736
3	SC ASTREA	9528t	91	13.5k	129.1m	0p	-	58T	A	BS	8917895
4	SC CONNECTOR	12251t	97	15.0k	154.5m	12P	-	124T	AS	MT	9131993
5	SEA-CARGO EXPRESS	6693t	12	16.0k	117.4m	0P	-	35T	A	MT	9358060
6	TRANS CARRIER	9953t	94	14.5k	145.2m	0P	-	94T	AS	BS	9007879

NORRLAND Built by J J Sietas KG, Hamburg, Germany for *Trailer Link* of Sweden. Chartered to *Sea-Cargo*.

SC AHTELA Built as the AHTELA by Brodogradiliste "Sava", Macvanska Mitrovica, Yugoslavia, completed by Fosen Mekaniske Verksteder, Rissa, Norway for *Rederi AB Gustav Erikson* of Finland. Chartered to *Transfennica*. In 1995 chartered to *DFDS Tor Line*. In 1996 chartered to *Finncarriers Oy* of Finland and in 1997 renamed the FINNOAK. In 2007 sold to *Hollming Oy* of Finland and in 2008 the charter ended and she was renamed the AHTELA. Chartered to *Navirail* of Estonia to operate between Helsinki and Muuga (Estonia). Between February and May 2011 chartered to *Sea-Cargo* to operate between Esbjerg (Denmark) and Egersund (Norway). In October 2012 purchased by *Sea-Cargo* and renamed the SC AHTELA.

SC ASTREA Built as the ASTREA by Tangen Verft Kragerø A/S, Kragerø, Norway for *Finncarriers* of Finland. Operated between Finland and Spain – Portugal via Antwerp. In 2006 chartered to *Danish MoD*. In 2007 chartered to *Sea-Cargo*. In August 2011 purchased by *Sea-Cargo* and renamed the SC ASTREA. Until early 2016 used primarily for moving windfarm equipment. In February placed on the Norway – Immingham service.

SC CONNECTOR Built as the UNITED EXPRESS by Fosen Mekaniske Verksteder A/S, Rissa, Norway for *United Shipping* (a subsidiary of *Birka Shipping*) of Finland and chartered to *Transfennica*. During 2000 used on their Kemi – Oulu – Antwerp – Felixstowe service. In 2001 the route was transferred to *Finnlines* and the vessel used sub-chartered to them (charter later transferred to *Finnlines*). In 2002 *United Shipping* was renamed *Birka Cargo* and she was renamed the BIRKA EXPRESS. In 2008 the charter was extended a further four years. In June 2013 renamed the EXPRESS. In November 2013 chartered to *Transfennica*. In April 2014 sold to *Sea-Cargo* but initially continued to operate for *Transfennica*. During winter 2015 re-engined and modified to allow to side loading. In February 2015 renamed the SC CONNECTOR. Entered service in late April.

SEA-CARGO EXPRESS One of two vessels ordered in 2005 from Bharati Ratnagiri Ltd, Mumbai, India for *Sea-Cargo*. The order for the second ship was cancelled. Trailers are carried on the main deck only. Containers

Stena Foreteller *(John Bryant)*

Seatruck Power *(George Holland)*

are carried on the weather deck and pallets on the lower decks. A crane is provided for the containers and a side door for pallets. She operates on the Aberdeen – Norway service.

TRANS CARRIER Built as the KORSNÄS LINK by Brodogradiliste Kraljevica, Kraljevica, Croatia for *SeaLink AB* of Sweden and due to be time-chartered to *Korsnäs AB*, a Swedish forest products company. However, due to the war in Croatia, delivery was seriously delayed and she was offered for sale. In 1994 sold to the *Swan Group* and renamed the SWAN HUNTER. She was placed on the charter market. In 1997 she was chartered to *Euroseabridge* and renamed the PARCHIM. In 1999 the charter ended and she resumed the name SWAN HUNTER. In 1999 she was sold to *SeaTrans* and renamed the TRANS CARRIER. She operated for *Sea-Cargo*. In 2005 chartered to *Finnlines* and used on the Finland to Spain/Portugal service. In 2006 returned to *Sea-Cargo*. In January and February 2009 lengthened by 18.9 metres in Poland.

SEATRUCK FERRIES

THE COMPANY *Seatruck Ferries Ltd* is a British private sector company. It is part of the *Clipper Group*.

MANAGEMENT Chairman Flemming Steen, **CEO** Alistair Eagles.

ADDRESSES *Heysham (HQ)* North Quay, Heysham Port, Heysham, Morecambe, Lancs LA3 2UH, *Warrenpoint* Seatruck House, The Ferry Terminal, Warrenpoint, County Down BT34 3JR, *Liverpool:* Seatruck Ferry Terminal, Brocklebank Dock, Port of Liverpool, L20 1DB, *Dublin:* Seatruck Dublin, Alexandra Road, Dublin 1 Irish Republic.

TELEPHONE Administration +44 (0)1524 855377, **Reservations** *Heysham* +44 (0)1524 853512. *Warrenpoint* +44 (0)28 754400, *Liverpool* + (0)151 9333660, *Dublin* + (0) 353 18230492.

FAX Administration +44 (0)28 4175 4545, **Reservations** *Warrenpoint* +44 (0)28 4177 3737, *Heysham* +44 (0)1524 853549.

INTERNET Email aje@seatruckgroup.co.uk **Websites** www.seatruckferries.com *(English)*

ROUTES OPERATED Heysham – Warrenpoint (9 hrs; *CLIPPER PENNANT, SEATRUCK PANORAMA*; 2 per day), Heysham – Dublin (9 hrs; *CLIPPER RANGER*; 1 per day), Liverpool – Dublin (9 hrs; *SEATRUCK PACE, SEATRUCK POWER, SEATRUCK PROGRESS*; up to 3 per day).

1	CLIPPER PENNANT	14759t	09	22.0k	142.0m	12P	-	120T	A	CY	9372688
2	CLIPPER POINT	14759t	08	22.0k	142.0m	12P	-	120T	A	CY	9350666
3	CLIPPER RANGER	7606t	98	17.0k	122.3m	12P	-	84T	A	IM	9119402
4	SEATRUCK PACE	14759t	09	22.0k	142.0m	12P	-	120T	A	CY	9350678
5	SEATRUCK PANORAMA	14759t	09	22.0k	142.0m	12P	-	120T	A	CY	9372676
6	SEATRUCK POWER	19722t	11	21.0k	142.0m	12P	-	151T	A	IM	9506215
7	SEATRUCK PROGRESS	19722t	11	21.0k	142.0m	12P	-	151T	A	IM	9506203

CLIPPER PENNANT Built by Astilleros Sevilla SA, Seville, Spain for *Seatruck Ferries*. In January 2013 chartered to *Stena RoRo*.

CLIPPER POINT Built by Astilleros de Huelva SA, Huelva, Spain for *Seatruck Ferries*. In May 2012 chartered to *DFDS Seaways* and placed on the Immingham-Cuxhaven route. In April 2013 chartered to the organisers of the 'SATA Rally Azores 2013' car rally to take cars from Portugal to the Azores. In May began operating for *DFDS Seaways* in the Baltic. In October transferred to the Immingham – Cuxhaven route. In June 2015 the charter ended. In July she was chartered to *InterShipping*, of Morocco to operate between Algeciras and Tangiers.

CLIPPER RANGER Built as the LEMBITU by Astilleros de Huelva SA, Huelva, Spain for the *Estonian Shipping Company*. On completion chartered to *P&O European Ferries (Irish Sea)* and placed on their Liverpool – Dublin route. In Autumn 1998 she was chartered to *Dart Line* and placed on the Dartford – Vlissingen route. In 1999 she was renamed the DART 7. In Autumn 1999 the charter was ended and she was chartered to *Cetam* of France, resumed the name LEMBITU and was used on services between Marseilles and Tunis. In 2000 she was chartered to *P&O European Ferries (Irish Sea)* and renamed the CELTIC SUN; she operated between Liverpool and Dublin. In 2001 the charter ended; she then reverted to the name

LEMBITU and was chartered to *NorseMerchant Ferries* and placed on the Heysham – Dublin service. In late 2001 the charter ended and she returned to *ESCO* service in the Baltic. In 2003 chartered to *Scandlines AG* and placed on their Rostock – Helsinki – Muuga service. This service finished in December 2004 and she was chartered to *Channel Freight Ferries* in January 2005. In March 2005 chartered to *NorseMerchant Ferries* again and operated between Heysham and Belfast. Later purchased by *Elmira Shipping* of Greece and renamed the RR CHALLENGE. In June 2005 chartered to *Seatruck Ferries*. In October 2007 sold to *Attica Group* of Greece and renamed the CHALLENGE. She continued to be chartered to *Seatruck Ferries*. In January 2008 she was transferred to the Liverpool – Dublin route and in April sold to *Seatruck Ferries*. In July renamed the CLIPPER RANGER. In June 2009 replaced the SHIELD (now the HILDASAY) until the new CLIPPER PENNANT took over in October. In May 2010 inaugurated a new Heysham – Larne service. In October 2013 chartered to *Caledonian MacBrayne* to replace the MUIRNEAG. The charter ended in May 2015. In November 2015 placed on the Liverpool – Dublin route as third ship. In March transferred to the Heysham – Dublin service.

SEATRUCK PACE Built as the CLIPPER PACE by Astilleros Sevilla SA, Seville, Spain for *Seatruck Ferries*. In March 2012 renamed the SEATRUCK PACE. In January 2013 chartered to *Blue Water Shipping* of Denmark to carry wind turbine parts between Mostyn (Wales) and Esbjerg. Now operates Liverpool – Dublin.

SEATRUCK PANORAMA Built by Astilleros de Huelva SA, Huelva Spain for *Seatruck Ferries*. Launched as the CLIPPER PENNANT and renamed the CLIPPER PANORAMA before delivery. In December 2011 renamed the SEATRUCK PANORAMA.

SEATRUCK POWER, SEATRUCK PROGRESS Built by Flensburger Schiffbau-Gesellschaft, Flensburg, Germany for *Seatruck Ferries*.

Seatruck Ferries also own the ARROW currently on charter to *Isle of Man Steam Packet Company*, HELLIAR and HILDASAY, currently on charter to *NorthLink Ferries*, and the STENA PERFORMER and STENA PRECISION, currently on charter to *Stena Line*.

SOL CONTINENT LINE

THE COMPANY *SOL Continent Line* is a division of *Swedish Orient Line*, a Swedish private sector company.

MANAGEMENT Managing Director Ragnar Johansson, **General Manager** Jonas Wåhlin.

ADDRESSES Svenska Orient Linien AB, Klippan 1A, SE-414 51 Gothenburg, Sweden.

TELEPHONE +46 (0)31-354 40 00.

FAX +46 (0)31-354 40 07.

INTERNET Email info@sollines.se **Website** www.sollines.se/en/content/sol-continent-line

ROUTES OPERATED Gothenburg – Zeebrugge (34 hrs; **SCHIEBORG, SLINGEBORG**; 4 per week), Oulu-Kemi-Lübeck-Antwerp-Zeebrugge-Tilbury-Oulu (**BALTICA, ELISABETH RUSS, TRANSPULP, TRANSTIMBER**; 2 per week).

1	BALTICA	21224t	90	19.0k	157.7m	0P	-	163T	A	MT	8813154
2	ELISABETH RUSS	10471t	99	21.0k	153.5m	12P	-	120T	A2	AG	9186429
3	SCHIEBORG	21005t	00	18.0k	183.4m	12P	-	180T	A	NL	9188233
4	SLINGEBORG	21005t	00	18.0k	183.4m	12P	-	180T	A	NL	9188245
5	TRANSPULP	23128t	06	16.0k	190.7m	12P	-	200T	A	SE	9343261
6	TRANSTIMBER	23128t	07	16.0k	190.7m	12P	-	200T	A	SE	9343273

BALTICA Built by Hyundai Heavy Industries, Ulsan, South Korea as the AHLERS BALTIC for *Ahlers Line* and chartered to *Finncarriers*. In 1995 acquired by *Poseidon Schiffahrt AG* of Germany and renamed the TRANSBALTICA. She continued to be chartered to *Finncarriers* and was acquired by them when they purchased *Poseidon Schiffahrt AG* (now *Finnlines Deutschland AG*) in 1997. In 2003 sold to Norwegian interests and chartered back; She was renamed the BALTICA. In recent years she operated on the Helsinki – St Petersburg – Hamina – Helsinki – Zeebrugge – Tilbury – Amsterdam – Antwerp – service with the

TransTimber *(Nick Widdows)*

Seatruck Pace *(FotoFlite)*

MERCHANT. During 2007 she operated Helsinki – Turku – Antwerp on a one-week cycle. In January 2008 moved to Baltic services. In April 2011 chartered to *Power Line* to operate between Helsinki and Travemünde. In January 2013 returned to *Finnlines*. In October 2015 sold to *Godby Shipping* of Finland. In November chartered to *SOL Continent Line*.

ELISABETH RUSS Built by J J Sietas KG, Hamburg, Germany for *Ernst Russ* of Germany and chartered to *Transfennica*. In 2012 the charter ended and she was chartered to a number of operators. In November 2015 chartered to *SOL Continent Line*.

SCHIEBORG, SLINGEBORG, Built by Flender Werft AG, Lübeck, Germany for *Wagenborg* of The Netherlands and time-chartered to *Stora-Enso* to operate on the *Stora Enso/Cobelfret Ferries* service between Zeebrugge and Gothenburg. In November 2014 the arrangement between *Stora Enso* and *Cobelfret Ferries* ended and they were chartered to *SOL Continent Line* who took over the operation of the service.

TRANSPULP Built by Aker Finnyards, Rauma, Finland for *Baltic Container Shipping* of the UK and chartered to *Rederi AB Transatlantic* of Sweden. Operated on service operated for Stora Enso Paper Group, mainly in the Baltic. In early 2011 transferred to the Gothenburg – Tilbury (once weekly) and Gothenburg – Zeebrugge (*CLdN* service) (once weekly) services. In January 2013 began operating twice weekly to Tilbury, replacing the SELANDIA SEAWAYS of *DFDS Seaways*. In January 2015 chartered to *SOL Continent Line*.

TRANSTIMBER Built by Aker Finnyards, Rauma, Finland for *Baltic Container Shipping* of the UK and chartered to *Rederi AB Transatlantic* of Sweden. Operated on service operated for Stora Enso Paper Group, mainly in the Baltic. In January 2015 chartered to *SOL Continent Line*.

FLOTA SUARDIAZ

THE COMPANY *Flota Suardiaz SL* is owned by *Grupo Suardiaz,* a Spanish private sector logistics company which operates divisions in ports, bunkering, warehousing, haulage, freight forwarding and shipping.

MANAGEMENT Presidente Don Juan Riva, **Director General** Alfredo Menendez Garcia.

ADDRESSES Spain Calle Ayala, 6 28001 Madrid, Spain, **UK** Suardiaz Shipping Ltd, Suardiaz House, 193 Shirley Road, Southampton SO15 3FG.

TELEPHONE Spain +34 914 31 66 40, **UK** +44 (0) 2380 211 981.

FAX Spain + 34 914 36 46 74, **UK** +44 (0) 2380 335309.

INTERNET Email infoweb@suardiaz.com, **Website** www.suardiaz.com *(English, Spanish).*

ROUTES OPERATED Channel Line (3 times per week) Sheerness – Zeebrugge, Grimsby – Zeebrugge. **North Sea Line** (weekly) Cuxhaven – Immingham, **Cantabrian Line** (weekly) Teesport – Cuxhaven – Zeebrugge – Southampton – Le Havre – Santander, **Atlantic Line** (weekly) Vlissingen – Zeebrugge – Southampton – Vigo – Setubal – Las Palmas – Tenerife – Casablanca – Barcelona – Sete – Barcelona – Casablanca – Setubal – Sheerness – Newcastle **Biscay Line** (3 per week) St Nazaire – Vigo, **Canaries Line** (weekly) Barcelona – Tarragona – Las Palmas – Tenerife **Algeria Line** Barcelona – Mostagenem (weekly).

Services listed carry unaccompanied ro-ro cargo together with large volumes of trade cars for vehicle manufacturers and distributors. The Cantabrian and Channel Line services are operated by SCSC (Suardiaz CAT Shipping Co) a joint venture with European Car distributor CAT. The Biscay Line is operated with European Union funding from the TEN-T Programme and supported by a car carrying contract to GEFCO. Vessels are regularly transferred between routes and are often chartered out for short periods to other operators and vehicle manufacturers. In view of this the following is a list of all vessels in the *Flota Suardiaz* fleet at the present time including those that do not currently serve the UK.

1	AUTO BALTIC	18979t	96	20.0k	138.5m	12P	1452C	105T	A2	FI	9121998
2	BOUZAS	15224t	02	18.5k	149.4m	12P	1265C	105T	A	ES	9249996
3	GALICIA	16361t	03	15.0k	149.4m	12P	1390C	110T	A	ES	9268409
4	GRAN CANARIA CAR	9600t	01	18.0k	132.5m	0P	1150C	42T	AS	ES	9218014
5	IVAN	8191t	96	14.6k	102.5m	0P	853C	73T	A	PT	9112040

6	L'AUDACE	15222t	99	18.5k	149.4m	12P	1233C	105T	A	ES	9187318
7	LA SURPRISE	15222t	00	18.5k	149.4m	12P	1233C	105T	A	ES	9198719
8	SUAR VIGO	16361t	03	18.5k	149.4m	12P	1356C	110T	A	ES	9250000
9	TENERIFE CAR	13122t	02	20.0k	149.4m	12P	1354C	54T	AS	ES	9249984

AUTO BALTIC Built as the TRANSGARD by Umoe Sterkoder, Kristiansund, Norway for *Bror Husell Chartering* of Finland for long-term charter to *Transfennica* and used between Rauma and Antwerp and Hamina and Lübeck. Later chartered to *Finncarriers*. In 2005 she underwent conversion in Poland to add a garage on top of the original weather deck and was placed on long-term charter to *UECC* with options to purchase. Generally used on the Baltic or Iberian services. In 2007 renamed AUTO BALTIC. In January 2016 chartered to *Flotta Suardiaz*.

BOUZAS, GALICIA, L'AUDACE, LA SURPRISE, SUAR VIGO Built by Hijos de J. Barreras SA, Vigo, Portugal for *Flota Suardiaz* of Spain for use on services in the Mediterranean and to the Canaries, U.K. and Benelux. The vessels are highly flexible with a 12 driver capacity and three full height freight decks, each fitted with a mezzanine deck for cars, together with a further dedicated car deck. In addition to operating for *Flota Suardiaz* a number of vessels have spent periods on charter to *UECC*. In January and February 2014 L'AUDACE was chartered to *P&O Ferries* to operate between Hull and Zeebrugge.

GRAN CANARIA CAR Built as HARALD FLICK by Hijos de J. Barreras SA, Vigo, Portugal for *Naviera del Odiel*, one of the shareholders in Barreras and placed on 10 year charter to *Flota Suardiaz* of Spain for use on services in the Mediterranean and to the Canaries, U.K. and Benelux. Renamed GRAN CANARIA CAR before entering service. In 2008 ownership passed to *Navicar SA* a subsidiary of *Flota Suardiaz*. In addition to operating for *Flota Suardiaz* has been chartered to *UECC* on a number of occasions.

IVAN Built by Astilleros De Murueta, Vizcaya, Spain for *Adamastor – Sociedade de Navegação, Lda* a subsidiary of *Flota Suardiaz* for use on short sea services. In recent years she has been used on services between Sheerness, Grimsby and Calais. This service no longer operates.

TENERIFE CAR Built by Hijos de J. Barreras SA, Vigo, Portugal for *Navicar SA* a subsidiary of *Flota Suardiaz* for use on services in the Mediterranean and to the Canaries, U.K. and Benelux.

TRANSFENNICA

THE COMPANY *Transfennica Ltd* is a Finnish private sector company wholly owned by *Spliethoff Bevrachtingskantoor* of The Netherlands.

MANAGEMENT Managing Director Dirk P. Witteveen, **Sales Director (UK)** Andrew Clarke.

ADDRESSES *Finland* Eteläranta 12, 00130 Helsinki, Finland, *UK* Finland House, 47 Berth, Tilbury Port, Tilbury, Essex RM18 7EH.

TELEPHONE Administration & Reservations *Finland* +358 (0)9 13262, *UK* +44 (0)1375 363 900.

FAX Administration & Reservations *Finland* +358 (0)9 652377, *UK* +44 (0)1375 840 888.

INTERNET Email *Finland* info@transfennica.fi *UK* info.uk@transfennica.com *(English)*

Website www.transfennica.com *(English)*

ROUTES OPERATED Tilbury (twice weekly) to various destinations in Finland and Russia. Please see the website. All *Transfennica* ships are listed below as ships are sometimes moved between routes.

1	GENCA	28301t	07	22.0k	205.0m	12P	-	200T	A2	NL	9307372
2	KRAFTCA	28301t	06	22.0k	205.0m	12P	-	200T	A2	NL	9307360
3	MIRANDA	10471t	98	22.0k	153.5m	12P	-	112T	A	FI	9183790
4	MISANA	14100t	07	20.0k	163.9m	12P	-	150T	A	FI	9348936
5	MISIDA	14100t	07	20.0k	163.9m	12P	-	150T	A	FI	9348948
6	PAULINE RUSS	10488t	99	22.0k	153.5m	12P	-	120T	A2	AG	9198989
7	PLYCA	28301t	09	22.0k	205.0m	12P	-	200T	A2	NL	9345398

Auto Bay and Yasmine *(John Bryant)*

Autoprestige *(John Bryant)*

SECTION 3 – FREIGHT ONLY FERRIES

8	PULPCA	28301t	08	22.0k	205.0m	12P	-	200T	A2	NL	9345386
9	SEAGARD	10488t	99	21.0k	153.5m	12P	-	134T	A2	FI	9198977
10	STENA FORERUNNER	24688t	02	22.0k	195.3m	12P	-	210T	A2	SE	9214666
11	TIMCA	28301t	06	22.0k	205.0m	12P	-	200T	A2	NL	9307358
12	TRICA	28301t	07	22.0k	205.0m	12P	-	200T	A2	NL	9307384

GENCA, KRAFTCA, PLYCA, PULPCA, TIMCA, TRICA Built by New Szczecin Shipyard (SSN), Szczecin, Poland for *Spliethoff Bevrachtingskantoor*, owners of *Transfennica*.

MIRANDA Built by J J Sietas KG, Hamburg, Germany for *Godby Shipping AB* of Finland. Initially chartered to *Transfennica*. In 2000 she was chartered to *Finnlines*. Until the end of 2007 used on a Helsinki – Hamina – Zeebrugge service only available northbound for general traffic. From January 2008 operated on *UPM-Kymmene Seaways'* service from Hamina to Lübeck, Amsterdam and Tilbury. In January 2013 chartered to *Acciona Trasmediterranea* for service in the Mediterranean. In January 2016 long-term chartered to *Stena RoRo*, who sub-chartered her to *Transfennica*.

MISANA, MISIDA Built by J J Sietas, Hamburg, Germany for *Godby Shipping AB* of Finland and time-chartered to *UPM-Kymmene* of Finland to operate between Finland, Spain and Portugal. In July 2013 charter taken over by *Finnlines*. In January 2016 long-term chartered to *Stena RoRo*, who then sub-chartered them to *Transfennica*.

PAULINE RUSS, Built by J J Sietas KG, Hamburg, Germany for *Ernst Russ* of Germany and chartered to *Transfennica*.

SEAGARD Built by J J Sietas KG, Hamburg, Germany for *Bror Husell Chartering* of Finland (later acquired by *Bore Shipowning* of Finland) and chartered to *Transfennica*.

STENA FORERUNNER Built by Dalian Shipyard Co Ltd, Dalian, China for *Stena RoRo* and chartered to *Transfennica*.

UECC

THE COMPANY *United European Car Carriers AS* is a Norwegian private sector company jointly owned in equal shares by *Nippon Yusen Kabushiki Kaisha (NYK)* of Japan and *Wallenius Lines* of Sweden. *UECC* consists of companies in Norway, Germany, Spain, France, Portugal and the UK. The fleet technical and ship management department is based in Grimsby (UK).

MANAGEMENT Chief Executive Officer Glenn Edvardsen **Sales Manager UK** Nick Clark.

ADDRESSES Norway Karenlyst Allè 57, 0277 Oslo, **UK** 17 St. Helen's Place, London EC3A 6DG and Units 5B & 5C Appian Way, Europa Park, Grimsby, DN31 2UT.

TELEPHONE Norway +47 21 00 98 00, **UK** +44 (0)207 628 2855 and +44 (0)1472 269429.

FAX Norway +47 21 00 98 01, **UK** +44 (0)207 628 2858.

INTERNET Email companymail@uecc.com, **Website** www.uecc.com *(English)*.

ROUTES OPERATED Bristol Service Portbury – Pasajes (*AUTOSUN*; every 4 days), **Biscay Services** Santander – Pasajes – Zeebrugge – Southampton – Santander (*AUTOSTAR*; weekly), Santander – Pasajes – Rotterdam – Zeebrugge – Santander (*AUTOSKY, AUTOPRIDE*; twice weekly), Santander – Zeebrugge – Southampton – Le Havre – Santander (*VIKING ODESSA*; weekly), **Atlantic Service** Santander – Le Havre – Zeebrugge – Vigo – Santander (*SPICA LEADER*; weekly), Vigo – Sheerness – Zeebrugge – Vigo (*BALTIC BREEZE*; weekly), Vigo – Santander – Le Havre – Zeebrugge – Vigo (*AGEAN BREEZE*; weekly), **North Sea Service** Southampton – Zeebrugge – Malmo – Cuxhaven – Southampton (*ASIAN BREEZE,* weekly), Southampton – Cuxhaven – Immingham – Cuxhaven – Southampton (*AUTORUNNER,* weekly), **Norway Service** Bremerhaven – Oslo – Drammen – Walhamn – Oslo – Drammen – Bremerhaven (*AUTOPROGRESS,* twice weekly), Bremerhaven – Drammen – Cuxhaven – Immingham – Zeebrugge – Grimsby, Zeebrugge – Ramsgate (*AUTOPREMIER*; weekly), **Baltic Service** Southampton – Zeebrugge – Gydnia –– Hanko – Ust Luga – St Petersburg – Uusikapunki – Bremerhaven – Southampton (*AUTO BAY,*

AUTO BANK; weekly), Southampton – Bremerhaven – Ust Luga – Cuxhaven – Immingham – Bremerhaven – Southampton **(AUTOPRESTIGE,** fortnightly), **North – South Service** Bremerhaven – Zeebrugge – Portbury – Vigo – Malaga – Sagunto – Tarragona – Livorno – Piraeus – Derince – Yenikoy – Borusan – Vigo – Bremerhaven (**OPAL LEADER, CORAL LEADER, EMERALD LEADER, JUPITER LEADER, VIKING CHANCE**; weekly), **Intra Med Service** Vigo – Djen Djen – Tunis – Misurata – Gioia Tauro –Vigo (**VARIOUS**, weekly).

Services listed carry unaccompanied ro-ro cargo together with large volumes of trade cars and may call at additional ports for an inducement and regular additional ports include Cork, Dublin, Immingham, Liverpool, Sheerness, Portbury, Tilbury, and Newcastle. A number of short-sea contract sailings for vehicle manufacturers and distributors are also operated serving additional ports in Northern Europe. Vessels are regularly transferred between routes and contracts and the following is a list of all owned and long term chartered vessels in the *UECC* fleet at the current time, including those that do not presently serve the UK. Additionally the fleet is regularly supplemented by short term chartered vessels from *Flota Suardiaz* and *Fret Cetam* (the *Louis Dreyfus Amateurs* and *Höegh Auto-liners* Airbus joint venture) and with deep sea ocean-going ro-ro vessels from Eukor and parent companies *NYK Line* and *Wallenius Lines*. Chartered vessels at the time of preparation and considered out of the scope of this book were the CORAL LEADER, EMERALD LEADER, OPAL LEADER, SPICA LEADER, JUPITER LEADER, VIKING ODESSA and VIKING CHANCE.

1	AEGEAN BREEZE	27876t	83	18.0k	164.0m	0P	3242C	260T	QRS	SG	8202367
2	ARABIAN BREEZE	27876t	83	18.0k	164.0m	0P	3242C	260T	QRS	SG	8202355
3	ASIAN BREEZE	27876t	83	18.0k	164.0m	0P	3242C	260T	QRS	SG	8202381
4	AUTO BANK	19107t	96	20.0k	138.8m	12P	1610C	105T	A2	FI	9160774
5	AUTO BAY	19094t	96	20.0k	138.8m	12P	1610C	105T	A2	FI	9122007
6	AUTOPREMIER	11591t	97	20.0k	128.8m	0P	1220C	-	AS	PT	9131943
7	AUTOPRESTIGE	11596t	99	20.0k	128.8m	0P	1220C	-	AS	PT	9190157
8	AUTOPRIDE	11591t	97	20.0k	128.8m	0P	1220C	-	AS	PT	9131955
9	AUTOPROGRESS	11591t	98	20.0k	128.8m	0P	1220C	-	AS	PT	9131967
10	AUTOSKY	21010t	00	20.9k	140.0m	0P	2080C	-	AS	PT	9206774
11	AUTOSTAR	21010t	00	20.9k	140.0m	0P	2080C	-	AS	PT	9206786
12	AUTOSUN	21094t	00	20.9k	140.0m	0P	1220C	-	AS	PT	9227053
13	BALTIC BREEZE	29979t	83	17.5K	164.0m	0P	3242C	260T	QRS	SG	8312590

AEGEAN BREEZE, ARABIAN BREEZE, ASIAN BREEZE Built by Kurushima Dockyard, Onishi, Japan for *Fuji Shipping* of Tokyo. Sold in 1988 to *Amon Shipping*. In 1990 sold to *Wallenius Lines*, Singapore and later chartered to *UECC*. Of deep-sea ocean-going ro-ro design with quarter ramps, each was re-engined and heavily rebuilt in 2008 at COSCO Dalian Shipyard, China to extend lifespan and improve suitability for short sea operation.

AUTO BANK Built as the SERENADEN by Umoe Sterkoder AS, Kristiansund, Norway for *Rederi AB Engship* of Finland and chartered to *Transfennica*. In 2006 *Rederi AB Engship* was taken over by *Rettig Group Bore*. In 2007 converted at COSCO Shipyard, Nantong, China to add a garage on top of the weather deck, renamed AUTO BANK and placed on long-term charter to *UECC*. Generally used on the Baltic or Iberian services.

AUTO BAY Built as the HERALDEN by Umoe Sterkoder AS, Kristiansund, Norway for *Rederi AB Engship* of Finland and chartered to *Transfennica*. In 2006 *Rederi AB Engship* was taken over by *Rettig Group Bore*. In 2007 converted at COSCO Shipyard, Nantong, China to add a garage on top of the weather deck, renamed AUTO BAY and placed on long-term charter to *UECC*. Generally used on the Baltic or Iberian services.

AUTOPREMIER, AUTOPRESTIGE, AUTOPROGRESS, AUTOPRIDE Built by Frisian Shipyard, Harlingen, the Netherlands for *UECC*. Designated P-class, they are an enlarged version of the R-class and built to a 'Grimsby-Max' specification with greater capacity for ro-ro cargo. Generally used on scheduled sailings between Iberia or Germany and Norway, the Benelux and UK.

AUTOSKY, AUTOSTAR, AUTOSUN Built by Tsuneishi Zosen, Tadotsu, Japan for *UECC*. Designated S-class, they are a further enlargement of the P-class and R-class designs and are normally used on Biscay routes.

BALTIC BREEZE Built by Kurushima Dockyard, Onishi, Japan for *Fuji Shipping Co* of Tokyo. Sold in 1988 to *Amon Shipping*. Sold to *Wallenius Lines*, Singapore in 1990. Chartered to *Eukor* then to *UECC*. Of deep-sea ocean-going ro-ro design with quarter ramps, she was re-engined and heavily rebuilt in 2008 at COSCO Dalian Shipyard, China to extend lifespan and improve suitability for short sea operation.

Under Construction

| 14 | NEWBUILDING 1 | 43,200t | 16 | 18.6K | 181.0m | 0P | 3800C | - | QRS | - | - |
| 15 | NEWBUILDING 2 | 43,200t | 16 | 18.6K | 181.0m | 0P | 3800C | - | QRS | - | - |

NEWBUILDING 1, NEWBUILDING 2 Dual fuel LNG Ice Class 1A pure car and truck carriers with side and quarter under construction by Kawasaki Heavy Industries at NACKS shipyard, Nantong, China for *UECC* and due for delivery in the second half of 2016. Intended for use on Baltic services, the vessels will be refuelled by specialist barge in Zeebrugge.

Stena Forerunner *(Andrew Cooke)*

SCA Östrand *(John Bryant)*

SECTION 3 – FREIGHT ONLY FERRIES

SECTION 4 – RO-RO OPERATORS CONVEYING PRIVATE TRAFFIC

The following operators employ ro-ro freight ships for the conveyance of their own traffic or traffic for a limited number of customers and do not solicit general traffic from hauliers or shippers.

FORELAND SHIPPING

THE COMPANY *Foreland Shipping Limited* (formerly *AWSR Shipping Limited*) is a UK private sector company. The principal shareholder in *Foreland Shipping* is *Hadley Shipping Group*.

MANAGEMENT Chairman Peter Morton, **Managing Director** Paul Trudgeon, **Operations Director** Stuart Williams.

ADDRESS 117-119 Houndsditch, London EC3A 7BT.

TELEPHONE +44 (0)20 7480 4140.

FAX +44 (0)20 7280 8790.

INTERNET Website www.foreland-shipping.co.uk *(English)*

ROUTES OPERATED No routes are operated. Ships are for charter to the *UK Ministry of Defence* for their 'Strategic Sealift Capability'.

1	ANVIL POINT	23235t	03	17.1k	193.0m	12P	-	180T	A	UK	9248540
2	EDDYSTONE	23235t	02	17.1k	193.0m	12P	-	180T	A	UK	9234070
3	HARTLAND POINT	23235t	03	17.1k	193.0m	12P	-	180T	A	UK	9248538
4	HURST POINT	23235t	02	17.1k	193.0m	12P	-	180T	A	UK	9234068

ANVIL POINT, HARTLAND POINT Built by Harland & Wolff, Belfast, UK for *AWSR Shipping*.

EDDYSTONE, HURST POINT Built by Flensburger Schiffbau-Gesellschaft, Flensburg, Germany for *AWSR Shipping*.

HOLMEN CARRIER

THE COMPANY *Holmen Carrier* is the branding of ships operated for *Holmen Paper AB*, an international company based in Sweden

MANAGEMENT President and CEO Henrik Sjölund.

ADDRESS Vattengränden 2, 601 88 Norrköping, Sweden.

TELEPHONE +46 11 23 50 00.

FAX +46 11 23 60 30.

INTERNET Website www.holmen.com/en **Email** info@holmen.com

ROUTES OPERATED Norrköping (Sweden) – Lübeck – Sheerness – Hull – Norrköping (2 weeks; *EXPORTER*, *SHIPPER*, 1 per week).

1	EXPORTER	6620t	91	16.5k	122.0m	0P	-	90T	A	FI	8820860
2	SHIPPER	6620t	91	16.5k	122.0m	0P	-	90T	A	FI	8911748

EXPORTER Built as the GRANÖ by Brodogradiliste "Sava", Macvanska Mitrovica, Yugoslavia (fitted out by Fosen Mekaniske Verksteder of Rissa, Norway) for *Rederi AB Gustav Erikson* of Finland and chartered to *Transfennica* for service between Finland and Germany. In 1995 the owning company became *United Shipping* and in 2002 *Birka Cargo AB*. In 2000 she was chartered to the *Korsnäs Paper Group* to carry their traffic from Gävle (Sweden) to Chatham and Terneuzen (The Netherlands). In 2002 she was renamed the BIRKA EXPORTER. In 2005 the charter and operation of the services were taken over by *DFDS Tor Line*. The northbound Terneuzen – Gävle section became a ferry route marketed as part of the *DFDS Tor Line* network. This arrangement ceased in 2006. In 2008 chartered to *Finnlines*. In January 2010 chartered to *Holmen Paper AB*. In June 2013 renamed the EXPORTER.

SHIPPER Built as the STYRSÖ and renamed the BIRKA SHIPPER in 2002 and the SHIPPER in June 2013. Otherwise all details as the EXPORTER.

SCA TRANSFOREST

THE COMPANY *SCA Transforest* is a Swedish company.

MANAGEMENT Managing Director (UK) Hugo Heij.

ADDRESS Sweden Box 805, 851 23, Sundsvall, Sweden, **UK** Interforest Terminal London Ltd, 44 Berth, Tilbury Dock, Essex RM18 7HP.

TELEPHONE Administration & Reservations Sweden +46 (0)60 19 35 00, **UK** +44 (0)1375 488500.

FAX Administration & Reservations Sweden +46 (0)60-19 35 65, **UK** +44 (0)1375 488503.

INTERNET Email Sweden info@transforest.sca.com **UK** interforest.london@sca.com

Website www.sca.com/transforest *(English)*

ROUTE OPERATED Umeå – Sundsvall – Sheerness – Rotterdam (Eemhaven) – Helsingborg – Umeå (8/9 day round trip; **SCA OBBOLA, SCA ORTVIKEN, SCA ÖSTRAND**; 1 per week), Umeå – Sundsvall – Sheerness – Rotterdam (Eemhaven) – Oxelösund – Umeå (8/9 day round trip; **SCA OBBOLA, SCA ORTVIKEN, SCA ÖSTRAND**; 1 per week).

1	SCA OBBOLA	20168t	96	16.0k	170.6m	0P	-	-	A	SE	9087350
2	SCA ORTVIKEN	20154t	97	16.0k	170.4m	0P	-	-	A	SE	9087374
3	SCA ÖSTRAND	20171t	96	16.0k	170.6m	0P	-	-	A	SE	9087362

SCA OBBOLA, SCA ORTVIKEN, SCA ÖSTRAND Built as the OBBOLA, ORTVIKEN and ÖSTRAND by Astilleros Españoles, Seville, Spain for Gorthon Lines and chartered to SCA Transforest. They are designed for the handling of forest products in non-wheeled 'cassettes' but can also accommodate trailers. The ORTVIKEN was lengthened during Autumn 2000 and the others during 2001. In June 2001 purchased by SCA Transforest. In spring 2016 renamed the SCA OBBOLA, SCA ORTVIKEN and SCA ÖSTRAND.

SMURFIT KAPPA GROUP

THE COMPANY *Smurfit Kappa Group* is an international company registered in the Irish Republic.

ADDRESS Beech Hill, Clonskeagh, Dublin 4, Irish Republic.

TELEPHONE +353 (0)1 202 7000.

INTERNET Website www.smurfitkappa.com *(English)*

ROUTE OPERATED Piteå (Sweden) – Södertälje (Sweden) – Bremen (Germany)- Sheerness – Terneuzen (Netherlands) – Cuxhaven (Germany) – Sodertalje – Piteå (12 days; **BALTICBORG, BOTHNIABORG**; 1 per week).

| 1 | BALTICBORG | 12460t | 04 | 16.5 k | 153.1m | 0P | - | 104T | A | NL | 9267716 |
| 2 | BOTHNIABORG | 12460t | 04 | 16.5 k | 153.1m | 0P | - | 104T | A | NL | 9267728 |

BALTICBORG, BOTHNIABORG Built by Bodewes Volharding, Volharding, The Netherlands (hull built by Daewoo Mangalia Heavy Industries SA, Mangalia, Romania) for *Wagenborg Shipping* of The Netherlands. Time-chartered to *Kappa Packaging* (now *Smurfit Kappa Group*). Placed on service between Piteå and Northern Europe. Northbound journeys (Terneuzen – Piteå) marketed as *RORO2 Stockholm*, with a call at Södertälje (Sweden (near Stockholm)) and, from 2005, the section Bremen – Sheerness – Terneuzen marketed as *RORO2London*. In 2007 these arrangements ceased and *Mann Lines* took over the marketing of northbound traffic, a northbound call at Harwich (Navyard) being introduced and the Södertälje call being replaced by a call at Paldiski in Estonia. This arrangement ceased in 2013 and they reverted to their previous schedules.

SECTION 5 – GB & IRELAND – CHAIN, CABLE ETC FERRIES

CUMBRIA COUNTY COUNCIL

Address Resources Directorate, Highways Transportation and Fleet, County Offices, Kendal, Cumbria LA9 4RQ **Tel** +44 (0)1539 713040, **Fax** +44 (0)1539 713035.

Internet Email peter.hosking@cumbria.gov.uk *(English)*

Website www.cumbria.gov.uk/roads-transport/highways-pavements/windermereferry.asp *(English)*

Route Bowness-on-Windermere – Far Sawrey.

1	MALLARD	-	90	-	25.9m	140P	18C	-	BA		

MALLARD Chain ferry built by F L Steelcraft, Borth, Dyfed for *Cumbria County Council*.

DARTMOUTH – KINGSWEAR FLOATING BRIDGE CO LTD

Address Dart Marina, Sandquay Road, Dartmouth, Devon TQ6 9PH. **Tel** +44 (0)7866 531687.

Internet Website www.dartmouthhigherferry.com *(English)*

Route Dartmouth – Kingswear (Devon) across River Dart (higher route) (forms part of A379).

1	HIGHER FERRY	540t	09	-	52.7m	240P	32C	-	BA		

HIGHER FERRY Built by Ravestein BV, Deest, The Netherlands under contract to Pendennis Shipyard, Falmouth, who fitted the vessel out between January and June 2009.

ISLE OF WIGHT COUNCIL (COWES FLOATING BRIDGE)

Address Ferry Office, Medina Road, Cowes, Isle of Wight PO31 7BX. **Tel** +44 (0)1983 293041.

Route West Cowes – East Cowes.

1	NO 5	-	76	-	33.5m	-	15C	-	BA		

NO 5 Chain ferry built by Fairey Marine, East Cowes, UK for *Isle of Wight County Council*, now *Isle of Wight Council*.

Under Construction

2	NEWBUILDING	-	17	-	37.0m	-	20C	-	BA		

NEWBUILDING Under construction by Mainstay Marine Solutions Ltd, Pembroke Dock, UK.

KING HARRY FERRY AND CORNWALL FERRIES

Address 2 Ferry Cottages, Feock, Truro, Cornwall TR3 6QJ. **Tel** +44 (0)1872 861917.

Internet Email beverley@kingharry.net **Website** www.falriver.co.uk *(English)*

Route Philliegh – Feock (Cornwall) (across River Fal)

1	KING HARRY FERRY	500t	06	-	55.2m	150P	34C	-	BA	UK	9364370

KING HARRY FERRY Chain ferry built by Pendennis Shipyard, Falmouth (hull constructed at Ravestein Shipyard, Deest, The Netherlands) to replace the previous ferry.

REEDHAM FERRY

Address Reedham Ferry, Ferry Inn, Reedham, Norwich NR13 3HA. **Tel** +44 (0)1493 700999.

Internet Email info@reedhamferry.co.uk **Website** www.reedhamferry.co.uk *(English)*

Route Acle – Reedham – Norton (across River Yare, Norfolk).

Higher Ferry *(John Hendy)*

Island Express *(Andrew Cooke)*

| 1 | REEDHAM FERRY | - | 84 | - | 11.3m | 20P | 3C | - | BA | | |

REEDHAM FERRY Chain ferry built by Newsons, Oulton Broad, Lowestoft, UK for *Reedham Ferry*. Maximum vehicle weight: 12 tons.

SANDBANKS FERRY

Address *Company* Bournemouth-Swanage Motor Road and Ferry Company, Shell Bay, Studland, Swanage, Dorset BH19 3BA. **Tel** +44 (0)1929 450203, **Fax** +44 (0)1929 450498), *Ferry* Floating Bridge, Ferry Way, Sandbanks, Poole, Dorset BH13 7QN. **Tel** +44 (0)1929 450203.

Internet Email email@sandbanksferry.co.uk **Website** www.sandbanksferry.co.uk *(English)*

Route Sandbanks – Shell Bay (Dorset).

| 1 | BRAMBLE BUSH BAY | 625t | 93 | - | 74.4m | 400P | 48C | - | BA | UK | 9072070 |

BRAMBLE BUSH BAY Chain ferry, built by Richard Dunston (Hessle) Ltd, Hessle, UK for the *Bournemouth-Swanage Motor Road and Ferry Company*.

SOUTH HAMS DISTRICT COUNCIL

Address Lower Ferry Office, The Square, Kingswear, Dartmouth, Devon TQ6 0AA. **Tel** +44 (0)1803 861234.

Internet Website www.southhams.gov.uk/DartmouthLowerFerry *(English)*

Route Dartmouth – Kingswear (Devon) across River Dart (lower route).

| 1 | THE TOM AVIS | - | 94 | - | 33.5m | 50P | 8C | - | BA |
| 2 | THE TOM CASEY | - | 89 | - | 33.5m | 50P | 8C | - | BA |

THE TOM AVIS Float (propelled by tugs) built by c Toms & Sons, Fowey, UK for *South Hams District Council*.

THE TOM CASEY Float (propelled by tugs) built by Cosens, Portland, UK for *South Hams District Council*.

TORPOINT FERRY

Address 2 Ferry Street, Torpoint, Cornwall PL11 2AX. **Tel** +44 (0)1752 812233, **Fax** +44 (0)1752 816873.

Internet Website www.tamarcrossings.org.uk *(English)*

Route Devonport (Plymouth) – Torpoint (Cornwall) across the Tamar. The three ferries operate in parallel, each on her own 'track'. Pre-booking is not possible and the above numbers cannot be used for that purpose.

1	LYNHER II	748t	06	-	73.0m	350P	73C	-	BA	UK	9310941
2	PLYM II	748t	04	-	73.0m	350P	73C	-	BA	UK	9310927
3	TAMAR II	748t	05	-	73.0m	350P	73C	-	BA	UK	9310939

LYNHER II, PLYM II, TAMAR II Chain ferries built by Ferguson Shipbuilders Ltd, Port Glasgow, UK to replace 1960s-built ships. Unlike previous ferries, they are registered as 'Passenger/Ro-Ro Cargo' ships and thus have gross tonnage, nation of registry and, being over 100t, an IMO number.

WATERFORD CASTLE HOTEL

Address The Island, Waterford, Irish Republic. **Tel** +353 (0)51 878203.

Internet Email info@waterfordcastleresort.com **Website** www.waterfordcastleresort.com *(English)*

Route Grantstown – Little Island (in River Suir, County Waterford).

| 1• | LORELEY | 110t | 59 | - | 32.0m | 57P | 12C | - | BA | | |
| 2 | MARY FITZGERALD | 122t | 72 | 10.0k | 35.0m | 100P | 14C | - | BA | IR | 8985531 |

LORELEY Chain ferry built as the LORELEY V by Ruthof, Mainz, Germany to operate between St Goarshausen and St Goar on the River Rhine. In 2004 replaced by a new vessel (the LORELEY VI) and became a reserve vessel In 2007, sold to the *Waterford Castle Hotel* and renamed the LORELEY and, in 2008 replaced the previous ferry. Self propelled and guided by cable. In August 2014 replaced by the MARY FITZGERALD and laid up.

MARY FITZGERALD Built as the STEDINGEN by Abeking & Rasmussen, Lemwerder, Germany for *Schnellastfähre Berne-Farge GmbH* (later *Fähren Bremen-Stedingen GmbH*) to operate across the River Weser (Vegesack – Lemwerder and Berne – Farge). In 2004 sold to the *Lough Foyle Ferry Company Ltd* and renamed the FOYLE RAMBLER. Generally used on the Buncrana – Rathmullan (Lough Swilly) service, which did not resume in summer 2014. In 2014 sold to *Waterford Castle Hotel* and renamed the MARY FITZGERALD. Modified to be cable guided.

SECTION 6 – GB & IRELAND – MAJOR PASSENGER-ONLY FERRIES

There are a surprisingly large number of passenger-only ferries operating in the British Isles, mainly operated by launches and small motor boats. There are, however, a few 'major' operators who operate only passenger vessels (of rather larger dimensions) and have not therefore been mentioned previously.

Aran Island Ferries BANRÍON NA FARRAIGE (117t, 27.4m, 1984, 188 passengers, IMO 8407709) (ex ARAN EXPRESS 2007), CEOL NA FARRAIGE (234t, 2001, 37.4m, 294 passengers, IMO 9246750), DRAÍOCHT NA FARRAIGE (318t, 1999, 35.4m, 294 passengers, IMO 9200897), GLÓR NA FARRAIGE (170t, 1985, 33.5m, 244 passenger, IMO 8522391) (ex ARAN FLYER 2007), SEA SPRINTER (16t, 11.6m, 35 passengers). **Routes operated** Rossaveal (Co Galway) – Inishmor, Rossaveal – Inis Meáin, Rossaveal – Inisheer. **Tel** +353 (0)91 568903 (572050 after 19.00), **Fax** +353 (0)91 568538, **Email** info@aranislandferries.com **Website** www.aranislandferries.com *(English)*

Brixham Express BRIXHAM EXPRESS (2015, 31t, 15.0m, 98 passengers) **Route operated** Brixham – Torquay. **Tel** +44 (0)7553 359596, **Email** info@brixhamexpress.com **Website** www.brixhamexpress.com

Clyde Cruises (Clyde Marine Services Ltd) CHIEFTAIN (ex SEABUS, 2014) (54t, 2007, 19.5m, 100 passengers)CLYDE CLIPPER (125t, 2009, 27m, 250 passengers), CRUISER (ex POOLE SCENE, 2001, HYTHE HOTSPUR, 1995, SOUTHSEA QUEEN, 1978) (119t, 1974, 24.4m, 245 passengers), FENCER (18t, 1976, 11.0m, 33 passengers), ROVER (48t, 1964, 19.8m, 120 passengers), THE SECOND SNARK (45t, 1938, 22.9m, 120 passengers). **Routes operated** Glasgow city cruise, Caledonian Canal sailings, Oban from Dunstaffnage Marina, Aberdeen Harbour tours and cruises and private charters around the Clyde area. **Tel** +44 (0)1475 721281, **Email** info@clydecruises.com **Website** www.clydecruises.com www.clyde-marine.co.uk *(English)*.

Clydelink ISLAND PRINCESS (1996, 13.7m, 96 passengers), **Route operated** Gourock – Kilcreggan (operated on behalf of *Strathclyde Partnership for Transport*), ISLAND TRADER (12 passengers), SILVER SWAN (12 passengers) **Route operated** Renfrew – Yoker (operated on behalf of *Strathclyde Partnership for Transport*). **Tel** 0871 705 0888, **Website** www.clydelink.co.uk *(English)*.

Dartmouth Steam Railway & Riverboat Company DARTMOUTH PRINCESS (ex DEVON BELLE II 2000) (22t, 1990, 18.3m, 156 passengers), KINGSWEAR PRINCESS (ex TWIN STAR II 2010) (27t, 1978, 19.1m, 150 passengers) **Route operated** Dartmouth – Kingswear. **Note:** River craft owned by this operator are also used for the ferry service on some occasions. **Tel** +44 (0)1803 555872, **Email** bookings@dsrrb.co.uk **Website** www.dartmouthrailriver.co.uk *(English)*

Doolin2Aran Ferries DOOLIN DISCOVERY (2009, 15.2m, 72 passengers), JACK B (2005, 15.2m, 67 passengers), HAPPY HOOKER (77t, 1989, 19.8m, 96 passengers), MACDARA (2010, 8.5m, 12 passengers), ROSE OF ARAN (113t, 1976, 20.1m, 96 passengers. IMO 7527916). **Routes operated** Doolin – Inisheer, Doolin – Inishmore, Doolin – Inishmaan. **Tel** +353 (0)65 707 5949, **Email** info@doolin2aranferries.ie **Website** www.doolin2aranferries.com *(English)*

Doolin Ferry (O'Brien Line) CAILIN OIR (1999, 15.2m, 72 passengers), QUEEN OF ARAN (113t, 1976, 20.1m, 96 passengers, IMO 7527928), TRANQUILITY (62t, 1988, 15.8m, 100 passengers). **Routes operated** Doolin – Inisheer, Doolin – Inishmaan, Doolin – Inishmore. Also cruises to Cliffs of Mohr. **Tel** +353 (0)65 707 5555, +353 (0)65 707 5618, **Email** info@doolinferry.com **Website** www.doolinferry.com *(English)*

SECTION 6 – MAJOR PASSENGER ONLY FERRIES

Ceol Na Farraige and Draiocht na Farraige *(Matthew Punter)*

Pirate Queen, Queen of Aran, Cailin Oir and Happy Hooker *(Matthew Punter)*

Exe to Sea Cruises MY QUEEN (ex GONDOLIER QUEEN) (1929, 37t, 18m, 127 passengers) (laid up), ORCOMBE (1954, 14.3m, 90 passengers), PRINCESS MARINA (1936, 15.8m, 60 passengers). **Route operated** Exmouth – Starcross. **Tel** +44 (0)1626 774770, **Email** info@exe2sea.co.uk **Website** www.exe2sea.co.uk *(English)*

Fleetwood – Knott End Ferry (operated by *Wyre Marine Services Ltd*) WYRE ROSE (2005, 32 passengers). **Route operated** Fleetwood – Knott End. **Route operated** Fleetwood – Knott End. **Tel** +44 (0)1253 871113, **Ferry mobile** +44 (0) 7793 270934, **Fax** +44 (0)1253 87 79 74 **Email** info@wyremarine.co.uk **Website** www.wyre.gov.uk (search for ferry) *(English)*

Gosport Ferry GOSPORT QUEEN (159t, 1966, 30.5m, 250 passengers, IMO 8633700), HARBOUR SPIRIT (293t, 2015, 32.8m, 297 passengers, IMO 9741669), SPIRIT OF GOSPORT (300t, 2001, 32.6m, 300 passengers, IMO 8972089), SPIRIT OF PORTSMOUTH (377t, 2005, 32.6m, 300 passengers, IMO 9319894) **Route operated** Gosport – Portsmouth. **Tel** +44 (0)23 9252 4551, **Fax:** +44(0)23 9252 4802, **Email** admin@gosportferry.co.uk **Website** www.gosportferry.co.uk *(English)*

Gravesend – Tilbury Ferry (operated by the *Lower Thames & Medway Passenger Boat Co Ltd*) DUCHESS M (ex VESTA 1979) (71t, 1956, 23.8m, 124 passengers), PRINCESS POCAHONTAS (ex FREYA II 1989, LABOE I 1985, LABOE 1984) (180t, 1962, 29.9m, 207 passengers, IMO 5201271). The PRINCESS POCAHONTAS is an excursion vessel operating regularly to Greenwich, Westminster, Chelsea and Southend, also occasionally to Rochester and Whitstable but sometimes covers the ferry roster. **Route operated** Gravesend (Kent) – Tilbury (Essex), **Tel** +44 (0)1732 353448, **Direct Line to Ferry** +44 (0)7973 390124, **Email** enquiry@princess-pocahontas.com   **Websites**   www.princess-pocahontas.com   *(English)* www.thurrock.gov.uk/ferry-services/tilbury-to-gravesend-timetable

Hamble – Warsash Ferry CLAIRE (2.1t, 1985, 7.3m, 12 passengers), EMILY (3.7t, 1990, 8.5m, 12 passengers), **Route operated** Hamble – Warsash (across Hamble River). **Tel** +44 (0)23 8045 4512, **Mobile** +44 (0) 7720 438402 **Email** mike@hambleferry.co.uk, **Website** www.hambllferry.co.uk *(English)*

Harwich Harbour Foot & Bicycle Ferry HARBOUR FERRY (8t, 2016, 11.4m, 58 passengers). **Routes operated** Harwich (Ha'penny Pier) – Shotley (Marina), Harwich – Felixstowe (Landguard Point) (Easter to end of September). **Tel** +44 (0) 7919 911440, **Email** chris@harwichharbourferry.com **Website** www.harwichharbourferry.com *(English)*

Hayling Ferry (now operated by Baker Trayte Marine Ltd on behalf of the Hayling Ferry Trust). PRIDE OF HAYLING (1989, 11.9m, 63 passengers), TINA MARIE (12 passengers) **Route operated** Eastney – Hayling Island.

Hovertravel FREEDOM 90 (1990, 25.4m, 95 passengers, BHC AP1-88/100S hovercraft, converted from AP1-88/100 in 1999), ISLAND EXPRESS (ex FREJA VIKING, 2002) (1985, 25.4m, 95 passengers, BHC AP1-88/100S hovercraft, converted from BHC AP1-88/100 in 2001), ISLAND FLYER (161t, 2016, 22.4m, 80 passengers, IMO 9737797, Griffon Hovercraft 12000TD/AP), SOLENT FLYER (161t, 2016, 40.0k, 22.4m, 80 passengers, IMO 9737785, Griffon Hovercraft 12000TD/AP), Route operated Southsea - Ryde. **Tel** +44 (0)8434 878887, **Fax** +44 (0)1983 562216, Email info@hovertravel.com **Website** www.hovertravel.com *(English)*

Hythe Ferry (White Horse Ferries) GREAT EXPECTATIONS (66t, 1992, 21.3m, 162 passengers – catamaran), URIAH HEEP (25.6t, 1999, 60 passengers (tri-maran)), **Tel**. *Head Office* +44 (0)1793 618566, *Local Office* +44 (0)23 8084 0722, **Email** post@hytheferry.co.uk **Website** www.hytheferry.co.uk *(English)*

Isle of Sark Shipping Company BON MARIN DE SERK (118t, 1983, 20.7m, 131 passengers, IMO 8303056), SARK BELLE (ex BOURNEMOUTH BELLE 2011) (50t, 1979, 26.2m, 180 passengers), SARK VENTURE (133t, 1986, 21.3m, 122 passengers, IMO 8891986), SARK VIKING (Cargo Vessel) (104t, 2007, 21.2m, 12 passengers, IMO 8648858). **Route operated** St Peter Port (Guernsey) – Sark. **Tel** +44 (0) 1481 724059, **Fax** +44 (0) 1481 713999, **Email** info@sarkshippingcompany.com **Website** www.sarkshippingcompany.com *(English)*

John O'Groats Ferries PENTLAND VENTURE (186t, 1987, 29.6m, 250 passengers, IMO 8834122). **Route operated** John O'Groats – Burwick (Orkney). **Tel** +44 (0)1955 611353, **Email** Office@jogferry.co.uk **Website** www.jogferry.co.uk *(English)*

Kintyre Express KINTYRE EXPRESS II (5.75t, 2011, 11.0m, 12 passengers), KINTYRE EXPRESS III (5.75t, 2012, 11.0m, 12 passengers), KINTYRE EXPRESS IV (5.75t, 2012, 11.0m, 12 passengers). **Routes operated** Campbeltown – Ballycastle, Port Ellen (Islay) – Ballycastle,. **Tel** +44 (0) 1586 555895, **Email** info@kintyreexpress.com **Website** www.kintyreexpress.com *(English)*

Lundy Company OLDENBURG (294t, 1958, 43.6m, 267 passengers, IMO 5262146). **Routes operated** Bideford – Lundy Island, Ilfracombe – Lundy Island. Also North Devon coastal cruises and River Torridge cruises. **Tel** +44 (0)1237 470074, **Fax** +44 (0)1237 477779, **Email** info@lundyisland.co.uk **Website** www.lundyisland.co.uk *(English)*

Manche Iles Express (trading name of Société Morbihannaise de Navigation) GRANVILLE (ex BORNHOLM EXPRESS 2014) (325t, 2006, 41.0m, 245 passengers, IMO 9356476 – catamaran), VICTOR HUGO (ex SALTEN 2003) (387t, 1997, 35.0m, 195 passengers, IMO 9157806 – catamaran). **Route operated** Granville – Jersey – Sark – Guernsey, Portbail or Carteret – Jersey, Guernsey and Sark, Diélette – Alderney – Guernsey. **Tel** +33 0825 131 050, **Fax** +33 02 33 90 03 49, **Website** www.manche-iles-express.com *(French, English)*

MBNA Thames Clippers (trading name of Collins River Enterprises Ltd) AURORA CLIPPER (181t, 2007, 37.8m, 27.5k, 220 passengers, IMO 9451824), CYCLONE CLIPPER (181t, 2007, 37.8m, 27.5k, 220 passengers, IMO 9451880), GALAXY CLIPPER (155t, 2015, 34.0m, 155 passengers, IMO 9783784), HURRICANE CLIPPER (181t, 2002, 37.8m, 27.5k, 220 passengers, IMO 9249702), METEOR CLIPPER (181t, 2007, 37.8m, 27.5k, 220 passengers, IMO 9451812), MONSOON CLIPPER (181t, 2007, 37.8m, 27.5k, 220 passengers, IMO 9451795), MOON CLIPPER (ex DOWN RUNNER 2005) (98t, 2001, 32.0m, 25.0k, 138 passengers, IMO 9245586), NEPTUNE CLIPPER (155t, 2015, 34.0m, 155 passengers, IMO 9783796), SKY CLIPPER (ex VERITATUM 1995, SD10 2000) (60t, 1992, 25.0m, 62 passengers), STAR CLIPPER (ex CONRAD CHELSEA HARBOUR 1995, SD9 2000) (60t, 1992, 25.0m, 62 passengers), STORM CLIPPER (ex DHL WORLDWIDE EXPRESS 1995, SD11 2000) (60t, 1992, 25.0m, 62 passengers), SUN CLIPPER (ex ANTRIM RUNNER 2005) (98t, 2001, 32.0m, 25.0k, 138 passengers, IMO 9232292), TORNADO CLIPPER (181t, 2007, 37.8m, 27.5k, 220 passengers, IMO 9451783), TWIN STAR (45t, 1974, 19.2m, 120 passengers), TYPHOON CLIPPER (181t, 2007, 37.8m, 27.5k, 220 passengers, IMO 9451771, (2015, 34.0m, 154 seats) The 'Typhoon', 'Tornado', 'Cyclone' and 'Monsoon', 'Aurora' and 'Meteor' Clippers were designed by AIMTEK and built by Brisbane Ship Constructions in Australia in 2007. 'Galaxy' and 'Neptune' were designed by One2three Naval Architects and built by Incat Tasmania, Hobart, Australia. **Routes operated** Embankment – Waterloo – Blackfriars – Bankside – London Bridge – Tower – Canary Wharf – Greenland – Masthouse Terrace – Greenwich – North Greenwich – Woolwich, Bankside – Millbank – St George (Tate to Tate Service), Putney – Wandsworth – Chelsea Harbour – Cardogan – Embankment – Blackfriars, Canary Wharf – Rotherhithe Hilton Docklands Hotel (TWIN STAR). +44 (0)870 781 5049, **Fax** +44 (0)20 7001 2222, **Email** web@thamesclippers.com **Website** www.thamesclippers.com (English).

Mersey Ferries ROYAL DAFFODIL (ex OVERCHURCH 1999) (751t, 1962, 46.6m, 860 passengers, IMO 4900868) (laid up), ROYAL IRIS OF THE MERSEY (ex MOUNTWOOD 2002) (464t, 1960, 46.3m, 750 passengers, IMO 8633712), SNOWDROP (ex WOODCHURCH 2004) (670t, 1960, 46.6m, 750 passengers, IMO 8633724). **Routes operated** Liverpool (Pier Head) – Birkenhead (Woodside), Liverpool – Wallasey (Seacombe) with regular cruises from Liverpool and Seacombe to Salford along the Manchester Ship Canal. **Tel** *Admin* +44 (0)151 639 0609, *Reservations* +44 (0)151 330 1444, **Fax** +44 (0)151 639 0578, **Email** info@merseyferries.co.uk **Website** www.merseyferries.co.uk *(English)*

Mudeford Ferry (Derham Marine) FERRY DAME (4t, 1989, 9.1m, 48 passengers), JOSEPHINE (10.5t, 1997, 10.7m, 70 passengers – catamaran), JOSEPHINE II (10.5t, 2013, 11.0m, 86 passengers – catamaran). **Route operated** Mudeford Quay – Mudeford Sandbank. **Tel** +44 (0)7968 334441 **Email** information@mudefordferry.co.uk **Website** www.mudefordferry.co.uk *(English)*

Nexus (trading name of Tyne & Wear Integrated Transport Authority) PRIDE OF THE TYNE (222t, 1993, 24.0m, 240 passengers, IMO 9062166), SPIRIT OF THE TYNE (174t, 2006, 25.0m, 200 passengers). **Route operated** North Shields – South Shields. Also cruises South Shields – Newcastle. **Tel** +44 (0)191 2020747, **Email** customerservices@nexus.org **Website** www.nexus.org.uk/ferry *(English)*

Harbour Spirit *(Nick Widdows)*

Pride of the Tyne *(Nick Widdows)*

Balmoral *(John Hendy)*

Starlight Ferries MERSEY ROSE (14t, 1988, 11.6m, 12 passengers) (ex RNLI 'Mersey Class' lifeboat PEGGY AND ALEX CAIRD 2015) **Route operated** Lymington – Yarmouth. **Tel** +44(0)7810 892 **Email** contact@starlightferries.com **Website** www.starlightferries.com

Travel Trident HERM TRIDENT V (79t, 1989, 25.9m, 250 passengers), TRIDENT VI (79t, 1992, 22.3m, 250 passengers). **Route operated** St Peter Port (Guernsey) – Herm. **Tel** +44 (0)1481 721379, **Fax** +44 (0)1481 700226, **Email** peterwilcox@cwgsy.net **Website** www.traveltrident.com *(English)*

Waverley Excursions WAVERLEY (693t, 1947, 73.2m, 925 passengers, IMO 5386954). **Routes operated** Excursions all round British Isles. However, regular cruises in the Clyde, Bristol Channel, South Coast and Thames provide a service which can be used for transport purposes and therefore she is in a sense a ferry. She is the only seagoing paddle steamer in the world. **Tel** +44 (0)845 130 4647, **Fax** +44 (0)141 248 2150, **Email** info@waverleyexcursions.co.uk **Website** www.waverleyexcursions.co.uk *(English)*

Western Isles Cruises Ltd VANGUARD (12t, 2006, 13.0m, 12 passengers). VENTURER (12t, 2006, 13.0m, 12 passengers), WESTERN ISLES (45t, 1960, 18.0m, 84 passengers). **Route Operated** Mallaig – Inverie (Knoydart) – Tarbet. **Tel** +44 (0)1687 462233, **Email** info@westernislescruises.co.uk, **Website** www.westernislescruises.co.uk *(English)*

Western Lady Ferry Service WESTERN LADY VI (ex TORBAY PRINCESS ex DEVON PRINCESS II) (50t, 1981, 19.2m, 173 passengers), WESTERN LADY VII (ex TORBAY PRINCESS II, ex BRIXHAM BELLE II, ex DEVON PRINCESS III) (46t, 1984, 19.8m, 177 passengers). **Route Operated** Torquay – Brixham. **Tel** +44 (0)1803 293797, **Website** www.westernladyferry.com *(English)* Note: The service is now part of *Dartmouth Steam Railway & Riverboat Company* but is marketed separately.

White Funnel BALMORAL (735t, 1949, 62.2m, 800 passengers, IMO 5034927) Excursions in Bristol Channel, North West, South Coast, Thames and Clyde. Regular cruises in the Bristol Channel provide a service which can be used for transport purposes and therefore she is in a sense a ferry. **Tel** +44 (0)117 325 6200 **Email** balmoral@whitefunnel.co.uk **Website** www.whitefunnel.co.uk

Twin Star *(Nick Widdows)*

Tornado Clipper *(Nick Widdows)*

Tom Sawyer *(John Bryant)*

SCANDINAVIAN & NORTHERN EUROPE REVIEW 2015-16

The following geographical review again takes the form of a voyage along the coast of the Netherlands and Germany, round the southern tip of Norway, down the Kattegat, through the Great Belt and into the Baltic, then up to the Gulf of Finland and Gulf of Bothnia.

FRISIAN ISLANDS & ELBE

TESO introduced its new *Texelstroom* on the service between Den Helder and the island of Texel in June 2016 after an eighteen month period of construction at Sestao. She is similar in size and with a slightly larger capacity than her fleetmate *Dokter Wagemaker* and has replaced the *Schulpengat* , which has been sold.

Rederij Doeksen announced plans during 2015 to convert its freighter *Nord-Nederland* to LNG-powered passenger configuration, but this was shelved later in the year. Instead, the company announced in early 2016 its plans to construct a pair of catamarans in Vietnam to replace the *Midsland* and relegating the *Friesland* to back-up vessel.

Tuule Grupp's new Elb-Link service began in July 2015, utilising the *Hiiumaa* and the *Saaremaa* which had been removed from their previous operation to the Estonian islands when their owners lost the contract for the services earlier in the year. The new Cuxhaven – Brunsbüttel route takes 75 minutes in each direction with up to ten departures a day. The two vessels have been given the marketing names of "Anne-Marie" (*Saaremaa*) and "Grete" (*Hiiumaa*) but have not been formally re-registered.

NORWEGIAN DOMESTIC

Hurtigruten has invested heavily in their expedition cruise fleet during the course of the last year. The company purchased the *Atlântida* from her Spanish builders in 2015, renaming her the *Spitsbergen* and commencing a lengthy conversion to meet the company's requirements. The vessel was originally constructed in 2008 but was rejected by her original owners. In April 2016, the company announced a memorandum of understanding with the Norwegian shipyard Kleven for an order for two further expedition ships with options for two additional units.

Several of Hurtigruten's fleet underwent extensive refits during 2015 to modernise their interiors: the *Polarys*, the *Nordkapp*, the *Nordnorge* and *Kong Harald* have all received stylish and modern interiors befitting their growing role as cruise vessels more than coastal ferries.

Bastø-Fosen's first new ship was launched in mid-April taking the name *Bastø VI*. The other two vessels in the class will be named *Bastø VII* and *Bastø VIII*.

SKAGERRAK & KATTEGAT

Stena Line introduced the ro-pax *Ask* onto the Frederikshavn – Gothenburg route in March 2016, renaming her the *Stena Gothica*. She replaced the veteran train ferry *Stena Scanrail* which was sold to Turkey for further service as the *Birdeniz*.

DANISH DOMESTIC

Mols-Linien celebrated the fiftieth anniversary of its foundation in May 2016, having started in 1966 between Ebeltoft and Sjællands Odde. In the intervening half century, the company has carried over 93 million passengers. Earlier in the year, the company announced it had placed an order with Tasmanian fast ferry builder InCat for a catamaran to join its fleet in May 2017. To be named the *KatExpress 3*, the new catamaran will be a third 102 metre vessel in the fleet, joining the *KatExpress 1* and *KatExpress 2*. She will replace the 91 metre *Max Mols*.

The new vessel represents something of a vote of confidence by Mols Linien in its service since the turbulent period of recent years as they switched from a mixed fleet to a solely fast ferry fleet. Passenger traffic on the services between Arhus/Ebeltoft and Sjaellands Odde has increased by 33 per cent in the last four years and the replacement of the smaller catamaran will not only provide much needed extra capacity, but will mean a fleet of near identical ships for the first time in decades.

Huckleberry Finn *(Miles Cowsill)*

Sassnitz *(Miles Cowsill)*

Leonora Christina *(Miles Cowsill)*

Kong Harald *(Miles Cowsill)*

Mols-Linien has also been awarded the contract for ferry services to the Danish island of Bornholm, replacing the incumbent BornholmFaergen which, via its predecessors, has operated to the island for 150 years. Mols Linien has ordered a replacement ro-pax vessel for the Køge – Rønne service from Rauma Marine Constructions and a 109m catamaran from Austal Ships in Australia for the Ystad – Rønne service.

Having welcomed the arrival of the new *Samsø* into service in March 2015, owners Samsø Rederi decided in June to change her name to *Prinsesse Isabella*. Rival operators SamsøFaergen subsequently renamed their own vessel *Kanhave*, adopting the now vacant name *Samsø*.

Læsø Færgen is also planning on ordering a new vessel during the next year with delivery planned for 2019. The new ship would be designed to replace both of the existing vessels on the service, although the *Margrete Læsø* would be retained as back-up provision.

SOUTH BALTIC

The first of Scandlines' long-delayed "GR12" vessels finally entered service in late May 2016. The *Berlin* was the lead vessel, having been rebuilt at Odense alongside her sister, the *Copenhagen*. Despite plans, when they were repurchased from the bankrupt shipyard at Stralsund, to have them in service by autumn 2015, the rebuild proved far more complex than anticipated and delivery dates were frequently delayed throughout the latter part of 2015 and into 2016. The company announced it was to retain the *Kronprins Frederik* to act as a spare vessel for the Gedser – Rostock service (as well as Puttgarden – Rødby) in the event of teething problems with the new ship but as summer 2016 approached, it became obvious that the *Copenhagen* would be delayed until the autumn and the *Kronprins Frederik* would be required on the service opposite the *Berlin*.

The company sold the *Prins Joachim* to European Seaways of Greece for further service in the Mediterranean renamed (temporarily) the *Prince*.

Wolin *(John Bryant)*

Destination Gotland has opted to take up the option on a second LNG-powered newbuild from Guangzhou shipyard in china, which is currently working on the first order for the company.

After more than two years of attempting to start a rival service to the island, Gotlandsbåten finally managed to secure a vessel late in 2015 with the purchase of P&O's *Express* which had been withdrawn from their Cairnryan and Troon to Larne services. The new service began operations in late April 2016, with weekend only crossings from Nynäshamn and daily operations during the summer peak, including sailings from Västervik.

Stena disposed of the train ferry *Trelleborg* which was withdrawn from the Trelleborg – Sassnitz service in 2014. She was purchased by unknown buyers, renamed *Sunny* and towed to Piraeus, pending further deployment.

CROSS BALTIC

In November 2015, a continuing decline in traffic to Russia forced DFDS to close their Kiel – Ust Luga freight service, operated by the *Botnia Seaways*. Instead, they agreed with Finnlines to purchase slots on their weekly Lübeck – St Petersburg service. The *Botnia Seaways* was transferred to the Fredericia – Copenhagen – Klaipėda route and the previous vessel on the service, the *Corona Seaways*, to the North Sea.

At the end of March 2015, Finnlines withdrew passenger facilities from the TransRussiaExpress service and replaced the ro-pax ferries used with a freighter.

NORTH BALTIC

The construction of Tallink's new LNG powered 'Shuttle' vessel for service between Tallinn and Helsinki started on 4th August with a steel-cutting ceremony at Turku where she is being constructed by Meyer Werft. It was announced in early 2016 that the new vessel would take the name *Megastar* (following a competition on Facebook) and that she would replace the *Superstar* which was sold to Corsica Ferries and chartered back for the 2016 season. The *Superstar* will be delivered to her new owners on the arrival of the *Megastar* in early 2017 and is likely to be renamed *Mega Express 6* for service in the Mediterranean. Tallink decided to let an option for a second vessel lapse during early 2016.

Tallink introduced a fourth vessel onto the Tallinn – Helsinki service from March 2016 with the *Silja Europa* being returned from her charter to Bridgemans in Australia. She was placed onto a new cruise roster opposite the *Baltic Queen* whilst the *Star* and *Superstar* maintained the Shuttle service.

Construction has been ongoing on the four new vessels for the Port of Tallinn's service linking the Estonian mainland with the islands of Saaremaa and Hiiumaa. The first two vessels were launched in Poland in December 2015 and January 2016, taking the names *Tõll* and *Piret* respectively. The third vessel was launched at Sefine in Turkey as the *Tiiu* in April. The company has announced the new service will be marketed as Praamid and unveiled a striking livery for the fleet featuring traditional designs and each vessel in a different primary colour. The new service will start in September 2016, taking over from Saaremaa Laevakompanii .

Following the announcement of the new contract for Port of Tallinn in early 2015, the incumbents Tuule Grupp were quick to redeploy their best tonnage on a new service across the River Elbe (see above), replacing the *Saaremaa* and the *Hiiumaa* with the previously redundant *St Ola* and the chartered *Ionas* from Greece.

Matthew Punter

Silja Serenade *(Matthew Punter)*

SECTION 7 - NORTHERN EUROPE

ÆRØFÆRGERNE

THE COMPANY *Ærøfærgerne* is a Danish company, owned by the municipality of Ærø.

MANAGEMENT Managing Director Kelda Møller, **Marketing Coordinator** Jeanette Erikson.

ADDRESS Vestergade 1, 5970 Ærøskøbing, Denmark.

TELEPHONE Administration & Reservations +45 62 52 40 00.

FAX Administration & Reservations +45 62 52 20 88.

INTERNET Email info@aeroe-ferry.dk **Website** www.aeroe-ferry.dk *(Danish, English, German)*

ROUTE OPERATED Ærøskøbing (Ærø) – Svendborg (Fyn) (1hr 15mins; **ÆRØSKØBING, MARSTAL**; every 1/2 hours), Søby (Ærø) – Faaborg (Fyn) (1hr; **SKJOLDNÆS**; 3 per day), Søby (Ærø) – Fynshav (Als) (1hr 10mins; **SKJOLDNÆS**; 3 per day).

1	ÆRØSKØBING	1617t	99	12.0k	49.0m	395P	42C	-	BA	DK	9199086
2	MARSTAL	1617t	99	12.0k	49.0m	395P	42C	-	BA	DK	9199074
3	SKJOLDNÆS	986t	79	11.0k	47.1m	245P	31C	-	BA	DK	7925649

ÆRØSKØBING, MARSTAL Built by EOS, Esbjerg, Denmark for *Ærøfærgerne*.

SKJOLDNÆS Built as the SAM-SINE by Søren Larsen & Sønner Skibsværft A/S, Nykøbing Mors, Denmark for *Hou-Sælvig Ruten Aps* of Denmark. Operated between Hou (Jutland) and Sælvig (Samsø). In 1995 she was taken over by *Samsø Linien*. In 2001 she was lengthened by Ørskov Christensen's Staalskibsværft, Frederikshavn, Denmark. In 2009 sold to *Ærøfærgerne* and renamed the SKJOLDNÆS.

BASTØ FOSEN

THE COMPANY *Bastø Fosen* is a Norwegian private sector company, a subsidiary of *Torghatten ASA – Brønnøysund*.

MANAGEMENT Managing Director May Kristin Salberg.

ADDRESS PO Box 94, 3191 Horten, Norway.

TELEPHONE Administration +47 33 03 17 40, **Reservations** +47 33 03 17 40 (buses only).

FAX Administration +47 33 03 17 49, **Reservations** +47 33 03 17 49 (buses only).

INTERNET Email bastohorten@fosen.no **Website** www.basto-fosen.no *(Norwegian)*

ROUTE OPERATED Moss – Horten (across Oslofjord, Norway) (30 mins; **BASTØ I, BASTØ II, BASTØ III, BASTØ VII, BASTØ VIII**; up to every 15 mins).

1	BASTØ I	5505t	97	14.0k	109.0m	550P	200C	18L	BA	NO	9144081
2	BASTØ II	5505t	97	14.0k	109.0m	550P	200C	18L	BA	NO	9144093
3	BASTØ III	7310t	05	18.0k	116.2m	540P	212C	18L	BA	NO	9299408
4	BASTØ VII	2835t	86	13.5k	80.1m	456P	140C	12L	BA	NO	8512114
5	BASTØ VIII	3397t	90	16.0k	92.0m	650P	155C	-	BA	NO	8917340

BASTØ I, BASTØ II Built by Fosen Mekaniske Verksteder, Frengen, Norway for *Bastø Fosen*.

BASTØ III Built by Stocznia Remontowa, Gdansk, Poland for *Bastø Fosen*.

BASTØ VII Built as the AUSTRHEIM by Trønderverftet A/S, Hommelvik, Norway for *A/S Bergen-Nordhordland Rutelag (BNR)*, operating between Steinestø and Knarvik. In 1993 chartered to *Rogaland Trafikkselskap A/S* and operated between Stavanger and Tau. In 1995 sold to *Hardanger Sunnhordlandske Dampskibsselskap (HSD)* of Norway and renamed the BJØRNEFJORD. Operated between Valevåg and Skjersholmane. In 2001 sold to *Boknafjorden Ferjeselskap A/S* and renamed the BOKNAFJORD. Later transferred to *Båtbygg A/S* and

Marstal *(Peter Therkildsen)*

Superspeed 1 *(Miles Cowsill)*

operated between Mortaviken and Arsvågen. In 2002 transferred to *Rogaland Trafikkselskap Ferjer A/S* and in 2003 transferred to *Stavangerska Ferjer A/S*. In 2008 and 2009 she was briefly chartered to a number of operators and in 2008 sold to *Tide Sjø AS*. In December 2010 she was sold to Bastø *Fosen* and renamed the BASTØ IV. In February 2016 renamed the BASTØ VII.

BASTØ VIII Built as the NORDKAPPHORN by *Trønderverftet A/S*, Hommelvik, Norway for Finnmark Fylkesrederi og Ruteselskap AS of Norway. In 1992 chartered to *Rogaland Trafikkselskap A/S* and renamed the RENNESØY. In January 2012 sold to *Torghatten Nord A/S* and renamed the TRANØY. In September 2012 sold to *Bastø Fosen* and renamed the BASTØ V. In February 2016 renamed the BASTØ VIII.

Under Construction

6	BASTØ IV	7700t	16	16.0k	142.9m	600P	200C	30L	BA	NO	9769219
7	BASTØ V	7700t	17	16.0k	142.9m	600P	200C	30L	BA	NO	-
8	BASTØ VI	7700t	17	16.0k	142.9m	600P	200C	30L	BA	NO	-

BASTØ IV, BASTØ V, BASTØ VI Under construction by Cemre Shipyard, Yalova, Turkey. They will replace two older ships and a five ship service will continue to be operated. A sixth ship will be kept in reserve.

COLOR LINE

THE COMPANY *Color Line ASA* is a Norwegian private sector stock-listed limited company. The company merged with *Larvik Scandi Line* of Norway (which owned *Larvik Line* and *Scandi Line*) in 1996. In 1997 the operations of *Larvik Line* were incorporated into *Color Line*; *Scandi Line* continued as a separate subsidiary until 1999, when it was also incorporated into *Color Line*. The marketing name *Color Scandi Line* was dropped at the end of 2000.

MANAGEMENT Managing Director Trond Kleivdal.

ADDRESS *Commercial* Postboks 1422 Vika, 0115 Oslo, Norway, *Technical Management* Color Line Marine AS, PO Box 2090, 3210 Sandefjord, Norway.

TELEPHONE Administration +47 22 94 44 00, **Reservations Germany** +49 40 381096 9113, *Denmark* +45 99 56 10 00, **Norway** +47 81 00 08 11.

INTERNET Website www.colorline.com *(English, Danish, German, Norwegian, Swedish,)*

ROUTES OPERATED Conventional Ferries Oslo (Norway) – Kiel (Germany) (19 hrs 30 mins; *COLOR FANTASY, COLOR MAGIC*; 1 per day), Kristiansand (Norway) – Hirtshals (3 hrs 15 mins; *SUPERSPEED 1*; 4 per day), Larvik (Norway) – Hirtshals (Denmark) (3 hrs 45 mins; *SUPERSPEED 2*; up to 2 per day), Sandefjord (Norway) – Strömstad (Sweden) (2 hrs 30 mins; *BOHUS, COLOR VIKING*; up to 4 per day).

1	BOHUS	9149t	71	20.5k	123.4m	1165P	240C	34T	BA	NO	7037806
2	COLOR FANTASY	75027t	04	22.3k	224.0m	2750P	750C	90T	BA	NO	9278234
3	COLOR MAGIC	75100t	07	22.3k	223.7m	2750P	550C	90T	BA	NO	9349863
4	COLOR VIKING	19763t	85	16.4k	134.0m	2000P	320C	40T	BA2	NO	8317942
5	SUPERSPEED 1	36822t	08	27.0k	211.3m	2250P	525C	121T	BA2	NO	9374519
6	SUPERSPEED 2	34231t	08	27.0k	211.3m	1800P	525C	121T	BA2	NO	9378682

BOHUS Built as the PRINSESSAN DESIREE by Aalborg Værft A/S, Aalborg, Denmark for *Rederi AB Göteborg-Frederikshavn Linjen* of Sweden (trading as *Sessan Linjen*) for their service between Gothenburg and Frederikshavn. In 1981 the company was taken over by *Stena Line* and she became surplus to requirements. During 1981 she had a number of charters including *B&I Line* of Ireland and *Sealink UK*. In 1982 she was chartered to *Sally Line* to operate as second vessel on the Ramsgate – Dunkerque service between June and September. She bore the name 'VIKING 2' in large letters on her hull although she was never officially renamed. In September 1982 she returned to *Stena Line* and in 1983 she was transferred to subsidiary company *Varberg-Grenaa Line* for their service between Varberg (Sweden) and Grenaa (Denmark), renamed the EUROPAFÄRJAN. In 1985 she was renamed the EUROPAFÄRJAN II. In 1986, following a reorganisation within *Stena Line*, ownership was transferred to subsidiary company *Lion Ferry*

AB and she was named the LION PRINCESS. In 1993 she was sold to *Scandi Line* and renamed the BOHUS. In 1999 *Scandi Line* operations were integrated into *Color Line*.

COLOR FANTASY Built by Kværner Masa-Yards, Turku, Finland for *Color Line* to replace the PRINSESSE RAGNHILD on the Oslo – Kiel service.

COLOR MAGIC Built by Aker Yards, Turku, Finland (hull construction) and Rauma, Finland (fitting out), for the Oslo – Kiel route.

COLOR VIKING Built as the PEDER PAARS by Nakskov Skibsværft A/S, Nakskov, Denmark for *DSB (Danish State Railways)* for their service between Kalundborg (Sealand) and Århus (Jutland). In 1990 purchased by *Stena Line* of Sweden for delivery in 1991. In that year renamed the STENA INVICTA and entered service on the *Sealink Stena Line* Dover – Calais service. She was withdrawn from the route in February 1998, before the formation of *P&O Stena Line,* but ownership was transferred to that company. In Summer 1998, she was chartered to *Silja Line* to operate between Vaasa and Umeå under the marketing name 'WASA JUBILEE'. In Autumn 1998 she was laid up at Zeebrugge. She remained there until Autumn 1999 when she was chartered to *Stena Line* to operate between Holyhead and Dublin. In 2000 she was chartered to *Color Line*, renamed the COLOR VIKING and in April entered service on the Sandefjord – Strömstad service. In 2002 purchased by *Color Line*.

SUPERSPEED 1, SUPERSPEED 2 Built by Aker Yards, Rauma, Finland for the Kristiansand – Hirtshals and Larvik – Hirtshals routes. In January 2011, the SUPERSPEED 1 was modified to provide additional facilities and increase passenger capacity.

DESTINATION GOTLAND

THE COMPANY *Destination Gotland AB* is a Swedish private sector company owned by *Rederi AB Gotland*.

MANAGEMENT Managing Director Christer Bruzelius, **Marketing Manager** Per-Erling Evensen.

ADDRESS PO Box 1234, 621 23 Visby, Gotland, Sweden.

TELEPHONE Administration +46 (0)498-20 18 00, **Reservations** +46 (0)771-22 33 00.

FAX Administration & Reservations +46 (0)498-20 13 90.

INTERNET Email info@destinationgotland.se **Website** www.destinationgotland.se *(Swedish, English, Finnish, German)*

ROUTES OPERATED Fast Conventional Ferries Visby (Gotland) – Nynäshamn (Swedish mainland) (3 hrs 15 mins; **GOTLAND, VISBY**; 1/2 per day), Visby – Oskarshamn (Swedish mainland) (2 hrs 55 mins; **GOTLAND, VISBY**; 1/4 per day). **Fast Ferries (Summer only)** Visby – Nynäshamn (3 hrs 15 mins; **GOTLANDIA II**; up to 3 per day), Visby – Oskarshamn (Swedish mainland) (2 hrs 55 mins; **GOTLANDIA**; 1 per day (selected)).

1	GOTLAND	29746t	03	28.5k	195.8m	1500P	500C	118T	BAS2	SE	9223796
2»	GOTLANDIA	5632t	99	35.0k	112.5m	700P	140C	-	A	SE	9171163
3»	GOTLANDIA II	6554t	06	36.0k	122.0m	780P	160C	-	A	SE	9328015
4	VISBY	29746t	03	28.5k	195.8m	1500P	500C	118T	BAS2	SE	9223784

GOTLAND, VISBY Built by Guangzhou Shipyard International, Guangzhou, China for *Rederi AB Gotland* for use on *Destination Gotland* services.

GOTLANDIA Alstom Leroux Corsair 11500 monohull vessel built as the GOTLAND at Lorient, France for *Rederi AB Gotland* and chartered to *Destination Gotland*. In 2003 renamed the GOTLANDIA. In 2006 laid up. In 2007 inaugurated a new route between Visby and Grankullavik (Öland). In 2014 will operate between Visby and Oskarshamn.

GOTLANDIA II Fincantieri SF700 monohull fast ferry built at Riva Trigoso, Italy for *Rederi AB Gotland* for use by *Destination Gotland*.

Color Magic *(John Bryant)*

Patria Seaways *(Rob der Visser)*

Under Construction

| 5 | NEWBUILDING 1 | 4800t | 17 | - | 200.0m | 1650P | - | 110L | BAS2 | SE | - |
| 6 | NEWBUILDING 2 | 4800t | 18 | - | 200.0m | 1650P | - | 110L | BAS2 | SE | - |

NEWBUILDING 1, NEWBUILDING 2 Under construction by Guangzhou Shipyard International, Guangzhou, China for *Rederi AB Gotland* for use on *Destination Gotland* services. To be LNG powered.

DFDS SEAWAYS

THE COMPANY *DFDS Seaways* is a division of *DFDS A/S*, a Danish private sector company.

MANAGEMENT CEO DFDS A/S Niels Smedegaard, **Executive Vice-President Shipping Division** Peder Gellert Pedersen, **Head of Baltic Sea Business Area** Anders Refsgaard.

ADDRESS *Copenhagen* Sundkrogsgade 11, 2100 Copenhagen Ø, Denmark.

TELEPHONE Administration +45 33 42 33 42, **Reservations** *Denmark* +45 78 79 55 36, *Germany* +49 (0)40-389030, *Lithuania* +370 46 393616, *Sweden* +46 454 33680

FAX Administration +45 33 42 33 41. **INTERNET Administration** incoming@dfdsseaways.dk, **Reservations** *Denmark* incoming@dfdsseaways.dk *Germany* service.de@dfds.com *Lithuania* booking.lt@dfds.com, *Sweden* pax@dfds.com

Website www.dfdsseaways.com *(English, Danish, Dutch, German, Italian, Japanese, Norwegian, Polish, Swedish)*

ROUTES OPERATED *Passengers services* Copenhagen – Oslo (Norway) (16 hrs 30 mins; *CROWN SEAWAYS, PEARL SEAWAYS*; 1 per day), Klaipėda (Lithuania) – Kiel (Germany) (21 hrs; *ATHENA SEAWAYS, REGINA SEAWAYS*; 7 per week), Klaipėda – Karlshamn (Sweden) (14 hrs; *OPTIMA SEAWAYS, PATRIA SEAWAYS, VICTORIA SEAWAYS*; 10 per week), Paldiski (Estonia) – Kapellskär (Sweden) (10 hrs; *LIVERPOOL SEAWAYS*; 6 per week), *Freight only service* Fredericia – Copenhagen – Klaipėda (*BOTNIA SEAWAYS*; 2 per week).

See Section 1 for services operating to Britain.

1	ATHENA SEAWAYS	24950t	07	23.0k	199.1m	500P	-	190T	A	LT	9350680
2F	BOTNIA SEAWAYS	11530t	00	20.0k	162.2m	12P	-	140T	A	LT	9192129
3	CROWN SEAWAYS	35498t	94	22.0k	169.4m	1940P	450C	50T	BA	DK	8917613
4	KAUNAS SEAWAYS	25606t	89	16.3k	190.9m	262P	460C	93Tr	A2	LT	8311924
5	LIVERPOOL SEAWAYS	21856t	97	20.0k	186.0m	320P	100C	135T	A	LT	9136034
6	OPTIMA SEAWAYS	25206t	99	21.5k	186.3m	327P	164C	150T	A	LT	9188427
7	PATRIA SEAWAYS	18332t	92	17.0k	154.0m	242P	-	114T	BA2	LT	8917390
8	PEARL SEAWAYS	40039t	89	21.0k	178.4m	2090P	350C	70T	BA	DK	8701674
9	REGINA SEAWAYS	25518t	10	24.0k	199.1m	600P	-	190T	A	LT	9458535
10	VICTORIA SEAWAYS	24950t	09	23.0k	199.1m	600P	-	190T	A	LT	9350721
11	VILNIUS SEAWAYS	22341t	87	16.3k	190.9m	132P	460C	112Tr	A2	LT	8311900

ATHENA SEAWAYS Built as the CORAGGIO by Nuovi Cantieri Apuani, Marina di Carrara, Italy. First of an order of eight vessels for *Grimaldi Holdings* of Italy. Used on *Grimaldi Lines* Mediterranean services. In September 2010, bare-boat chartered to *Stena Line* to operate between Hook of Holland and Killingholme. In November 2011 replaced by the new STENA TRANSIT and returned to Mediterranean service. In December 2013 renamed the ATHENA SEAWAYS, chartered to *DFDS* and replaced the LIVERPOOL SEAWAYS on the Klaipėda – Kiel service. In May 2016 purchased by *DFDS*.

BOTNIA SEAWAYS Built as the FINNMASTER by Jinling Shipyard, Nanjing, China for the *Macoma Shipping Group* and chartered to *Finncarriers*. In 2008 sold to *DFDS Lisco* and in January 2009 delivered, chartered to *DFDS Tor Line* and renamed the TOR BOTNIA. Operated on the Immingham – Rotterdam route until December 2010. In January 2011 moved to the Kiel – St Petersburg route. In January 2013 renamed the BOTNIA SEAWAYS.

CROWN SEAWAYS Launched as the THOMAS MANN by Brodogradevna Industrija, Split, Croatia for *Euroway AB* for their Lübeck – Travemünde – Malmö service. However, political problems led to serious delays and, before delivery, the service had ceased. She was purchased by *DFDS*, renamed the CROWN OF SCANDINAVIA and introduced onto the Copenhagen – Oslo service. In January 2013 renamed the CROWN SEAWAYS.

KAUNAS SEAWAYS Train ferry built as the KAUNAS by VEB Mathias-Thesen-Werft, Wismar, Germany (DDR) for *Lisco* of the former Soviet Union and operated between Klaipėda and Mukran in Germany (DDR). She was part of a series of vessels built to link the USSR and Germany (DDR), avoiding Poland. In 1994/95 she was modified to offer passenger facilities and placed on the Klaipėda – Kiel service. In 2003 transferred to the Klaipėda – Karlshamn route. Early in 2004 chartered to *DFDS Tor Line* to operate between Lübeck and Riga. In 2005 returned to the Klaipėda – Karlshamn route. In May 2009 replaced by the LISCO OPTIMA and laid up. In October 2009 placed on the Travemünde – Riga route; this route ceased in January 2010 and she was laid up again. In May 2010 chartered to *Scandlines* and placed on a new Travemünde – Liepaja (Latvia) service. In December 2010 returned to *DFDS Seaways*. In March 2011 chartered to *Baltic Scandinavian Line* to operate between Paldiski (Estonia) and Kapellskär. In May returned to *DFDS Seaways* and inaugurated a new service between Kiel and Ust Luga (Russia). In May 2012 she was renamed the KAUNAS SEAWAYS and in June transferred to the Klaipėda – Sassnitz route. At the end of September 2013 this route closed and in October she was transferred to the Paldiski – Kapellskär service. After a period of lay up, in August 2015 she was chartered to *UKR Ferry* of The Ukraine to operate between Ilyichevsk, Batumi, Poti and Constanta.

LIVERPOOL SEAWAYS Built as the LAGAN VIKING by CN Visentini, Donada, Italy for *Levantina Trasporti* of Italy and chartered to *Norse Irish Ferries*, operating between Liverpool and Belfast. In 1999 the charter was taken over by *Merchant Ferries*. Purchased by *NorseMerchant Ferries* in 2001. In 2002 the service transferred to Twelve Quays River Terminal, Birkenhead. In January 2005 renamed the LIVERPOOL VIKING and in December moved to the Birkenhead – Dublin route. In August 2010 renamed the LIVERPOOL SEAWAYS. In February 2011 moved to the Klaipėda – Karlshamn service. In January 2014 chartered to *NaviRail*. In January 2015 returned to *DFDS* and placed on the Paldiski – Kapellskär service.

OPTIMA SEAWAYS Ro-pax vessel built as the ALYSSA by C N Visentini di Visentini Francesco & C Donada, Italy for *Levantina Trasporti* of Italy for charter. Initially chartered to *CoTuNav* of Tunisia for service between Marseilles, Genoa and Tunis and in 2000 to *Trasmediterranea* of Spain for service between Barcelona and Palma de Mallorca. In 2001 chartered to *Stena Line Scandinavia AB*, renamed the SVEALAND and placed as second vessel on the *Scandlines AB* freight-only Trelleborg – Travemünde service. In 2003 sub-chartered to *Scandlines AG* and placed on the Kiel – Klaipėda route, replacing the ASK and PETERSBURG. In 2004 sold to *Rederia AB Hornet*, a *Stena* company. In late 2005 the *Scandlines* Kiel – Klaipėda service ended. In early 2006 she was chartered to *TT-Line* to cover for the rebuilding of the engines of their four newest vessels. Later sold to *DFDS*, renamed the LISCO OPTIMA. In April 2012 renamed the OPTIMA SEAWAYS. Currently operates on the Karlshamn – Klaipėda route.

PATRIA SEAWAYS Ro-pax vessel built as the STENA TRAVELLER by Fosen Mekaniske Verksteder, Trondheim, Norway for *Stena RoRo*. After a short period with *Stena Line* on the Hook of Holland – Harwich service, she was chartered to *Sealink Stena Line* for their Southampton – Cherbourg route, initially for 28 weeks. At the end of the 1992 summer season she was chartered to *TT-Line* to operate between Travemünde and Trelleborg and was renamed the TT-TRAVELLER. In late 1995, she returned to *Stena Line*, resumed the name STENA TRAVELLER and inaugurated a new service between Holyhead and Dublin. In Autumn 1996 she was replaced by the STENA CHALLENGER (18523t, 1991). In early 1997 she was again chartered to *TT-Line* and renamed the TT-TRAVELLER. She operated on the Rostock – Trelleborg route. During Winter 1999/2000 her passenger capacity was increased to 250 and passenger facilities renovated. In early 2002 the charter ended and she was renamed the STENA TRAVELLER, chartered to *Stena Line* and placed on their Karlskrona – Gdynia service. This charter ended in May 2003 and she was sold to *Lisco Baltic Service* and renamed the LISCO PATRIA. Placed on the Klaipėda – Karlshamn service. In January 2006 transferred to the Klaipėda – Kiel service to replace the *Scandlines* vessel SVEALAND following that company's withdrawal from the joint route. In Spring 2006 returned to the Klaipėda – Karlshamn route. In May 2011 chartered to *Baltic Scandinavia Lines* and placed on their Paldiski – Kapellskär service. In September 2011 a

Regina Seaways *(Henk van der Lugt)*

Pearl Seaways *(John Bryant)*

controlling interest in this service was acquired by *DFDS Seaways*. In January 2012 renamed the PATRIA SEAWAYS. In September 2014 replaced by the *Sirena Seaways* and became a relief vessel. In April 2015 chartered as a windfarm accommodation vessel off Esbjerg. In January 2016 chartered to *P&O Ferries* to cover for refits on the Hull routes. In April 2016 became third vessel on the Klaipėda – Karlshamn route.

PEARL SEAWAYS Built as the ATHENA by Wärtsilä Marine, Turku, Finland for *Rederi AB Slite* of Sweden (part of *Viking Line*) and used on 24-hour cruises from Stockholm to Mariehamn (Åland). In 1993 the company went into liquidation and she was sold to *Star Cruises* of Malaysia for cruises in the Far East. She was renamed the STAR AQUARIUS. Later that year she was renamed the LANGKAPURI STAR AQUARIUS. In February 2001 sold to *DFDS* and renamed the AQUARIUS. After rebuilding, she was renamed the PEARL OF SCANDINAVIA and introduced onto the Copenhagen – Oslo service. In January 2011 renamed the PEARL SEAWAYS.

REGINA SEAWAYS Built as the ENERGIA by Nuovi Cantieri Apuani, Marina di Carrara, Italy for *Grimaldi Holdings* of Italy. In August 2011 chartered to DFDS Seaways and moved to Klaipėda for modifications. In September 2011 renamed the REGINA SEAWAYS and placed on the Klaipėda – Kiel service.

VICTORIA SEAWAYS Built by Nuovi Cantieri Apuani, Marina di Carrara, Italy. Launched as the FORZA. Fifth of an order of eight vessels for *Grimaldi Holdings* of Italy. Whilst under construction, sold to *DFDS Tor Line*. On delivery renamed the LISCO MAXIMA. In March/April 2012 renamed the VICTORIA SEAWAYS. Operates between Karlshamn and Klaipėda.

VILNIUS SEAWAYS Train ferry as KAUNAS SEAWAYS. Built as the VILNIUS. In 1993 rebuilt in Liverpool to convert from a 12 passenger freight vessel to a 120 passenger ro-pax vessel. Operated on the Klaipėda – Kiel service until June 2003. Later chartered to *DFDS Tor Line* to operate between Lübeck and Riga. In Summer 2006 transferred to the *DFDS Lisco* Klaipėda – Sassnitz route. In January 2011 renamed the VILNIUS SEAWAYS. In June 2012 she was transferred to the Kiel – Ust Luga service. In June 2013 she was chartered to *Ukrferry* of the Ukraine for service in the Black Sea.

REDERIJ DOEKSEN

THE COMPANY *BV Rederij G. Doeksen en Zn BV* is a Dutch private sector company. Ferries are operated by subsidiary *Terschellinger Stoomboot Maatschappij*, trading as *Rederij Doeksen*.

MANAGEMENT Managing Director P J M Melles, **Manager Operations** R. de Vries, **Controller** R. Herrema, **Manager Hospitality, FO & CC** Dirk Spoor, **Manager Personnel & Organization** A. Idzinga, **Manager Marketing & Communications** A. van Brummelen.

ADDRESS Waddenpromenade 5, 8861 NT Harlingen, The Netherlands.

TELEPHONE *In The Netherlands* 088 – 9000 888, *From abroad* +31 562 442 002.

FAX +31 (0)517 413303.

INTERNET Email info@rederij-doeksen.nl **Website** www.rederij-doeksen.nl *(Dutch, English, German))* **Facebook** www.facebook.com/rederijdoeksen **Twitter** www.twitter.com/rederijdoeksen

ROUTES OPERATED Conventional Ferries Harlingen (The Netherlands) – Terschelling (Frisian Islands) (2 hrs; *FRIESLAND, MIDSLAND)* (up to 6 per day), Harlingen – Vlieland (Frisian Islands) (1 hr 45 mins; *VLIELAND*; 3 per day). **Fast Passenger Ferries** Harlingen – Terschelling (45 mins; *KOEGELWIECK, TIGER*; 3 to 6 per day), Harlingen – Vlieland (45 mins; *KOEGELWIECK, TIGER*; 2 per day), Vlieland – Terschelling (30 mins; *KOEGELWIECK, TIGER*; 2 per day). **Freight Ferry** Harlingen – Terschelling (2 hrs; *NOORD-NEDERLAND*), Harlingen – Vlieland (1hr 45 mins; *NOORD-NEDERLAND*).

1	FRIESLAND	3583t	89	14.0k	69.0m	1100P	122C	12L	BA	NL	8801058
2»p	KOEGELWIECK	439t	92	33.0k	35.5m	315P	0C	0L	-	NL	9035582
3	MIDSLAND	1812t	74	15.5k	77.9m	700P	55C	6L	BA	NL	7393066
4F	NOORD-NEDERLAND	361t	02	14.0k	48.0m	12P	-	9L	BA	NL	9269611
5»p	TIGER	660t	02	37.0k	52.0m	414P	0C	0L	BA	NL	9179191
6	VLIELAND	2726t	05	15.0k	64.1m	1950P	58C	4L	BA	NL	9303716

FRIESLAND Built by Van der Giessen-de Noord, Krimpen aan den IJssel, Rotterdam, The Netherlands for *Rederij Doeksen*. Used on the Harlingen – Terschelling route.

KOEGELWIECK Harding 35m catamaran built at Rosendal, Norway for *Rederij Doeksen* to operate between Harlingen and Terschelling, Harlingen and Vlieland and Terschelling and Vlieland.

MIDSLAND Built as the RHEINLAND by Werftunion GmbH & Co, Cassens-Werft, Emden, Germany for *AG Ems* of Germany. In 1993 purchased by *Rederij Doeksen* and renamed the MIDSLAND. Used mainly on the Harlingen – Terschelling route but also used on the Harlingen – Vlieland service. She is now a reserve vessel.

NOORD-NEDERLAND Catamaran built by ASB, Harwood, New South Wales, Australia for *Rederij Doeksen*. Used on freight services from Harlingen to Terschelling and Vlieland.

TIGER Catamaran built as the SUPERCAT 2002 by FBMA Babcock Marine, Cebu, Philippines for *SuperCat* of the Philippines. In 2007 purchased by *Rederij Doeksen* and renamed the TIGER. Operates from Harlingen to Terschelling and Vlieland.

VLIELAND Catamaran built by FBMA Babcock Marine, Cebu, Philippines for *Rederij Doeksen* to operate between Harlingen and Vlieland.

Under Construction

| 7 | NEWBUILDING 1 | - | 18 | 14.0k | 70.0 | 600P | 64C | - | BA | NL | - |
| 8 | NEWBUILDING 1 | - | 18 | 14.0k | 70.0 | 600P | 64C | - | BA | NL | - |

NEWBUILDING 1, NEWBUILDING 2 Under construction by Strategic Marine, Vun Tau, Vietnam. They will be aluminium catamarans and LNG powered.

REDERI AB ECKERÖ

THE COMPANY *Rederi AB Eckerö* is an Åland Islands company. It operates two ferry companies, a cruise operation from Stockholm (*Birka Cruises*), a ro-ro time chartering company (*Eckerö Shipping*) and a bus company on Åland (*Williams*).

ADDRESS PO Box 158, AX-22101 Mariehamn, Åland, Finland.

TELEPHONE Administration +358 (0)18 28 030.

FAX Administration +358 (0)18 12 011.

INTERNET Email info@rederiabeckero.ax **Website** www.rederiabeckero.ax *(English, Swedish)*

ECKERÖ LINE

THE COMPANY *Eckerö Line Ab Oy* is a Finnish company, 100% owned by *Rederi Ab Eckerö* of Åland, Finland. Until January 1998, the company was called *Eestin-Linjat*.

MANAGEMENT Managing Director Irja Hanelius, **Marketing Director** Ida Toikka-Everi.

ADDRESS PO Box 307, 00181 Helsinki, Finland.

TELEPHONE Administration & Reservations +358 9 (0)9 685 3957.

INTERNET Email info@eckeroline.fi **Website** www.eckeroline.fi *(Swedish, Finnish, English)*

ROUTE OPERATED Passenger Service Helsinki (Länsisatama) – Tallinn (Estonia) (2 hrs 30 mins; *FINLANDIA*; up to 2 per day).

| 1 | FINLANDIA | 36093t | 01 | 27.0k | 175.0m | 1880P | 665C | 116T | BA | FI | 9214379 |

FINLANDIA Built as the MOBY FREEDOM by Daewoo Shipbuilding & Heavy Machinery Ltd, Okpo, South Korea for *Moby SpA (Moby Line)* of Italy. Operated on their Genoa/Civitavecchia/Livorno – Olbia routes. In March 2012 sold to *Eckerö Line*, and renamed the FREEDOM. Refitted at Landskrona and, in June, renamed the FINLANDIA. She entered service on 31st December 2012.

Finlandia *(Darren Holdaway)*

Povl Anker *(Darren Holdaway)*

ECKERÖ LINJEN

THE COMPANY Eckerö Linjen is an Åland Islands company 100% owned by Rederi AB Eckerö.

MANAGEMENT Managing Director Tomas Karlsson, **Marketing Manager** Maria Hellman.

ADDRESS Torggatan 2, Box 158, AX-22100 Mariehamn, Åland.

TELEPHONE Administration +358 (0)18 28 000, **Reservations** +358 (0)18 28 300.

FAX Administration +358 (0)18 28 380. **Reservations** +358 (0)18 28 230.

INTERNET Email info@eckerolinjen.ax **Website** www.eckerolinjen.se (Swedish, Finnish, English)

ROUTE OPERATED Eckerö (Åland) – Grisslehamn (Sweden) (2 hrs; **ECKERÖ**; 3 per day).

1	ECKERÖ	12358t	79	19.5k	121.1m	1500P	265C	34T	BA	SE	7633155

ECKERÖ Built as the JENS KOFOED by Aalborg Værft A/S, Aalborg, Denmark for Bornholmstrafikken. Used on the Rønne – Copenhagen, Rønne – Ystad and (until December 2002) Rønne – Sassnitz services. Rønne – Copenhagen service became Rønne – Køge in September 2004. In October 2004 sold to Eckerö Linjen for delivery in May 2005. Renamed the ECKERÖ and substantially rebuilt before entering service in early 2006. In January 2009 transferred from the Finnish to the Swedish flag.

AG EMS

THE COMPANY AG Ems is a German public sector company.

MANAGEMENT Managing Director & Chief Executive Dr Bernhard Brons, **Marine Superintendent** Knut Gerdes, **Operations Manager** Hans-Jörg Oltmanns.

ADDRESS Am Aussenhafen, Postfach 1154, 26691 Emden, Germany.

TELEPHONE Administration & Reservations +49 (0)1805-180182.

FAX Administration & Reservations +49 (0)4921-890740.

INTERNET Email info@ag-ems.de **Website** www.ag-ems.de (German) www.borkumlijn.nl (Dutch) www.helgolandlinie.de (German)

ROUTES OPERATED Conventional Ferries Emden (Germany) – Borkum (German Frisian Islands) (2 hrs; **MÜNSTERLAND, OSTFRIESLAND**; up to 4 per day), Eemshaven (The Netherlands) – Borkum (55 mins; **GRONINGERLAND**; up to 4 per day), Wilhelmshaven – Heligoland (3 hrs; **WESTFALEN**; 1 per day) (Operated by subsidiary Reederei Cassen Eils – tourist cars not conveyed). **Fast Ferries** Emden – Borkum (1 hr; **NORDLICHT** up to 4 per day), Eemshaven – Borkum (30 mins; **NORDLICHT**; 1 per week in summer).

1	GRONINGERLAND	1070t	91	12.0k	44.4m	621P	30C	-	BA	DE	9002465
2	MÜNSTERLAND	1859t	86	15.5k	78.7m	1200P	70C	10L	BA	DE	8601989
3p»	NORDLICHT	435t	89	33.0k	38.8m	272P	0C	0L	-	DE	8816015
4	OSTFRIESLAND	1859t	85	16.0k	78.7m	1200P	70C	10L	BA	DE	8324622
5p	WAPPEN VON BORKUM	287t	76	11.5k	42.8m	358P	0C	0L	-	DE	7525918
6	WESTFALEN	1812t	72	15.5k	77.9m	1200P	65C	10L	BA	DE	7217004

GRONINGERLAND Built by Husumer Schiffswerft, Husum, Germany as the HILLIGENLEI for Wyker Dampfschiffs-Reederei Föhr-Amrum GmbH of Germany. Operated Schlüttsiel – Halligen – Wittdün (North Frisian Islands). In 2004 laid up. In late 2005 sold to AG Ems. In 2006 renamed the GRONINGERLAND and placed on the Eemshaven – Borkum route.

MÜNSTERLAND Built by Martin Jansen GmbH & Co KG Schiffswerft, Leer, Germany for AG Ems.

NORDLICHT Fjellstrand 38m passenger-only catamaran built at Mandal, Norway for AG Ems.

OSTFRIESLAND Built by Martin Jansen GmbH & Co KG Schiffswerft, Leer, Germany for AG Ems. In 2015 lengthened by 15.4 m by BVT Brenn-und Verformtechnik GmbH, Bremen, Germany.

WAPPEN VON BORKUM Built as the HANNOVER by Schiffswerft Schlömer GmbH & Co KG, Oldersum, Germany for *Friesland Fahrlinie* of Germany. In 1979 sold to *AG Ems* and renamed the STADT BORKUM. In 1988 sold to *ST-Line* of Finland, operating day trips from Rauma and renamed the PRINCESS ISABELLA. In 1994 returned to *AG Ems* and renamed the WAPPEN VON BORKUM.

WESTFALEN Built by as the WESTFALEN by C Cassens Schiffswerft, Emden, Germany for *AG Ems*. Rebuilt in 1994. In 2006 renamed the HELGOLAND and inaugurated a new Wilhelmshaven – Helgoland service for subsidiary *Helgoland Linie*. In January 2016 reverted to the name WESTFALEN.

FÆRGEN

THE COMPANIES *Danske Færger A/S* trading as *Færgen (previously Nordic Ferry Services A/S)* is a Danish mixed public and private sector company.

MANAGEMENT CEO John Steen-Mikkelsen.

ADDRESSES Dampskibskajen 3, 3700 Rønne, Denmark.

TELEPHONE Administration & Reservations +45 70 23 15 15. (Reservations not possible on FanøFærgen).

INTERNET Website www.faergen.com *(Danish, German, English)*

ROUTES OPERATED

AlsFærgen Fynshav (Als) – Bøjden (Fyn) (50 mins; **FRIGG SYDFYEN, FYNSHAV**; hourly (summer) two-hourly (winter)), *BornholmerFærgen* **Conventional Ferries** Rønne (Bornholm, Denmark) – Køge (5 hrs 30 mins; **HAMMERODDE**; 1 per day, *April-October only:* Rønne – Sassnitz (Germany) (3 hrs 30 mins; **POVL ANKER**; 1 per day). **Fast Ferry** Rønne – Ystad (Sweden) (1 hr 20 mins; **LEONORA CHRISTINA, VILLUM CLAUSEN**; **Peak season**: departure every 2 hours. **Low season:** 3 trips a day), *FanøFærgen* Esbjerg (Jutland) – Nordby (Fanø) (12 mins; **FENJA, MENJA, SØNDERHO**; every 20-40 mins), *LangelandsFærgen* Spodsbjerg (Langeland) – Tårs (Lolland) (45 mins; **LANGELAND, LOLLAND**; hourly), *SamsøFærgen* Kalundborg – Ballen (Samsø) (1 hr 15 min; **SAMSØ**; up to 4 per day).

1	FENJA	751t	98	11.5k	49.9m	396P	34C	4L	BA	DK	9189378
2	FRIGG SYDFYEN	1676t	84	13.5k	70.1m	338P	50C	8L	BA	DK	8222824
3	FYNSHAV	3380t	98	14.5k	69.2m	450P	96C	8L	BA	DK	9183025
4	HAMMERODDE	13906t	05	18.5k	124.9m	400P	342C	106T	A	DK	9323699
5	LANGELAND	4500t	12	16.0k	99.9m	600P	122C	36L	BA	DK	9596428
6»	LEONORA CHRISTINA	8235t	11	40.0k	112.6m	1400P	359C	-	BA	DK	9557848
7	LOLLAND	4500t	12	16.0k	99.9m	600P	122C	36L	BA	DK	9594690
8	MENJA	751t	98	11.5k	49.9m	396P	34C	4L	BA	DK	9189380
9	POVL ANKER	12131t	78	19.5k	121.0m	1500P	262C	26T	BA	DK	7633143
10	SAMSØ	4250t	08	16.0k	91.4m	600P	122C	30L	BA	DK	9548562
11p	SØNDERHO	93t	62	10.0k	26.3m	163P	0C	0L	-	DK	
12»	VILLUM CLAUSEN	6402t	00	40.0k	86.6m	1055P	200C	-	BA	DK	9216250

FENJA Built by Morsø Værft A/S, Nykøbing Mors, Denmark for *Scandlines Sydfyenske A/S* for the Esbjerg – Nordby service.

FRIGG SYDFYEN Built by Svendborg Skibsværft A/S, Svendborg, Denmark for *Sydfyenske Dampskibsselskab (SFDS)* of Denmark for the service between Spodsbjerg and Tårs. In June 2012 moved to the Fynshav – Bøjden route.

FYNSHAV Built as the KYHOLM by Ørskov Staalskibsværft, Frederikshavn, Denmark for *Samsø Linien* of Denmark. In October 2008 chartered to *Nordic Ferry Services* and in July 2009 sold to them. Used on the Kalundborg – Koby Kås service. In March 2015 renamed the FYNSHAV and moved to the Fynshav – Bøjden service.

Langeland *(Matthew Punter)*

Hammerodde *(John Bryant)*

HAMMERODDE Built by Merwede Shipyard, Hardinxveld-Giessendam, The Netherlands for *Bornholmstrafikken*. In Winter 2010 an additional vehicle deck was added for freight and some additional cabins.

LANGELAND Built by Sietas Werft, Hamburg, Germany for the Spodsbjerg – Tårs route.

LEONORA CHRISTINA Austal Auto-Express 113 catamaran built at Fremantle, Australia for *Færgen*. Used on the Rønne – Ystad route.

LOLLAND Built by Sietas Werft, Hamburg, Germany. She was launched as the SAMSØ and it was intended that she would be operated on the Hou – Sælvig service, being owned by *Samsø Linien* and operated by *Færgen*. However, these plans were dropped and in February 2012 she was renamed the LOLLAND. After delivery in March 2012 she was, in April, placed on the Spodsbjerg – Tårs route.

MENJA Built by Morsø Værft A/S, Nykøbing Mors, Denmark for *Scandlines Sydfyenske A/S* for the Esbjerg – Nordby service.

POVL ANKER Built by Aalborg Værft A/S, Denmark for *Bornholmstrafikken*. Used on the Rønne – Copenhagen (until September 2004), Rønne – Køge (October 2004-date), Rønne – Ystad and Rønne – Sassnitz services. In recent years she has operated between Rønne and Sassnitz and Rønne and Ystad in the peak summer period.

SAMSØ Built as the KANHAVE by Frantzis Shipyard, Perama, Greece. Used on the Hou – Sælvig route. In January 2015 transferred to the Kalundborg – Koby Kås (Samsø) service. Later in January 2015 the Samsø terminal was moved to Ballen. In August 2015 renamed the SAMSØ.

SØNDERHO Passenger-only ferry built by Esbjerg Jernstøberi & Maskinfabrik A/S, Esbjerg, Denmark for *Post & Telegrafvæsenet* (Danish Post Office). In 1977 taken over by *DSB*. Used on extra peak sailings and late night and early morning sailings between Esbjerg and Nordby.

VILLUM CLAUSEN Austal Auto-Express 86 catamaran built at Fremantle, Australia for *Bornholmstrafikken*. Used on the Rønne – Ystad service. Car capacity increased in 2005.

FINNLINES

THE COMPANY *Finnlines plc* is a Finnish private sector company. The Italian company *Grimaldi Compagnia de Navigazione SpA* has a controlling interest. It operates four passenger brands: *Finnlines HansaLink*, *Finnlines NordöLink* and *FinnLink*.

MANAGEMENT President and CEO Emanuele Grimaldi, **Head of Passenger Services and Line Manager HansaLink & Hanko–Rostock** Kielo Vesikko, **Line Manager NordöLink, Finnlink and Russia** Antonio Raimo

ADDRESS PO Box 197, 00180 Helsinki, Finland.

TELEPHONE Administration +358 (0)10 343 50**, Passenger Reservations** +358 (0)9 231 43 100.

INTERNET *Finnlines* Email info.fi@finnlines.com **Website *Finnlines*** www.finnlines.com *(English, Finnish, German, Polish, Swedish)*

ROUTES OPERATED *Finnlines Hansalink* branded routes Helsinki (Vuosaari) – Travemünde (27 hrs; **FINNLADY, FINNMAID, FINNSTAR**; 7 per week).

***Finnlines NordöLink* branded route** Malmö – Travemünde (9 hrs; **FINNPARTNER, FINNTRADER, NORDLINK**; up to 3 per day).

***FinnLink* branded route** Naantali (Finland) – Långnäs – Kapellskär (Sweden) (6 hrs; **FINNCLIPPER, FINNFELLOW,** 2 per day).

1	FINNCLIPPER	29841t	99	22.0k	188.3m	440P	-	210T	BA2	SE	9137997
2	FINNEAGLE	29841t	99	22.0k	188.3m	440P	-	185T	BA2	FI	9138006
3	FINNFELLOW	33769t	00	22.0k	188.3m	452P	-	220T	BA	FI	9145164

4	FINNLADY	45923t	07	25.0k	216.0m	500P	-	300T	BA2	FI	9336268
5	FINNMAID	45923t	06	25.0k	216.0m	500P	-	300T	BA2	FI	9319466
6	FINNPARTNER	32534t	94	21.3k	183.0m	270P	-	236T	A2	SE	9010163
7	FINNSTAR	45923t	06	25.0k	216.0m	500P	-	300T	BA2	FI	9319442
8	FINNTRADER	32534t	95	21.3k	183.0m	270P	-	220T	BA2	SE	9017769
9	NORDLINK	45923t	07	25.0k	216.0m	500P	-	300T	BA2	SE	9336256

FINNCLIPPER 'Ro-pax' ferry built by Astilleros Españoles, Cadiz, Spain. Ordered by *Stena RoRo* of Sweden and launched as the STENA SEAPACER 1. In 1998 sold, before delivery, to *Finnlines* and renamed the FINNCLIPPER. Entered service on the Helsinki – Travemünde route in 1999. During Winter 1999/2000 she was converted to double-deck loading. In 2003 transferred to *FinnLink*. In 2007 an additional freight deck was added.

FINNEAGLE 'Ro-pax' vessel built by Astilleros Españoles, Cadiz, Spain. Ordered by *Stena RoRo* of Sweden and launched as the STENA SEAPACER 2. In 1998 sold, before delivery, to *Finnlines* and renamed the FINNEAGLE. Although expected to join her sister the FINNCLIPPER on the Helsinki – Travemünde route, on delivery in November 1999 she entered service with *FinnLink*. During Winter 1999/2000 she was modified for two-deck loading. She has operated on both the *FinnLink* and *Finnlines Nordö-Link* services. In July 2016 charterd to *Grimalidi Line* to operate between Barcelona and Tangiers.

FINNFELLOW 'Ro-pax' ferry built as the STENA BRITANNICA by Astilleros Españoles, Cadiz, Spain for *Stena RoRo* and chartered to *Stena Line BV* to operate between Hook of Holland and Harwich. In 2003 replaced by a new STENA BRITANNICA, sold to *Finnlines*, renamed the FINNFELLOW and placed on the Helsinki – Travemünde route. In 2004 transferred to *FinnLink*.

FINNLADY, FINNMAID Built by Fincantieri-Cantieri Navali Italiani SpA, Ancona, Italy to operate between Helsinki and Travemünde.

FINNPARTNER 'Ro-pax' vessel built by Stocznia Gdanska SA, Gdansk, Poland for *Finnlines Oy* of Finland to provide a daily service conveying both freight and a limited number of cars and passengers on the previously freight-only route between Helsinki and Travemünde. In February 2007 replaced by the FINNLADY and placed on the Turku – Travemünde freight service; in May sent to the Remontowa Shipyard in Gdansk for rebuilding to increase passenger capacity and allow for two-deck through loading. Currently operating on the Travemünde – Malmö and Lübeck – St Petersburg services.

FINNSTAR Built by Fincantieri-Cantieri Navali Italiani SpA, Castellamare, Italy to operate between Helsinki and Travemünde.

FINNTRADER 'Ro-pax' vessel built by Stocznia Gdanska SA, Gdansk, Poland for *Finnlines Oy* of Finland to provide a daily service conveying both freight and a limited number of cars and passengers on the previously freight-only route between Helsinki and Travemünde. In 2006/07 rebuilt to increase passenger capacity and allow for two-deck through loading. In 2007 transferred to the Malmö – Travemünde route.

NORDLINK Built by Fincantieri-Cantieri Navali Italiani SpA, Castellamare, Italy for *Finnlines* to operate for *Finnlines NordöLink* between Travemünde and Malmö. Currently operating on the Travemünde – Malmö service.

FJORD LINE

THE COMPANY *Fjord Line* is a Norwegian company. During 2007 most of the shares of the company were purchased by *Frode and Ole Teigen*. The company bought and merged with *Master Ferries* during December 2007 and all operations are branded as *Fjord Line*.

MANAGEMENT CEO Rickard Ternblom, **Communications Director** Eva Sørås Mellgren.

ADDRESS PO Box 513, 4379 Egersund, Norway.

TELEPHONE Administration +47 55 54 87 00, **Reservations** +47 51 46 40 99.

INTERNET Email info@fjordline.com **Website** www.fjordline.com *(English, Danish, German, Dutch, Polish, Norwegian,)*

ROUTE OPERATED Conventional Ferry Bergen (Norway) – Stavanger – Hirtshals (Denmark) (17 hrs; **BERGENSFJORD, STAVANGERFJORD**; daily), Langesund (Norway) – Hirtshals (4 hrs 30 mins; **BERGENSFJORD, STAVANGERFJORD,** daily), Sandefjord (Norway) – Strömstad (Sweden) (2 hrs 30 mins; **OSLOFJORD**; 2 per day), **Fast Ferry May-August** Kristiansand (Norway) – Hirtshals (Denmark) (2 hrs 15 min); **FJORD CAT**; up to 3 per day).

1	BERGENSFJORD	31678t	13	21.5k	170.0m	1500P	600C	90T	BA	DK	9586617
2»	FJORD CAT	5619t	98	43.0k	91.3m	663P	220C	-	A	DK	9176060
3	OSLOFJORD	16794t	93	19.0k	134.4m	882P	350C	44T	BA	DK	9058995
4	STAVANGERFJORD	31678t	13	21.5k	170.0m	1500P	600C	90T	BA	DK	9586605

BERGENSFJORD, STAVANGERFJORD Built by Bergen Group Fosen AS, Rissa, Norway for *Fjord Line*. They operate on LNG.

FJORD CAT Incat 91-metre catamaran, built speculatively at Hobart, Tasmania, Australia. In Spring 1998, following *Incat's* acquisition of a 50% share in *Scandlines Cat-Link A/S*, she was chartered by *Nordic Catamaran Ferries K/S* to that company, operating between Århus and Kalundborg and named the CAT-LINK V. She is the current holder of the Hales Trophy for fastest crossing of the Atlantic during her delivery voyage between the USA and Falmouth, UK (although this claim is disputed because it was not a genuine commercial service). In 1999 the charter was transferred to *Mols-Linien*, she was renamed the MADS MOLS and operated between Århus and Odden. Charter ended in July 2005. Laid up and renamed the INCAT 049. In 2006 sold to *Gabriel Scott Rederi (Master Ferries)* and renamed the MASTER CAT. In December 2008 purchased by *Fjord Line* renamed the FJORD CAT. Did not operate in 2009 but service resumed in 2010.

OSLOFJORD Built by Fosen Mekaniske Verksteder, Rissa, Norway for *Rutelaget Askøy-Bergen* as the BERGEN and used on the *Fjord Line* Bergen – Egersund – Hanstholm service. In April 2003 chartered to *DFDS Seaways*, renamed the DUCHESS OF SCANDINAVIA and, after modifications, introduced onto the Harwich – Cuxhaven service. In 2004 sold to *Bergensfjord KS* of Norway and chartered to *DFDS Seaways*. In 2005 sub-chartered to *Fjord Line* for 5 months (with *DFDS* officers and deck-crew) and renamed the ATLANTIC TRAVELLER. In 2006 chartered directly to *Fjord Line*. In March 2008 purchased by *Fjord Line* and renamed the BERGENSFJORD. In January 2014 renamed the OSLOFJORD, rebuilt as a day ferry by STX Finland, Rauma, Finland and, in June 2014, inaugurated a new service between Sandefjord and Strömstad.

GOTLANDSBÅTEN

THE COMPANY *Gotlandsbåten* is a Swedish private sector company.

MANAGEMENT CEO Lars Meijer, **Marketing Manager** Julia Bendelin.

ADDRESS Färjeleden 2, 621 57, Visby, Sweden.

TELEPHONE *Administration & Reservation* +46 (0)771 40 30 25.

INTERNET Email info@gotlandsbaten.se **Website** gotlandsbaten.se *(Swedish)*

ROUTE OPERATED Västervik (Sweden) – Visby (Gotland) (3 hrs 10 min; **EXPRESS**; up to 2 per day).

1»	EXPRESS	5902t	98	43.0k	91.3m	868P	195C	-	A	SE	9176046

EXPRESS Incat 91m catamaran built at Hobart, Tasmania, Australia for *Buquebus* of Argentina as the CATALONIA 1 and used by *Buquebus España* on their service between Barcelona (Spain) and Mallorca. In April 2000 chartered to *P&O Portsmouth* and renamed the PORTSMOUTH EXPRESS. During Winter 2000/01 she operated for *Buquebus* between Buenos Aires (Argentina) and Piriapolis (Uruguay) and was renamed the CATALONIA. Returned to *P&O Portsmouth* in Spring 2001 and was renamed the PORTSMOUTH EXPRESS. Returned to *Buquebus* in Autumn 2001 and then returned to *P&O Portsmouth* in Spring 2002. Laid up in Europe during Winter 2002/03 and renamed the CATALONIA. She returned to *P&O Ferries* in Spring 2003 trading under the marketing name 'Express'. In November she was renamed the EXPRESS. In 2004 she operated as the 'Cherbourg Express'. In 2005 transferred to *P&O Irish Sea* and operated on the Larne – Cairnryan/Troon service. Charter ended in October 2015. Chartered to *Gotlandsbåten*. Entered service in April 2016.

Finntrader *(Miles Cowsill)*

Express *(Peter Therkildsen)*

HURTIGRUTEN

THE COMPANY Hurtigruten AS is a Norwegian private sector company. The service was originally provided by a consortium of companies. By 2006, through mergers and withdrawal from the operation, there were just two companies – Troms Fylkes D/S and Ofotens og Vesteraalens D/S and in that year Hurtigruten ASA was formed.In September 2015 it was taken over by Silk Bidco AS of Norway and the company changed its name to Hurtigruten AS.

MANAGEMENT Chairman Trygve Hegnar, **Chief Executive Officer** Daniel Skjeldam.

ADDRESS Hurtigruten ASA, Fredrik Lamges gate 14, Postboks 6144, 9291 Tromsø, Norway.

TELEPHONE Administration +47 970 57 030, **Reservations *Norway*** +47 810 03 030,

UK +44 (0)203 131 5966.

INTERNET Email firmapost@hurtigruten.com uk.sales@hurtigruten.com

Websites www.hurtigruten.co.uk *(English)* www.hurtigruten.no *(Norwegian)* www.hurtigruten.de *(German)* www.hurtigruten.fr *(French)* www.hurtigruten.us *(US English)*

ROUTE OPERATED 'Hurtigruten' sail every day throughout the year from Bergen and calls at 34 ports up to Kirkenes and takes you along one of the world's most exciting coast lines, where you will find yourself close to nature, people and traditions. Daily departures throughout the year. The round trip takes just under 11 days.

1	FINNMARKEN	15539t	02	18.0k	138.5m	1000P	47C	0L	S	NO	9231951
2p	FRAM	11647t	07	18.0k	110.0m	500P	0C	0L	S	NO	9370018
3	KONG HARALD	11204t	93	18.0k	121.8m	691P	45C	0L	S	NO	9039119
4	LOFOTEN	2621t	64	16.0k	87.4m	410P	0C	0L	C	NO	5424562
5	MIDNATSOL	16151t	03	18.0k	135.7m	1000P	45C	0L	S	NO	9247728
6	NORDKAPP	11386t	96	18.0k	123.3m	691P	45C	0L	S	NO	9107772
7	NORDLYS	11204t	94	18.0k	121.8m	691P	45C	0L	S	NO	9048914
8	NORDNORGE	11384t	97	18.0k	123.3m	691P	45C	0L	S	NO	9107784
9	POLARLYS	11341t	96	18.0k	123.0m	737P	35C	0L	S	NO	9107796
10	RICHARD WITH	11205t	93	18.0k	121.8m	691P	45C	0L	S	NO	9040429
11	SPITSBERGEN	7025t	09		97.5m	320P	0C	0L	S	NO	9434060
12	TROLLFJORD	16140t	02	18.0k	135.7m	822P	45C	0L	S	NO	9233258
13	VESTERÅLEN	6262t	83	18.0k	108.6m	560P	35C	0L	S	NO	8019368

FINNMARKEN Built by Kværner Kleven Skeppsvarv, Ulsteinvik, Norway for Ofotens og Vesteraalens D/S. In October 2009 chartered as a support vessel for the Gorgon Project (natural gas) in Western Australia. In November 2011 returned to Hurtigruten and, in February 2012, returned to service.

FRAM Built by Fincantieri-Cantieri Navali Italiani SpA at Trieste for Hurtigruten Group ASA (ordered by OVDS). Since 2007 she has operated cruises around Greenland and Svalbad during the summer period and in South America during the winter and this has been the pattern since. She is named after Fridtjof Nansen's expedition ship FRAM and has ice class 1A/1B.

KONG HARALD Built by Volkswerft, Stralsund, Germany for Troms Fylkes D/S.

LOFOTEN Built by A/S Aker Mekaniske Verksted, Oslo, Norway for Vesteraalens D/S. In 1988 she was sold to Finnmark Fylkesrederi og Ruteselskap. In 1996 she was sold to Ofotens og Vesteraalens D/S. In 2002 she was replaced by the FINNMARKEN but she then operated summer cruises and in the winter months substituted for the NORDNORGE when that vessel was sailing in the Chilean Fjords and Antarctica. Since 2008 she has operated on the main Hurtigruten roster.

MIDNATSOL Built by Fosen Mekaniske Verksteder, Rissa, Norway for Troms Fylkes D/S. From 2016 also used as an expedition ship in the Antarctic.

NORDKAPP Built by Kværner Kleven Skeppsvarv, Ulsteinvik, Norway for *Ofotens og Vesteraalens D/S*. During the winters of 2005/06 and 2006/07 she operated cruises in South America but following the delivery of the FRAM she now remains on the Hurtigruten throughout the year.

NORDLYS Built by Volkswerft, Stralsund, Germany for *Troms Fylkes D/S*. In 2002 sold to *Kilberg Shipping KS* of Norway and leased back on 15 year bareboat charter with options to repurchase. She was laid up during winter 2008/09 until required to replace the damaged RICHARD WITH from the end of January. She now operates full-time on the Hurtigruten roster.

NORDNORGE Built by Kværner Kleven, Ulsteinvik, Norway for *Ofotens og Vesteraalens D/S*. During winters 2002/03 – 2007/08 she operated cruises in South America. During most of Winter 2008/09 she was used as an accommodation vessel for a liquefied natural gas field. Laid up at Bremerhaven during winter 2009/10.

POLARLYS Built by Ulstein Verft A/S, Ulsteinvik, Norway for *Troms Fylkes D/S*.

RICHARD WITH Built by Volkswerft, Stralsund, Norway for *Ofotens og Vesteraalens D/S*. In 2002 sold to *Kystruten KS*, of Norway and leased back on 15 year bareboat charter with options to re-purchase.

SPITSBERGEN Built as the ATLANTIDA by Estaleiros Navais de Viana do Castelo, Viana do Castelo, Portugal for *Atlanticoline* of Portugal to operate in the Azores. Although completed in 2009, she was never delivered because she did not meet the required specification. In June 2015 purchased by *Hurtigruten* and renamed the NORWAY EXPLORER. Taken to the Öresund Drydocks shipyard, Landskrona, Sweden for rebuilding to make her suitable for *Hurtigruten* service. In May 2016 renamed the SPITSBERGEN and entererd service on the *Hurtigruten*, running along-side the LOFOTEN. In autumn 2016 she will go cruising in Antarctica.

TROLLFJORD Built by Fosen Mekaniske Verksteder, Rissa, Norway for *Troms Fylkes D/S*.

VESTERÅLEN Built by Kaarbös Mekaniske Verksted A/S, Harstad, Norway for *Vesteraalens D/S*. From 1987 owned by *Ofotens og Vesteraalens D/S* and from 2006 by *Hurtigruten Group ASA*.

Under Construction

| 14 | NEWBUILDING 1 | - | 18 | - | 140.0m | 600P | - | 0L | S | NO | - |
| 15 | NEWBUILDING 2 | - | 19 | - | 140.0m | 600P | - | 0L | S | NO | - |

NEWBUILDING 1, NEWBUILDING 2 Under construction by Kleven Verft, Ulsteinvik, Norway. They are designed to cope with both polar waters and service on the regular routes along the Norwegian coastline. There is an option for two more.

FÆRGESELSKABET LÆSØ

THE COMPANY *Færgeselskabet Læsø K/S* is a Danish public sector company, 50% owned by the county of North Jutland and 50% by the municipality of Læsø.

MANAGEMENT Managing Director Lars Ricks, **Marketing Manager** Bente Faurholt.

ADDRESS Havnepladsen 1, Vesterø Havn, 9940 Læsø, Denmark.

TELEPHONE Administration & Reservations +45 98 49 90 22

FAX Administration +45 98 49 95 22.

INTERNET Email info@laesoe-line.dk **Website** www.laesoe-line.dk *(Danish, German)*

ROUTE OPERATED Læsø – Frederikshavn (Jutland) (1 hr 30 mins; **ANE LÆSØ**, **MARGRETE LÆSØ**; up 7 per day).

| 1 | ANE LÆSØ | 2208t | 95 | 12.0k | 53.8m | 440P | 72C | - | BA | DK | 9107370 |
| 2 | MARGRETE LÆSØ | 3668t | 97 | 13.5k | 68.5m | 586P | 76C | 12L | BA | DK | 9139438t |

ANE LÆSØ Built as the VESBORG by Ørskov Stålskibsværft, Ørskov, Denmark for *Samsø Linien*. In March2012 sold to *Læsø Færgen*. Rebuilt by Soby Yard, Aerø, Denmark and renamed the ANE LÆSØ. Between

Vesteralen *(Miles Cowsill)*

KatExpress I *(Peter Therkildsen)*

September 2014 and February 2015 she operated on the Hou – Sælvig (Samsø) service which had been taken over by *Samsø Rederi* before their new SAMSØ (now PRINSESSE ISABELLA) was delivered. She will continue to act as reserve vessel on this route.

MARGRETE LÆSØ Built as the LÆSØ FÆRGEN by A/S Norsdsøværftet, Ringkøbing, Denmark for *Andelsfærgeselskabet Læsø* of Denmark. In June 1997 renamed the MARGRETE LÆSØ. In July 1999 transferred to *Færgeselskabet Læsø*.

LINDA LINE

Lindaliini AS (trading as *Linda Line*) is an Estonian Company owned by three Estonian investors – Enn Rohula (26.8%), Urmas Sardis & Janek Veeber (73.2%).

MANAGEMENT CEO Enn Rohula.

ADDRESS Ädala 4A, Tallinn 10614, Estonia.

TELEPHONE Administration & Reservations +372 5252314

FAX Administration +372 6999 341.

INTERNET Email info@lindaline.ee **Website** www.lindaline.ee *(Estonian, Finnish, English Russian)*

ROUTE OPERATED Tallinn (Estonia) – Helsinki (Finland) (1hr 40 mins, *KAROLIN, MERILIN*; up 6 to per day (April – December) depending on winter ice conditions).

| 1p | KAROLIN | 636t | 00 | 40.0k | 42.0m | 402P | 0C | 0L | EE | 9124433 |
| 2p | MERILIN | 963t | 99 | 37.0k | 52.0m | 450P | 0C | 0L | EE | 9194256 |

KAROLIN Construction began 1995 at Austal Ships Pty Ltd (Hendersons) initially as the OCEANFAST FERRIES NO 16 and later the CARAIBE-JET but not completed until 2000. In 2000 sold to *AG Ems of Germany* as the POLARSTERN for services between from Emden and Frisian Island of Borkum and Helgoland (summer only). In 2009 sold to *Lindaliini AS* and renamed the KAROLIN**.**

MERILIN Built 1999 by Austal Freemantle for AG Reederei Norden-Frisa, Germany, for services between Norddeich and Norderney (German Frisian Islands). Originally named the NO 1 (1999) but upon entering service immediately renamed CAT 1. In 2007 bought by *Lindaliini AS* and renamed the MERILIN**.**

MOLS-LINIEN

THE COMPANY *Mols-Linien A/S* is a Danish private sector company; previously a subsidiary of *J Lauritzen A/S*, it was sold in 1988 to *DIFKO No LXII (Dansk Investeringsfond)*. Since 1994 shares in the company have been traded on the Stock Exchange. In January 1999 a 40% share in the company was acquired by *Scandlines Danmark A/S*. Their *Scandlines Cat-Link* Århus – Kalundborg service became part of *Mols-Linien* in February 1999 and the service was switched from Kalundborg to Odden in April 1999. The *Scandlines* share in the company was acquired by the *Clipper Group* in 2007.

MANAGEMENT CEO Søren Jespersen, **Marketing Manager** Mikkel Hybel.

ADDRESS Hveensgade 4, 8000 Aarhus C, Denmark.

TELEPHONE Administration +45 89 52 52 00, **Reservations** +45 70 10 14 18 (press 1).

FAX Administration +45 89 52 53 93.

INTERNET Email mols-linien@mols-linien.dk **Website** www.mols-linien.dk *(Danish, English, German)*

ROUTES OPERATED Århus – Odden (Sealand) (1 hr 5 mins; *KATEXPRESS 1, KATEXPRESS 2, MAX MOLS*; up to 7 per day), Ebeltoft (Jutland) – Odden (45 mins; *KATEXPRESS 1, KATEXPRESS 2, MAX MOLS*; up to 4 per day).

1»	KATEXPRESS 1	10504t	09	40.0k	112.6m	1200P	417C	34L	A	DK	9501590
2»	KATEXPRESS 2	10500t	13	40.0k	112.6m	1000P	417C	34L	A	DK	9561356
3»	MAX MOLS	5617t	98	43.0k	91.3m	800P	220C	-	A	DK	9176058

KATEXPRESS 1 Incat 112m catamaran built by Incat Tasmania Pty Ltd for *MGC Chartering* of the Irish Republic. Launched as the INCAT 066. On completion, sold to for *MGC Chartering* of the Irish Republic and renamed the MGC 66. In April 2009 chartered to *LD Lines*, renamed the NORMAN ARROW and, in June, placed on the Dover – Boulogne route. In November 2009 withdrawn and laid up for the winter. In April 2010 began operating on the Portsmouth Le Havre – route. In March 2012 chartered to *Mols-Linien* and renamed the KATEXPRESS 1 (Note: in upper and lower case spelt 'KatExpress 1'). Entered service in May 2012.

KATEXPRESS 2 Incat 112m catamaran built by Incat Tasmania Pty Ltd. Launched as INCAT 067. In March 2013 chartered to *Mols-Linien* and renamed the KATEXPRESS 2 for ten years with a purchase option. (Note: in upper and lower case spelt 'KatExpress 2'). Entered service in May 2013.

MAX MOLS Incat 91-metre catamaran, built speculatively at Hobart, Tasmania, Australia. In Spring 1998, following *Incat's* acquisition of a 50% share in *Scandlines Cat-Link A/S*, she was sold to that company and named the CAT-LINK IV. In 1999 purchased by *Mols-Linien* and renamed the MAX MOLS. In 2000 chartered to *Marine Atlantic* of Canada to operate between Port aux Basques (Newfoundland) and North Sydney (Nova Scotia). Returned to *Mols-Linien* in Autumn 2000. In Summer 2002 chartered to *Riga Sea Lines* to operate between Riga and Nynäshamn. Returned to *Mols-Linien* in Autumn 2002. In 2004 chartered to *P&O Ferries* to operate between Portsmouth and Caen. Operated under the marketing name 'Caen Express'. In November 2004 returned to *Mols-Linien* and placed on the Århus – Odden route to enhance the service.

Under construction

4»	KATEXPRESS 3	10841t	17	40.0k	112.6m	1000P	417C	34L	A	DK	-
5»	KATEXPRESS 4	-	18	40.0k	109.0m	1006P	425C	36L	A	DK	-
6	NEWBUILDING	-	18	-	158.0m	400P	-	90L	BA	DK	-

KATEXPRESS 3 Incat 112m catamaran under construction by Incat Tasmania Pty Ltd, Hobart, Australia.

KATEXPRESS 4 Austal 109m catamaran under construction by from Austal Ships, Fremantle, Australia. Likely to operate between Ystad (Sweden) and Rønne (Bornholm) when *Mols-Linien* takes over the Bornholm contract from *Danske Færger A/S* in September 2018.

NEWBUILDING 2 Under construction by Rauma Marine Constructions Oy, Rauma, Finland. She will operate between Køge and Rønne (Bornholm) when *Mols-Linien* takes over the Bornholm contract from *Danske Færger A/S* in September 2018.

NAVIRAIL

THE COMPANY *Navirail* is an Estonian company.

MANAGEMENT Managing Director Igor Zimin, **Marketing Manager** Jelena Andilevko.

ADDRESS Liimi 1, 10621 Tallinn, Estonia.

TELEPHONE Administration +372 666 16 81, **Reservations** +372 66 616 83.

FAX Administration & Reservations +372 66 616 59.

INTERNET Email navirail@navirail.com **Websites** www.navirail.com *(English, Estonian, Finnish, Polish, Russian)*

ROUTE OPERATED Paldiski Northern Port (Estonia) – Hanko (Finland) (3 hrs; **SAILOR**; 2 per day).

1	SAILOR	20921t	87	19.0k	157.6m	119P	50C	82L	A2	EE	8401444

SAILOR Built as the FINNSAILOR by Gdansk Shipyard, Gdansk, Poland for *Finnlines* of Finland for freight service between Finland and Germany. In 1996 converted to ro-pax format to inaugurate a new passenger/freight service between Helsinki and Norrköping (Sweden) for subsidiary *FinnLink*. In 1997 this service was transferred to the Kapellskär – Naantali route and passengers (other than lorry drivers) ceased to be conveyed. In 2000 she was chartered to *Nordö-Link* to operate between Travemünde and Malmö. In 2002 she returned to *FinnLink*. In 2004 transferred to *Nordö-Link*. In 2007 returned to *FinnLink* as fourth ship.

In early 2009 transferred to *Finnlines'* freight service operating between Helsinki, Turku and Travemünde but in April transferred back. In March 2011 moved back to *Finnlines Nordö-Link*. In November 2013 chartered to *Navirail* of Estonia to operate between Paldiski and Hanko. In January 2014 returned to *Finnlines* and placed on the Naantali – Kapellskär route. In January 2015 time chartered again to *Navirail*. In February 2015 demise chartered to *Navirail* and renamed the SAILOR.

REEDEREI NORDEN-FRISIA

THE COMPANY *Aktiengesellschaft Reederei Norden-Frisia* is a German public sector company.

MANAGEMENT President/CEO C U Stegmann, **Managing Director/CFO** Prok. Graw, **Technical Manager** Prok. H Stolle.

ADDRESS Postfach 1262, 26534 Norderney, Germany.

TELEPHONE *Administration* +49 (0)4931 987 0.

FAX *Administration* +49 (0)4931 987 1131.

INTERNET *Email* info@reederei-frisia.de *Website* www.reederei-frisia.de *(German)*

ROUTES OPERATED Car Ferries & Passenger Ferries Norddeich (Germany) – Norderney (German Frisian Islands) (1 hr; *FRISIA I, FRISIA III, FRISIA IV, FRISIA VI*; up to 15 per day), Norddeich – Juist (German Frisian Islands) (1 hr 20 mins; *FRISIA II, FRISIA V, FRISIA VII*; up to 15 per day). **Excursion Vessels** *(FRISIA IX, FRISIA X, RÜM HART, WAPPEN VON NORDENEY*; varies).

1	FRISIA I	1020t	70	12.3k	63.7m	1500P	53C	-	BA	DE	7018604
2	FRISIA II	1125t	78	12.0k	63.3m	1340P	53C	-	BA	DE	7723974
3	FRISIA III	1786t	15	12.0k	74.3m	1342P	60C	-	BA	DE	9732450
4	FRISIA IV	1574t	02	12.0k	71.7m	1342P	60C	-	BA	DE	9246839
5	FRISIA V	1007t	65	11.0k	63.8m	1442P	53C	-	BA	DE	8827181
6	FRISIA VI	768t	68	12.0k	54.9m	1096P	35C	-	BA	DE	8827179
7F	FRISIA VII	363t	84	12.0k	53.0m	12P	30C	-	BA	DE	8891807
8p	FRISIA IX	571t	80	11.0k	57.0m	785P	0C	-	-	DE	7924310
9p	FRISIA X	187t	72	12.0k	36.3m	290P	0C	-	-	DE	7222308
10p	RÜM HART	105t	69	12.0k	35.4m	940P	0C	-	-	DE	8137237
11p	WAPPEN VON NORDENEY	154t	67	14.0k	31.1m	200P	0C	-	-	DE	7935395

FRISIA I, FRISIA II, FRISIA V, FRISIA VI Built by Jos L Meyer Werft, Papenburg, Germany for *Reederei Norden-Frisia*. Passenger capacities relate to the summer season. Capacity is reduced during the winter.

FRISIA III Built by Cassen-Werft, Emden, Germany.

FRISIA IV Built by Schiffswerft und Maschinenfabrik Cassens GmbH, Emden, Germany for *Reederei Norden-Frisia* to replace the FRISIA VIII.

FRISIA VII Built by Schlömer Werft, Oldersum, Germany for *Reederei Norden-Frisia*. Conveys ro-ro freight to Norderney and Juist.

FRISIA IX, FRISIA X Built by Schiffswerft Julius Diedrich GmbH & Co. KG, Oldersum, Germany for *Reederei Norden-Frisia*. The FRISIA IX was built to convey 9 cars at the bow end but is now used in passenger-only mode. These ships are generally used for excursions.

RÜM HART Built by Julius Diedrich Schiffswerft, Odersum, Germany as the BALTRUM IV for *Baltrum-Linie* of Germany. In November 1982 sold to *Wyker Dampfschiffs-Reederei* and renamed the RÜM HART. In March 2014 sold to *Reederei Norden-Frisia*.

WAPPEN VON NORDENEY Built by Cassens-Werft, Emden, Germany for *Reederei Norden-Frisia*. Used for excursions.

Mazovia *(Miles Cowsill)*

Kronprins Frederik *(John Bryant)*

POLFERRIES

THE COMPANY *Polferries* is the trading name of *Polska Zegluga Baltycka SA (Polish Baltic Shipping Company)*, a Polish state-owned company.

MANAGEMENT President Piotr Redmerski.

ADDRESS ul Portowa 41, 78-100 Kolobrzeg, Poland.

TELEPHONE Administration +48 94 35 52 102, +48 94 35 52 103, **Reservations** +48 801 003 171.

INTERNET Email info@polferries.pl **Website** www.polferries.pl *(Polish, Danish, English, German, Swedish)*

ROUTES OPERATED Świnoujście – Ystad (7 hrs; *BALTIVIA, MAZOVIA*; 2 per day), Gdansk – Nynäshamn (Sweden) (18 hrs; *WAWEL*; 3 per week.

1	BALTIVIA	17790t	81	19.0k	146.9m	250P	30C	80L	BA	BS	7931997
2	MAZOVIA	25996t	96	21.0k	168.0m	200P	-	154T	BA2	BS	9010814
3	WAWEL	25318t	80	19.0k	163.9m	900P	550C	75L	A2	BS	7814462

BALTIVIA Built as the SAGA STAR by Fartygsentreprenader AB, Kalmar, Sweden for *TT-Saga-Line* and, from 1982, used on freight services between Travemünde and Trelleborg/Malmö. (Originally ordered by *Rederi AB Svea* as the SAGALAND). In 1989 sold to *Cie Meridionale* of France, renamed the GIROLATA and used on *SNCM* (later *CMR*) services in the Mediterranean. In 1993 she was chartered back to *TT-Line*, resumed her original name and was used on the Travemünde – Trelleborg service. Following delivery of the ROBIN HOOD and the NILS DACKE in 1995, she was transferred to the Rostock – Trelleborg route. In July 1997 she was purchased by *TT-Line* and in 1998 passenger facilities were completely renovated to full ro-pax format; following the delivery of the TOM SAWYER she was transferred back to the Travemünde – Trelleborg route, operating additional freight sailings. Briefly transferred back to Rostock – Trelleborg when the charter of the TT-TRAVELLER ended. Withdrawn in 2002, sold to *Transmanche Ferries* and renamed the DIEPPE. In 2006 replaced by the SEVEN SISTERS, sold to *Polferries*, renamed the BALTIVIA and, in 2007, placed on the Gdansk – Nynäshamn route. In February 2013 transferred to the Świnoujście – Ystad service.

MAZOVIA Built as the GOTLAND by Pt Dok Kodja Bahri, Kodja, Indonesia for *Rederi AB Gotland* for charter. In 1997 briefly chartered to *Tor Line* and then to *Nordic Trucker Line*, to operate between Oxelösund and St Petersburg (a ro-ro freight service). In June 1997 she was chartered to *SeaWind Line*, enabling a twice-daily passenger service to be operated. In late 1997 she was sold to *Finnlines* and renamed the FINNARROW. She started operating twice weekly between Helsinki and Travemünde. During Summer 1998 she was transferred to *FinnLink*; a bow door was fitted and she was modified to allow for two-level loading. In 2003 transferred to *Nordö Link*. In 2005 returned to *FinnLink*. In 2006 transferred to *Finnlines Nordö Link* again. In 2007 chartered to *Stena Line* to operate between Karlskrona and Gdynia. In December 2011 transferred to the Hook of Holland – Killingholme route. In March 2011 returned to *Finnlines* and placed on the Travemünde – Malmö service. In October 2011 transferred to *FinnLink*. Between January and March 2013 chartered to *Stena Line* to cover Irish Sea routes during the refit period but withdrawn from service prematurely following an accident. In April 2013 chartered to *Grimaldi Line* of Italy for five years and renamed the EUROFERRY BRINDISI. In October 2014 sold to the *Grimaldi Group* of Italy. In November sold to *Polferries* and renamed the MAZOVIA. Entered service in June 2015 on the Świnoujście – Ystad service.

WAWEL Built as the SCANDINAVIA by Kockums Varvet AB, Malmö, Sweden for *Rederi AB Nordö* of Sweden. After service in the Mediterranean for *UMEF*, she was, in 1981, sold to *SOMAT* of Bulgaria, renamed the TZAREVETZ and used on *Medlink* services between Bulgaria and the Middle East, later on other routes. In 1986 she was chartered to *Callitzis* of Greece for a service between Italy and Greece. In 1988 she was sold to *Sealink*, re-registered in The Bahamas and renamed the FIESTA. She was then chartered to *OT Africa Line*. During Autumn 1989 she was rebuilt at Bremerhaven to convert her for passenger use and in March 1990 she was renamed the FANTASIA and placed on the Dover – Calais service. Later in 1990 she was renamed the STENA FANTASIA. In 1998 transferred to *P&O Stena Line*. In 1999 she was renamed the P&OSL CANTERBURY. In 2002 renamed the PO CANTERBURY. In Spring 2003 replaced by the PRIDE OF CANTERBURY and laid up at Dunkerque. Later in the year sold to *GA Ferries* and renamed the ALKMINI A. In 2004 moved to Greece and, after a partial rebuild (including the welding up of the bow door) placed on the Igoumenitsa – Brindisi route.

Later in 2004 sold to *Polferries* and renamed the WAWEL; rebuilt to increase the number of cabins. In 2005 placed on the Świnoujście – Ystad service. In May 2015 transferred to the Gdansk – Nynäshamn route.

PRAAMID

THE COMPANY Praamid is the trading name of the ferry operation of the *Port of Tallinn*, a company owned by the Republic of Estonia. It takes over the operation of services to the islands of Hiiumaa and Saaremaa in October 2016.

INTERNET Email Website www.praamid.ee *(Estonia, English)*

ROUTES OPERATED (from 1st October 2016) Kuivastu – Virtsu (Saaremaa) (30 mins; *PIRET, TÕLL*; up to 34 per day), Rohuküla – Heltermaa (Hiiumaa) (1 hr 30 mins; *LEIGER, TIIU*; up to 11 per day).

1	LEIGER	4012t	16	10.0k	114.0m	700P	150C	-	BA	EE	9762675
2	PIRET	4012t	16	10.0k	114.0m	700P	150C	-	BA	EE	9762663
3	TIIU	4012t	16	10.0k	114.0m	700P	150C	-	BA	EE	-
4	TÕLL	4012t	16	10.0k	114.0m	700P	150C	-	BA	EE	9762651

LEIGER, TIIU Built by Sefine Shipyard, Yalova, Turkey. LNG powered. To enter service October 2016.

PIRET, TÕLL Built by Remontowa Shipyard, Gdansk, Poland (The PIRET's hull was subcontracted to Irko, Gdansk, Poland). LNG powered. To enter service October 2016.

SAAREMAA LAEVAKOMPANII

THE COMPANY Saaremaa Laevakompanii AS is an Estonian shipping company, founded in 1992. Subsidiary company is OÜ Väinamere Liinid, founded in 2005. Brand name "Tuule Laevad" (meaning Wind Ships) brings together different ferry services and is a part of Tuule Grupp identity which was created in 2007.

MANAGEMENT General Director Tõnis Rihvk.

ADDRESS Kohtu 1, 93819 Kuressaare, Estonia.

TELEPHONE Administration +372 452 4350, **Reservations** +372 452 4444.

INTERNET Email *customer service* info@tuulelaevad.ee, ***administration*** slk@laevakompanii.ee *ElbLink* mail@ElbLink.com **Websites** www.tuulelaevad.ee *(Estonian, English)* elblink.com *(German)* *ElbLink* www.elb-link.de *(German, English)*

ROUTES OPERATED Vehicle Ferries Kuivastu – Virtsu (Saaremaa) (30 mins; *HIIUMA, IONAS*,; up to 32 per day) (service to cease after 30th September 2016), Heltermaa (Hiiumaa) – Rohuküla (1 hr 30 mins;, *HARILAID, REGULA, ST OLA*; up to 15 per day) (service to cease after 30th September 2016), Triigi – Sõru (1 hr 5 mins; *KÕRGELAID*; 3 per day), **Summer only passenger service** Roomassaare – Ruhnu (2 hrs 10 mins, *RUNÖ*, up to 3 per week), Ruhnu – Pärnu (3 hrs 10 mins, *RUNÖ*, 3 per week), Munalaid – Ruhnu (2 hrs 45 mins, *RUNÖ*; 2 per week). **ElbLink vehicle service:** Cuxhaven – Brunsbüttel (across River Elbe, Germany) (1 hr 10 mins – 1 hr 30 mins; *MUHUMAA, SAAREMAA*; up to 10 per day). **Note:** The contract to operate the Kuivastu – Virtsu and Heltermaa (Hiiumaa) – Rohuküla services has been awarded to the Port of Tallinn with effect from October 2016 (see *Praamid*).

1p•	AEGNA	101t	79	18.0k	24.9 m	93P	0C	0L	-	EE	8874366
2	HARILAID	1028t	85	9.9k	49.9m	120P	35C	5L	BA	EE	8727367
3	HIIUMAA	5233t	11	15.0k	97.9m	600P	150C	20L	BA2	EE	9481805
4	IONAS	4296t	89	14.0k	95.0m	400P	85C	16L	BA	CY	8611659
5	KÖRGELAID	1028t	87	9.9k	49.9m	190P	35C	5L	BA	EE	8725577
6	MUHUMAA	5233t	10	15.0k	97.9m	600P	150C	12L	BA	EE	9474060
7	REGULA	3774t	71	14.5k	71.2m	580P	105C	20L	BA2	EE	7051058
8p	RUNÖ	169t	12	20.0k-	23.9m	60P	2C	0L	A	EE	9643336
9	SAAREMAA	5900t	10	15.0k	97.9m	600P	150C	12L	BA	EE	9474072
10	ST OLA	4833t	71	14.50k	85.9m	480P	120C	14L	BA	EE	7109609

AEGNA Built as the RÅSA by Fjellstrand, Omastrand, Norway for *Helgeland Trafikkselskap* of Norway. In 2003 sold to *Jan og Torleif Charter DA*. In 2005 sold to *Saaremaa Laevakompanii* and renamed the AEGNA. Inaugurated a passenger-only service between Saaremaa and Ruhnu and Pärnu. This no longer operates and she is now laid up.

HARILAID, KÖRGELAID Built by Riga Shiprepair Yard, Riga, Latvia (USSR) for *ESCO* of Estonia. In 1994 transferred to *Saaremaa Laevakompanii*.

HIIUMAA, MUHUMAA, SAAREMAA Built by Fiskerstrand Verft A/S, Aalesund, Norway for *Saaremaa Laevakompanii*. In summer 2015 the MUHUMAA and SAAREMAA were transferred to the new *ElbLink* service.

IONAS Built as the SUPERFLEX HOTEL by North East Shipbuilders Ltd, Sunderland, England for *VR Shipping Aps* of Denmark. Operated in the Øresund. In 1992 chartered to *Scarlett Line* of Sweden and in 1993 renamed the FREJA SCARLETT. In 1995 sold to *ISNASA-Islena de Navegacion SA* of Spain and renamed the MIGUEL HERNANDEZ. Operated on the Straits of Gilbraltar. In 2003 sold to *Enermar Trasporti Isole Sarde SrL* of Italy and renamed the BUDELLI. Operated between Palau and La Maddalena. In 2005 sold to *RFI SpA* of Italy and operated between Villa San Giovanni and Messina (Sicily). In April 2012 sold to *Corfu Superflex I Ltd* of the Marshall Islands and renamed the IONAS. In May 2014 chartered to *Kerch Ferry State Shipping* of Russia and operated on the Black Sea. In May 2015 chartered to *Saaremaa Laevakompanii*.

REGULA Built by Jos L Meyer, Papenburg, Germany for *Stockholms Rederi AB Svea* of Sweden for the service between Helsingborg and Helsingør operated by *Linjebuss International AB* (a subsidiary company). In 1980 she was sold to *Scandinavian Ferry Lines*. During Winter 1984/85 she was rebuilt to increase vehicle and passenger capacity. In 1991 ownership was transferred to *SweFerry* and operations to *ScandLines* on the Helsingborg – Helsingør service. Ownership later transferred to *Scandlines AB*. In 1997 sold to *Saaremaa Laevakompanii*.

RUNÖ Built by Baltic Workboats AS, Nasva, Saaremaa, Estonia for the Government of Estonia. Chartered to *Saaremaa Laevakompanii*.

ST OLA Built as the SVEA SCARLETT for by Jos L Meyer, Papenburg, Germany *Stockholms Rederi AB Svea* of Sweden and used on the *SL (Skandinavisk Linjetrafik)* service between Copenhagen (Tuborg Havn) and Landskrona (Sweden). In 1980 she was sold to *Scandinavian Ferry Lines* of Sweden and *Dampskibsselskabet Øresund A/S* of Denmark (jointly owned). Initially she continued to serve Landskrona but later that year the Swedish terminal became Malmö. In 1981 she operated on the Helsingborg – Helsingør service for a short while, after which she was withdrawn and laid up. In 1982 she was sold to *Eckerö Linjen* of Finland, renamed the ECKERÖ and used on services between Grisslehamn (Sweden) and Eckerö (Åland Islands). In 1991 she was sold to *P&O Scottish Ferries* and renamed the ST OLA. In March 1992 she replaced the previous ST OLA (1345t, 1974) on the Scrabster – Stromness service. In September 2002 withdrawn and sold to *Saaremaa Laevakompanii*. In 2011 laid up. Re-entered service in summer 2015 on the Heltermaa – Rohuküla service.

SAMSØ REDERI

THE COMPANY *Samsø Rederi* is a Danish public sector company owned by the Samsø Municipality.

MANAGEMENT Managing Director Carsten Kruse.

ADDRESS Sælvig 64, 8305 Samsø, Denmark.

TELEPHONE Administration and Reservations + 45 7022 5900.

INTERNET Email tilsamsoe@samsoe.dk **Website** www.tilsamsoe.dk (Danish, German, English).

ROUTE OPERATED Sælvig (Samsø) – Hou (Jutland) (1 hr; *PRINSESSE ISABELLA*; up to 7 per day).

| 1 | PRINSESSE ISABELLA | 5478t | 15 | 9.9k | 100.0m | 600P | 160C | 16T | BA | DK | 9692806 |

PRINSESSE ISABELLA Built as the SAMSØ by Stocznia Remontowa, Gdansk, Poland. Entered service in March 2015. In June 2015 renamed the PRINSESSE ISABELLA.

SASSNITZ – UST LUGA FERRY

THE COMPANY The *Sassnitz – Ust Luga Ferry* is operated by *Black Sea Ferry* in partnership with *Russian Railways* and *AnRuss Trans*. *Trans-Exim* act as agents.

ADDRESS Trans-Exim, 45 Suvorova street, Kaliningrad, Russia.

TELEPHONE Administration +7 (4012) 66 04 70, **Reservations** +7 (4012) 66 04 73.

FAX Administration & Reservations +7 (4012) 66 04 76.

INTERNET Email info@transexim.ru **Website** transexim.ru/en/ferry-schedule *(English, Russian)*

ROUTE OPERATED Ust Luga (Russia) – Baltiysk (Kaliningrad, Russia) – Sassnitz (Germany) (*PETERSBURG*; 1 per week).

1	PETERSBURG	25353t	86	16.0k	190.8m	144P	329C	110T	A2	RU	8311883

PETERSBURG Built Mathias Thesen Werft, Wismar, East Germany as the MUKRAN for *DSR* of Germany (DDR) to operate between Mukran (Sassnitz) and Klaipėda, a joint service with *Lisco* of Lithuania. In 1994 the service was taken over by *Euroseabridge*. In 1995 she was rebuilt to introduce road vehicle and additional passenger capacity and was renamed the PETERSBURG. In 2001 she was transferred to the Kiel – Klaipėda service, replacing the sister vessel GREIFSWALD whose charter was ended. In April 2003, the service became part of *Scandlines* and she was transferred to transferred to the Karlshamn – Liepaja (Latvia) route. In 2009, the charter ended and she returned to her owners. In October 2010 she was sold to *Baltic Fleet LLC* of Russia and the following month placed on a service between Baltiysk (Kaliningrad) and Ust Luga. In June 2012 she inaugurated a new service between Sassnitz and Ust Luga via Baltiysk.

SCANDLINES

THE COMPANY In 2007, the owners of *Scandlines AG*, the Danish Ministry of Transport and Energy and Deutsche Bahn AG, decided to sell their shares. The new owner was a consortium of the 3i Group (UK), Allianz Capital Partners GmbH (Germany) (40% of the shares each) and *Deutsche Seereederei GmbH* (Germany) (20% of the shares). The company was subsequently transformed into a private limited company and now trades under the name Scandlines GmbH, uniting the companies *Scandlines Deutschland GmbH* and *Scandlines Danmark A/S*. With *Deutsche Seereederei GmbH* selling its shares in *Scandlines GmbH* in 2010, 3i and Allianz Capital Partners held 50% of the shares each. During 2012 *Stena Line* took over the Travemünde – Ventspils, Travemünde – Liepaja and Nynäshamn – Ventspils routes, took full control of the joint routes – Rostock – Trelleborg and Sassnitz – Trelleborg services and took over the vessels used. The freight-only route between Rostock and Hanko passed to *SOL*. The Helsingborg – Helsingør service remains jointly operated and continues to be branded *Scandlines*. In November 2013 3i Group purchased Allianz Capital Partners' share and now control 100% of the company.

MANAGEMENT CEO Søren Poulsgaard Jensen, **Managing Director & Chief Customer Officer** Morten Haure-Petersen.

ADDRESS Am Bahnhof 3a, 18119 Rostock, Germany.

TELEPHONE Administration & Reservations *Denmark* +45 33 15 15 15, *Germany* +49 (0)381-77 88 77 66.

FAX Administration *Germany* +49 (0)381-29 22 05 71.

INTERNET Email info@scandlines.com **Website** www.scandlines.com *(Danish, German, English)*,

ROUTES OPERATED Rødby (Lolland, Denmark) – Puttgarden (Germany) (45 mins; *DEUTSCHLAND, HOLGER DANSKE, PRINS RICHARD, PRINSESSE BENEDIKTE, SCHLESWIG-HOLSTEIN (HOLGER DANSKE specially for dangerous goods)*; half-hourly train/vehicle ferry + additional road freight-only sailings), Gedser (Falster, Denmark) – Rostock (Germany) (2 hours; *BERLIN, COPENHAGEN, KRONPRINS FREDERIK*; every 2 hours.

1	BERLIN	22319t	16	20.5k	169.5m	1300P	460C	96L	BA2	DE	9587855

2	DEUTSCHLAND	15187t	97	18.5k	142.0m	1200P	364C	30Lr	BA2	DE	9151541
3F	HOLGER DANSKE	2779t	76	14.9k	86.8m	12P	-	12L	BA	DK	7432202
4	KRONPRINS FREDERIK	16071t	81	20.5k	152.0m	1082P	210C	46T	BA	DK	7803205
5	PRINS RICHARD	14822t	97	18.5k	142.0m	1100P	364C	36Lr	BA2	DK	9144419
6	PRINSESSE BENEDIKTE	14822t	97	18.5k	142.0m	1100P	364C	36Lr	BA2	DK	9144421
7	SCHLESWIG-HOLSTEIN	15187t	97	18.5k	142.0m	1200P	364C	30Lr	BA2	DE	9151539

BERLIN Partly built by Volkswerft Stralsund, Stralsund, Germany for *Scandlines* to operate on the Gedser – Rostock route. The propulsion system allows for adaption to LNG. Originally due to enter service in Spring 2012, construction was seriously delayed. It was then found that she did not meet the specification and the order was cancelled. She was 90% finished and had undertaken sea trials. In March 2014, purchased by *Scandferries ApS* of Denmark (an associated company) and towed, firstly to Blohm + Voss Shipyards, Hamburg and then to Fayard Shipyard, Odense to be completed with an almost completely new superstructure to make her suitable for the Gedser – Rostock route. Her engines were also modified from straight diesel to diesel-electric hybrid. In May 2016 chartered to *Scandlines* and entererd service on the Gedser – Rostock route,

DEUTSCHLAND Train/vehicle ferry built by Van der Giessen-de Noord, Krimpen aan den IJssel, Rotterdam, The Netherlands for *DFO* for the Puttgarden – Rødby service. During Winter 2003/04 a new hoistable deck was added for cars by Neptun Yard Rostock, (Germany).

HOLGER DANSKE Built by Aalborg Værft A/S, Aalborg, Denmark as a train/vehicle ferry for *DSB* for the Helsingør – Helsingborg service. In 1991 transferred to the Kalundborg – Samsø route (no rail facilities). In 1997 transferred to subsidiary *SFDS A/S*. Withdrawn at the end of November 1998 when the service passed to *Samsø Linien*. In 1999 began operating between Rødby and Puttgarden as a road-freight-only vessel, carrying, among others, loads which cannot be conveyed on passenger vessels.

KRONPRINS FREDERIK Train/vehicle ferry built by Nakskov Skibsværft A/S, Nakskov, Denmark for *DSB* for the Nyborg – Korsør service. Withdrawn in 1997. After conversion to a car/lorry ferry, she was transferred to the Gedser – Rostock route (no rail facilities). She will be retained as a reserve vessel when the COPENHAGEN is delivered in Autumn 2016.

PRINS RICHARD, PRINSESSE BENEDIKTE Train/vehicle ferries, built by Ørskov Christensen Staalskibsværft A/S, Frederikshavn, Denmark for *Scandlines A/S* for the Rødby – Puttgarden service. During Winter 2003/04 a new hoistable deck was added for cars by Neptun Yard Rostock, (Germany).

SCHLESWIG-HOLSTEIN Train/vehicle ferry built by Van der Giessen-de Noord, Krimpen aan den IJssel, Rotterdam, The Netherlands for *DFO* for the Puttgarden – Rødby service. During Winter 2003/04 a new hoistable deck was added for cars by Neptun Yard Rostock, (Germany).

Under construction

8	COPENHAGEN	22319t	16	20.5k	169.5m	1300P	460C	96L	BA2	DK	9587867

COPENHAGEN As the BERLIN except that at the time of purchase by *Scandlines*, she had been launched but was only 50% finished. Due to enter service in Autumn 2016.

SCANDLINES HELSINGØR – HELSINGBORG

THE COMPANY *Scandlines Helsingør – Helsingborg* is a Swedish private sector company owned by First State Investments, a subsidiary of Commonwealth Bank of Australia. Previously a joint venture between *Scandlines* and *Stena Line*, it was acquired by First State Investments in January 2015. Although now a separate company, it currently operates as part of the *Scandlines* network.

TELEPHONE *Reservations* +45 33 151515.

INTERNET Email info@scandlines.com **Website** www.scandlines.com *(Danish, German, English)*,

ROUTES OPERATED Helsingør (Sealand, Denmark) – Helsingborg (Sweden) (20 mins; *AURORA AF HELSINGBORG, MERCANDIA IV, MERCANDIA VIII, HAMLET, TYCHO BRAHE*; every 15 mins)

1	AURORA AF HELSINGBORG	10918t	92	14.0k	111.2m	1250P	225C	25Lr	BA	SE	9007128
2	HAMLET	10067t	97	13.5k	111.2m	1000P	244C	34L	BA	DK	9150030
3	MERCANDIA IV	4296t	89	13.0k	95.0m	420P	170C	18L	BA	DK	8611685
4	MERCANDIA VIII	4296t	87	13.0k	95.0m	420P	170C	18L	BA	DK	8611623
5	TYCHO BRAHE	11148t	91	14.5k	111.2m	1250P	240C	35Lr	BA	DK	9007116

AURORA AF HELSINGBORG Train/vehicle ferry built by Langsten Verft A/S, Tomrefjord, Norway for *SweFerry* for *ScandLines* joint *DSB/SweFerry* service between Helsingør and Helsingborg.

HAMLET Road vehicle ferry built by Finnyards, Rauma, Finland for *Scandlines* (50% owned by *Scandlines AG* and 50% owned by *Scandlines AB* of Sweden) for the Helsingør – Helsingborg service. Sister vessel of the TYCHO BRAHE but without rail tracks.

MERCANDIA IV Built as the SUPERFLEX NOVEMBER by North East Shipbuilders Ltd, Sunderland, UK for *Vognmandsruten* of Denmark. In 1989 sold to *Mercandia* and renamed the MERCANDIA IV. In 1990 she began operating on their *Kattegatbroen* Juelsminde – Kalundborg service. In 1996 she was transferred to their *Sundbroen* Helsingør – Helsingborg service. In 1997 the service and vessel were leased to *HH-Ferries*. In 1999 she was purchased by *HH-Ferries*. She has been equipped to carry dangerous cargo. Now owned by *Scandlines Helsingør – Helsingborg*.

MERCANDIA VIII Built as the SUPERFLEX BRAVO by North East Shipbuilders Ltd, Sunderland, UK for *Vognmandsruten* of Denmark and used on their services between Nyborg and Korsør and Copenhagen (Tuborg Havn) and Landskrona (Sweden). In 1991 she was chartered to *Scarlett Line* to operate on the Copenhagen and Landskrona route. In 1993 she was renamed the SVEA SCARLETT but later in the year the service ceased and she was laid up. In 1996 she was purchased by *Mercandia*, renamed the MERCANDIA VIII and placed on their *Sundbroen* Helsingør – Helsingborg service. In 1997 the service and vessel were leased to *HH-Ferries*. In 1999 she was purchased by *HH-Ferries*. Now owned by *Scandlines Helsingør – Helsingborg*. Now reserve vessel. Between April and July 2015 she operated between Puttgarden and Rødby for *Scandlines*, following damage sustained by the PRINSESSE BENEDIKTE at Gdansk during a refit.

TYCHO BRAHE Train/vehicle ferry, built by Tangen Verft A/S, Tomrefjord, Norway for *DSB* for the Helsingør – Helsingborg service.

SMYRIL LINE

THE COMPANY *Smyril Line* is a Faroe Islands company.

MANAGEMENT Adm. Director Rúni Vang Poulsen, **Accounting and Department Manager** Nina Djurhuus.

ADDRESS Yviri við Strond 1, PO Box 370, 110 Tórshavn, Faroe Islands.

TELEPHONE Administration & Reservations +298-34 59 00.

FAX +298-345901.

INTERNET Email office@smyrilline.com **Website** www.smyrilline.com *(English, French, Dutch German)* www.smyrilline.fo *(Danish, Faroese, Icelandic)*

ROUTES OPERATED *Winter/Early Spring* Tórshavn (Faroes) – Hirtshals (Denmark) (36 hrs; *NORRÖNA*; 1 per week), *Spring/Early Summer/Autumn* Tórshavn – Hirtshals (36 hrs; *NORRÖNA*; 1 per week), Tórshavn – Seyðisfjördur (Iceland) (19 hrs; *NORRÖNA*; 1 per week), *Summer* Tórshavn – Hirtshals (Denmark) (30 hrs; *NORRÖNA*; 2 per week), Tórshavn – Seyðisfjördur (Iceland) (19 hrs; *NORRÖNA*; 2 per week). *Freight service* Tórshavn – Hirtshals – St Petersburg *EYSTNES*, *HVITANES*.

1F	EYSTNES	4610t	81	15.0k	102.2m	0P	-	24T	AS	FO	7922166
2F	HVITANES	4636t	80	12.0k	77.3m	0P	-	14T	AS	FO	7915541
3	NORRÖNA	35966t	03	21.0k	164.0m	1482P	800C	134T	BA	FO	9227390

EYSTNES Con-ro vessel (only the main deck can take trailers) built as the COMETA by Fosen Mekaniske Verksteder, Rissa, Norway for *Nor-Cargo*. Until 2010 she operated for *Sea-Cargo* between Norwegian ports

Mercandia IV *(Henk van der Lugt)*

Hamlet *(Henk van der Lugt)*

SPL Princess Anastasia *(Darren Holdaway)*

Stena Danica *(Miles Cowsill)*

and Immingham; afterwards she operated on *Nor-Cargo* Norwegian domestic services. In September 2015 sold to *Smyril Line* and renamed the EYSTNES.

HVITANES Con-ro vessel (only the main deck can take trailers) built as the TANAGER by Bergen Mekaniske Verksteder, Bergen, Norway for *NorCargo* of Norway. In September 2015 sold to *Smyril Line* and renamed the EYSTNES.

NORRÖNA Built by Flender Werft, Lübeck, Germany for *Smyril Line*, to replace the existing NORRÖNA. Originally due to enter service in Summer 2002, start of building was delayed by financing difficulties. She was to have been built at Flensburger Schiffbau-Gesellschaft, Flensburg, Germany, but delays in arranging finance led to change of shipyard.

ST. PETER LINE

THE COMPANY *St. Peter Line* is a Russian owned, EU registered private sector company.

MANAGEMENT CEO Sergei Kotenev.

ADDRESS Ostrovskogo sq. 7, St. Petersburg, 191025 Russia.

TELEPHONE *Russia* +7 (812) 337-20-60, ***Finland*** +358 (0)9 6187 2000

INTERNET Email sales@stpeterline.com **Website** www.stpeterline.com/en

(Russian, English, Estonian, Finnish, Swedish)

ROUTES OPERATED Helsinki (Finland) – St Petersburg (Russia) (12 hours 30 mins; ***PRINCESS MARIA***; 3/4 per week), St Petersburg – Helsinki – Stockholm – Tallinn – St Petersburg; ***SPL PRINCESS ANASTASIA***; 1/2 per week).

1	PRINCESS MARIA	34093t	81	20.0k	168.1m	1638P	360C	54T	A	MT	7911533
2	SPL PRINCESS ANASTASIA	37583t	86	22.0k	177.0m	2500P	380C	42L	BA	MT	8414582

PRINCESS MARIA Built as the FINLANDIA by Oy Wärtsilä Ab, Turku, Finland for *EFFOA* of Finland for *Silja Line* services between Helsinki and Stockholm. In 1990 she was sold to *DFDS*, renamed the QUEEN OF SCANDINAVIA and introduced onto the Copenhagen – Helsingborg – Oslo service. In 2000 rebuilt at Gdynia. In 2001 transferred to the Newcastle – IJmuiden route. In May 2007 moved to the Newcastle – Norway route. This service ended at the end of August 2008 and she was laid up. In 2009 used for ten weeks as an accommodation vessel at Oskarshamn and in December in Copenhagen. In April 2010 time chartered to *Inflot Cruise and Ferry Ltd* of Russia for three years for use by *St. Peter Line* and renamed the PRINCESS MARIA.

SPL PRINCESS ANASTASIA Built as the OLYMPIA by Oy Wärtsilä Ab, Turku, Finland for *Rederi AB Slite* of Sweden for *Viking Line* service between Stockholm and Helsinki. In 1993 she was chartered to *P&O European Ferries* to inaugurate a new service between Portsmouth and Bilbao. Renamed the PRIDE OF BILBAO. During the summer period she also operated, at weekends, a round trip between Portsmouth and Cherbourg. In 1994 she was purchased by the *Irish Continental Group* and re-registered in the Bahamas. In 2002 her charter was extended for a further five years and again for a further three years from October 2007. The Cherbourg service ended at the end of 2004. In September 2010 redelivered to *Irish Continental Group*. In October 2010 renamed the BILBAO. In November 2010 chartered to *St. Peter Line*, in February 2011 renamed the SPL PRINCESS ANASTASIA and in April 2011 inaugurated a new Stockholm – St Petersburg service. In February 2011 purchased by an associated company of *St. Peter Line*. During January and February 2014 she served as a floating hotel at the Winter Olympics in Sochi, Russia.

STENA LINE

THE COMPANY *Stena Line Scandinavia AB* is a Swedish private sector company. During 2012, the operations of subsidiary *Scandlines AB* of Sweden were absorbed and some of the Baltic operations and vessels of *Scandlines GmbH* of Germany were taken over.

MANAGEMENT CEO Carl-Johan Hagman, **Chief Operating Officer** Hans Nilsson.

ADDRESS Danmarksterminalen, 405 19 Gothenburg, Sweden.

TELEPHONE Administration +46 (0)31-85 80 00, **Reservations** +46 (0)31 704 00 00.

INTERNET Email info@stenaline.com **Website** www.stenaline.com *(Czech, Danish, Dutch, English, French, German, Latvian, Lithuanian, Norwegian, Polish, Russian, Swedish)*

ROUTES OPERATED Conventional Ferries Gothenburg (Sweden) – Frederikshavn (Denmark) (3 hrs 15 mins; *STENA DANICA, STENA JUTLANDICA*; up to 6 per day), Gothenburg – Kiel (Germany) (14 hrs; *STENA GERMANICA, STENA SCANDINAVICA*; 1 per day), Frederikshavn – Oslo (Norway) (8 hrs 45 mins; *STENA SAGA*; 1 per day), Varberg (Sweden) – Grenaa (Denmark) (4 hrs; *STENA NAUTICA*; 2 per day), Karlskrona (Sweden) – Gdynia (Poland) (10 hrs 30 mins; *STENA BALTICA, STENA SPIRIT, STENA VISION*; 2/3 per day), Rostock (Germany) – Trelleborg (Sweden) (7 hrs); *MECKLENBURG-VORPOMMERN, SKÅNE*; 3 per day)), Sassnitz (Germany) – Trelleborg (4 hrs 15 mins; *SASSNITZ*; 1 per day), Travemünde (Germany) – Ventspils (Latvia) (25 hrs; *STENA FLAVIA*; 1 per week), Travemünde (Germany) – Liepaja (Latvia) (28 hrs 30 mins; *URD*; 2 per week), Nynäshamn (Sweden) – Ventspils (Latvia) (12 hrs; *SCOTTISH VIKING, STENA FLAVIA*; 6 per week). **Freight Ferry** Gothenburg – Frederikshavn (3 hrs 45 mins; *STENA GOTHICA*; 2 per day).

1	MECKLENBURG-VORPOMMERN	36185t	96	22.0k	199.9m	600P	445C	230Tr	A2	DE	9131797
2	SASSNITZ	21154t	89	18.5k	171.5m	875P	314C	50Tr	BA2	DE	8705383
3	SCOTTISH VIKING	26500t	09	24.0k	186.5m	800P	185C	120L	A	IT	9435454
4	SKÅNE	42705t	98	21.0k	200.2m	600P	520C	240Tr	AS2	SE	9133915
5	STENA BALTICA	22542t	07	23.0k	167.0m	160P	-	140L	BA2	UK	9364978
6»•	STENA CARISMA	8631t	97	40.0k	88.0m	900P	210C	-	A	SE	9127760
7	STENA DANICA	28727t	83	19.5k	154.9m	2274P	555C	120T	BAS2	SE	7907245
8	STENA FLAVIA	26904t	08	24.0k	186.5m	852P	185C	120L	A	DK	9417919
9	STENA GERMANICA	44372t	01	22.0k	240.1m	900P	-	250L	BA	SE	9145176
10F	STENA GOTHICA	13144t	82	18.0k	171.0m	186P	-	104T	AS	SE	7826867
11	STENA JUTLANDICA	29691t	96	21.5k	183.7m	1500P	550C	156T	BAS2	SE	9125944
12	STENA NAUTICA	19504t	86	19.4k	134.0m	700P	330C	70T	BA2	SE	8317954
13	STENA SAGA	33750t	81	22.0k	166.1m	2000P	510C	76T	BA	SE	7911545
14	STENA SCANDINAVICA	55050t	03	22.0k	240.1m	900P	-	260L	BA	SE	9235517
15	STENA SPIRIT	39169t	88	20.0k	175.4m	2400P	550C	120T	BAS2	BS	7907661
16	STENA VISION	39178t	87	20.0k	175.4m	2400P	550C	120T	BAS2	SE	7907659
18	URD	13144t	81	17.5k	171.0m	186P	-	104T	AS	DK	7826855

MECKLENBURG-VORPOMMERN Train/vehicle ferry built by Schichau Seebeckwerft, Bremerhaven, Germany for *DFO* for the Rostock – Trelleborg service. During Winter 2002/03 modified to increase freight capacity and reduce passenger capacity. In September 2012 sold to *Stena Line.*

SASSNITZ Train/vehicle ferry built by Danyard A/S, Frederikshavn, Denmark for *Deutsche Reichsbahn*. In 1993 ownership transferred to *DFO*. Used on the Sassnitz – Trelleborg service. In September 2012 sold to *Stena Line.*

SCOTTISH VIKING Built by CN Visentini, Porto Viro, Italy for *Epic Shipping* of the UK and chartered to *Norfolkline*. Operated between Zeebrugge and Rosyth until December 2010. In January 2010 chartered to *Scandlines* and placed on the Nynäshamn – Ventspils service. In September 2012 charter transferred to *Stena Line.*

Stena Baltica *(Miles Cowsill)*

Stena Germanica *(Henk van der Lugt)*

SKÅNE Train/vehicle ferry built by Astilleros Españoles, Cadiz, Spain for an American trust and chartered to *Scandlines*. She is used on the Trelleborg – Rostock service.

STENA BALTICA Built as the COTENTIN by STX Finland, Helsinki, Finland for *Brittany Ferries*. Used on freight service from Poole to Cherbourg and Santander. In March 2013 replaced by the BARFLEUR (operating to Cherbourg only). During summer 2013 operated twice weekly from Poole to Bilbao and Santander. In October 2013 sold to *Stena RoRo* and renamed the STENA BALTICA. In November 2013 chartered to *Stena Line* and replaced the STENA ALEGRA on the Karlskrona – Gdynia route.

STENA CARISMA Westamarin HSS 900 craft built at Kristiansand, Norway for *Stena Line* for the Gothenburg – Frederikshavn service. Work on a sister vessel, approximately 30% completed, was ceased. She has not operated since 2013.

STENA DANICA Built by Chantiers du Nord et de la Méditerranée, Dunkerque, France for *Stena Line* for the Gothenburg – Frederikshavn service.

STENA FLAVIA Built by CN Visentini, Porto Viro, Italy for *Epic Shipping* of the UK. Launched as the WATLING STREET. On delivery, chartered to *ISCOMAR* of Spain and renamed the PILAR DEL MAR. In 2009 laid up until February 2010 when she was chartered to *Acciona Trasmediterranea* of Spain and operated between Barcelona and Tangiers. Later that month, chartered to *T-Link* and resumed the name WATLING STREET. In May 2011 chartered to *Scandlines* and placed on the Travemünde – Ventspils service. In April 2012, sold to *Stena RoRo*; she continued to be chartered to *Scandlines*. In September 2012 charter transferred to *Stena Line*. In April 2013 renamed the STENA FLAVIA. Now .operates one weekly roundtrip from Nynäshamn to Liepaja, two roundtrips to Nynäshamn to Ventspils and once weekly Ventspils – Travemünde.

STENA GERMANICA Ro-pax ferry built as the STENA HOLLANDICA by Astilleros Españoles, Cadiz, Spain for *Stena RoRo* and chartered to *Stena Line BV* to operate between Hook of Holland and Harwich. In 2007 lengthened by 50m at Lloyd Werft, Bremerhaven and passenger capacity increased to 900. Between May and August 2010 refurbished at Gdansk and had an 100 additional cabins added. At the end of August entered service on the Gothenburg – Kiel route, renamed the STENA GERMANICA III. In September, after the previous STENA GERMANICA had been renamed the STENA VISION, she was renamed the STENA GERMANICA.

STENA GOTHICA Built as the LUCKY RIDER by Nuovi Cantieri Apuania S.P.A., Marina De Carrara, Italy, a ro-ro freight ferry, for *Delpa Maritime* of Greece. In 1985 she was acquired by *Stena Line* and renamed the STENA DRIVER. Later that year she was acquired by *Sealink British Ferries* and renamed the SEAFREIGHT FREEWAY to operate freight-only services between Dover and Dunkerque. In 1988 she was sold to *SOMAT* of Bulgaria for use on *Medlink* services in the Mediterranean and renamed the SERDICA. In 1990 she was sold and renamed the NORTHERN HUNTER. In 1991 she was sold to *Blæsbjerg* of Denmark, renamed the ARKA MARINE and chartered to *DSB*. She was then converted into a ro-pax vessel, renamed the ASK and introduced onto the Århus – Kalundborg service. Purchased by *Scandlines A/S* of Denmark in 1997. In 1999 she was, after some modification, transferred to *Scandlines Euroseabridge* and placed on the Travemünde – Klaipéda route. In 2000 she was transferred to the Rostock – Liepaja route. Lengthened by 20m in 2001 and, in late 2001, chartered to *Nordö Link* to operate between Travemünde and Malmö. In late 2002 replaced by the FINNARROW and returned to *Scandlines*. She was transferred to the Rostock – Trelleborg route whilst the MECKLENBURG-VORPOMMERN was being rebuilt. She was then transferred to the Kiel – Klaipéda route. In 2003 chartered to *Scandlines AB* to operate on the Trelleborg – Travemünde route. In April 2005 the charter ended and she returned to *Scandlines AG*. Initially she was due to replace the FELLOW on the Nynäshamn – Ventspils route during her annual refit. In Autumn 2005 moved to the Rostock – Ventspils route. In January 2009 moved to the Nynäshamn – Ventspils route. In January 2011 moved to the Travemünde – Liepaja route. In May 2011 laid up. In November introduced as second vessel. In September 2012 sold to *Stena Line*. In September 2015 to move to the Gothenburg – Frederikshavn freight service and renamed the STENA GOTHICA.

STENA JUTLANDICA Train/vehicle 'ro-pax' vessel built by Van der Giessen-de Noord, Krimpen aan den IJssel, Rotterdam, The Netherlands for *Stena Line* to operate between Gothenburg and Frederikshavn. She was launched as the STENA JUTLANDICA III and renamed on entry into service.

STENA NAUTICA Built as the NIELS KLIM by Nakskov Skibsværft A/S, Nakskov, Denmark for *DSB (Danish State Railways)* for their service between Århus (Jutland) and Kalundborg (Sealand). In 1990 she was purchased by *Stena Rederi* of Sweden and renamed the STENA NAUTICA. In 1992 she was chartered to *B&I Line*, renamed the ISLE OF INNISFREE and introduced onto the Rosslare – Pembroke Dock service, replacing the MUNSTER (8093t, 1970). In 1993 she was transferred to the Dublin – Holyhead service. In early 1995 she was chartered to *Lion Ferry*. She was renamed the LION KING. In 1996 she was replaced by a new LION KING and renamed the STENA NAUTICA. During Summer 1996 she was chartered to *Transmediterranea* of Spain but returned to *Stena RoRo* in the autumn and remained laid up during 1997. In December 1997 she was chartered to *Stena Line* and placed on the Halmstad – Grenaa route. This route ended on 31st January 1999 and she was transferred to the Varberg – Grenaa route. During Winter 2001/02 she was rebuilt to heighten the upper vehicle deck and allow separate loading of vehicle decks; passenger capacity was reduced. On 16th February 2004 she was hit by the coaster JOANNA and holed. Returned to service at the end of May 2004 after repairs at Gothenburg and Gdansk.

STENA SAGA Built as the SILVIA REGINA by Oy Wärtsilä Ab, Turku, Finland for *Stockholms Rederi AB Svea* of Sweden. She was registered with subsidiary company *Svea Line* of Turku, Finland and was used on *Silja Line* services between Stockholm and Helsinki. In 1981 she was sold to *Johnson Line* and in 1984 sold to a Finnish Bank and chartered back. In 1990 she was purchased by *Stena RoRo* of Sweden for delivery in 1991. In 1991 she was renamed the STENA BRITANNICA and took up service on the Hook of Holland – Harwich service for Dutch subsidiary *Stena Line BV*, operating with a British crew. In 1994 she was transferred to the Oslo – Frederikshavn route and renamed the STENA SAGA. During Winter 2002/03 rebuilt to increase passenger capacity by 200.

STENA SCANDINAVICA Ro-pax vessel built by Hyundai Heavy Industries, Ulsan, South Korea, for *Stena RoRo*. Launched and delivered in January 2003 as the STENA BRITANNICA II. Chartered to *Stena Line* for use on the Hook of Holland – Harwich service, replacing the 2000-built STENA BRITANNICA, now the FINNFELLOW of *FinnLink*. In March 2003 renamed the STENA BRITANNICA. In 2007 lengthened at Lloyd Werft, Bremerhaven. In September 2010 renamed the BRITANNICA. Between October 2010 and April 2011 refurbished and had 100 additional cabins added at Gdansk. In April 2011 renamed the STENA SCANDINAVICA IV and entered service on the Gothenburg – Kiel route. In May, after the previous STENA SCANDINAVICA had been renamed the STENA SPIRIT, she was renamed the STENA SCANDINAVICA.

STENA SPIRIT Built as the STENA SCANDINAVICA by Stocznia i Komuni Paryski, Gdynia, Poland for *Stena Line* for the Gothenburg – Kiel service (launched as the STENA GERMANICA and names swapped with sister vessel before delivery). There were originally intended to be four vessels. Only two were delivered to *Stena Line*. The third (due to be called the STENA POLONICA) was sold by the builders as an unfinished hull to *Fred. Olsen Lines* of Norway and then resold to *ANEK* of Greece who had her completed at Perama and delivered as EL VENIZELOS for service between Greece and Italy. The fourth hull (due to be called the STENA BALTICA) was sold to *A Lelakis* of Greece and was to be rebuilt as a cruise ship to be called REGENT SKY; however, the project was never completed. The hull was broken up in 2004. During the summer period on some days, the vessel arriving in Gothenburg overnight from Kiel operates a round trip to Frederikshavn before departing for Kiel the following evening. During Winter 1998/99 she was modified to increase freight capacity and reduce the number of cabins. In April 2011 replaced by the former STENA BRITANNICA (renamed the STENA SCANDINAVICA IV) and entered CityVarvet in Gothenburg for refurbishment. In June 2011 she was renamed the STENA SPIRIT and, in July 2011, transferred to the Karlskrona – Gydnia route.

STENA VISION Built as the STENA GERMANICA by Stocznia im Lenina, Gdansk, Poland for *Stena Line* for the Gothenburg – Kiel service. During the summer period on some days, the vessel arriving in Gothenburg overnight from Kiel operates a round trip to Frederikshavn before departing for Kiel the following evening. During Winter 1998/99 modified to increase freight capacity and reduce the number of cabins. In August 2010 replaced by the former STENA HOLLANDICA (renamed the STENA GERMANICA III initially) and entered CityVarvet in Gothenburg for refurbishment. In September she was renamed the STENA VISION and, in November, transferred to the Karlskrona – Gydnia route.

URD Built as the EASY RIDER by Nouvi Cantieri Aquania SpA, Venice, Italy, a ro-ro freight ferry, for *Delpa Maritime* of Greece and used on Mediterranean services. In 1985 she was acquired by *Sealink British Ferries*

Stena Vision *(Miles Cowsill)*

Silja Europa *(Kalle Id)*

and renamed the SEAFREIGHT HIGHWAY to operate a freight-only service between Dover and Dunkerque. In 1988 she was sold to *SOMAT* of Bulgaria for use on *Medlink* services in the Mediterranean and renamed the BOYANA. In 1990 she was sold to *Blæsbjerg* of Denmark, renamed the AKTIV MARINE and chartered to *DSB*. In 1991 she was converted into a ro-pax vessel, renamed the URD and introduced onto the Århus – Kalundborg service. Purchased by *Scandlines* in 1997. Withdrawn at the end of May 1999 and, after modification, transferred to the *Balticum Seaways* (later *Scandlines Balticum Seaways*) Århus – Aabenraa – Klaipėda route. In 2001 lengthened and moved to the Rostock – Liepaja route. In Autumn 2005 this route became Rostock – Ventspils. Withdrawn from Rostock – Ventspils in November 2009. Vessel inaugurated new service Travemünde – Ventspils in January 2010. Replaced by the WATLING STREET in May 2011 and moved to the Travemünde – Liepaja route. In October 2012 sold to *Sol Dru A/S* (a subsidiary of *Swedish Orient Line*) and chartered to *Stena Line*. In August 2013 sold to *Stena Line*.

Under Construction

19	NEWBUILDING 1	-	19	-	-	1000P	-	180L	BA	-	-
20	NEWBUILDING 2	-	19	-	-	1000P	-	180L	BA	-	-
21	NEWBUILDING 3	-	19	-	-	1000P	-	180L	BA	-	-
22	NEWBUILDING 4	-	19	-	-	1000P	-	180L	BA	-	-

NEWBUILDING 1, NEWBUILDING 2, NEWBUILDING 3, NEWBUILDING 3 Under construction by AVIC International Maritime Holdings, Weihai, China. They are designed to run on either methanol or LPG. Deployment has not yet been decided.

STRANDFARASKIP LANDSINS

THE COMPANY *Strandfaraskip Landsins* is owned by the Faroe Islands Government.

ADDRESS Sjógøta 5, Postboks 30, 810 Tvøroyri, Faroe Islands.

TELEPHONE Administration & Reservations +298 34 30 00.

FAX Administration & Reservations +298 34 30 01.

INTERNET Email fyrisitingssl.fo **Website** www.ssl.fo *(Faroese)*

ROUTES OPERATED Passenger and Car Ferries Tórshavn (Streymoy) – Tvøroyri (Suduroy) (1 hr 50 mins; **SMYRIL**; up to 2 per day), Klaksvík – Syòradali (20 min; **SAM**; up to 6 per day), Skopun – Gamlarætt (30 mins; **TEISTIN**; up to 9 per day). **Passenger-only Ferries** Sørvágur – Mykines (1 hr 15 mins; **SILJA STAR/FROYUR (chartered ships)**; up to 3 per day), Hvannasund – Svínoy (40 mins) – Kirkja (20 mins) – Hatlarvik (10 mins) – Svínoy (30 mins; **RITAN**; up to 4 per day), Sandur – Skúvoy (35 mins; **SILDBERIN**; up to 5 per day), Tórshavn – Nólsoy (25 mins; **TERNAN**; up to 5 per day).

1p	RITAN	81t	71	10.5k	22.1m	125P	0C	0L	-	FO	
2	SAM	217t	75	9.7k	30.2m	115P	17C	-	A	FO	7602168
3p	SILDBERIN	34t	79	7.5k	11.2m	30P	0C	0L	-	FO	
4	SMYRIL	12670t	05	21.0k	135.0m	976P	200C	32L	A	FO	9275218
5p	SÚLAN	11t	87	-	12.0m	40P	0C	0L	-	FO	
6	TEISTIN	1260t	01	11.0k	45.0m	288P	33C	2L	BA	FO	9226102
7	TERNAN	927t	80	12.0k	39.7m	319P	0C	0L	BA	FO	7947154

RITAN Built by Monnickenda, Volendam, The Netherlands. Used on the Hvannasund – Svínoy-Kirkja-Hattarvik service.

SAM Built by Blaalid Slip & Mek Verksted, Raudeberg, Norway. Used on the Klaksvik – Syòradali route and the Leirvik – Syòradali route.

SILDBERIN Built at Tvøroyri, Faroe Islands. Used on the Sandur – Skúvoy route.

SMYRIL Built by IZAR, San Fernando, Spain for *Strandfaraskip Landsins*. Operates on the Tórshavn – Tvøroyri service.

SÚLAN Built by Faaborg Værft A/S, Faaborg, Denmark. Used on the Sørvágur – Mykines service. Now conveys freight to Skúvoy.

TEISTIN Built by P/F Skipasmidjan a Skala, Skala, Faroe Islands for *Strandfaraskip Landsins*. Used on the Skopun – Gamlarætt service.

TERNAN Built by Tórshavnar Skipasmidja P/f, Tórshavn, Faroe Islands for *Strandfaraskip Landsins*. Used on the Tórshavn – Nólsoy service.

SYLTFÄHRE

THE COMPANY Syltfähre (*Syltfærge* in Danish) is the trading name of *Römö-Sylt Linie GmbH & Co. KG*, a German private sector company, a subsidiary of *FRS (Förde Reederei Seetouristik)* of Flensburg.

MANAGEMENT Managing Director FRS Birte Dettmers, **CEO Römö-Sylt Linie** Christian Baumberger, Götz Becker, Jan Kruse.

ADDRESS *Germany* Am Fähranleger 3, 25992 List, Germany, *Denmark* Kilebryggen, 6792 Rømø, Denmark.

TELEPHONE Administration +49 (0)461 864 0, **Reservations** *Germany* +49 (0)461 864 601, *Denmark* +49 461 864 601.

INTERNET Email info@rsl.de **Website** www.syltfaehre.de *(Danish, English, German)*

ROUTE OPERATED List auf Sylt (Sylt, Germany) – Havneby (Rømø, Denmark) (approx. 40 mins; **SYLTEXPRESS**; variable – approx two-hourly). **Note**: The Danish island of Rømø is linked to the Danish mainland by a toll-free road causeway; the German island of Sylt is linked to the German mainland by a rail-only causeway on which cars are conveyed on shuttle wagons.

1	SYLTEXPRESS	3650t	05	16.0k	88.2m	600P	80C	10L	BA	CY	9321823

SYLTEXPRESS Built by Fiskerstrand Verft A/S, Aalesund, Norway for *Römö-Sylt Linie*.

TALLINK/SILJA LINE

THE COMPANY *AS Tallink Grupp* is an Estonian private sector company. *Tallink Silja Oy* is a Finnish subsidiary, *Tallink Silja AB* is a Swedish subsidiary.

MANAGEMENT *AS Tallink Grupp:* **Chairman of Management Board** Janek Stalmeister, *Tallink Silja Oy* **Managing Director** Margus Schults, *Tallink Silja AB* **Managing Director** Marcus Risberg.

ADDRESSES *AS Tallink Grupp* Sadama 5/7, Tallinn 10111, Estonia, *Tallink Silja Oy* P.O. Box 100, 00181 Helsinki, Finland, *Tallink Silja AB* Box 27295, 10253 Stockholm, Sweden.

TELEPHONE *AS Tallink Grupp* +372 (0)640 9800, *Tallink Silja Oy* **Administration** +358 (0)9 18041, **Reservations** +358 (0)600 15700, *Tallink Silja AB* **Administration** +46 (0)8 6663300, **Reservations** +46 (0)8 222140.

FAX *AS Tallink Grupp* **Administration** + 372 (0)640 9810, *Tallink Silja Oy* **Administration** +358 (0)9 180 4633, *Tallink Silja AB* **Administration** +46 (0) 8 663400.

INTERNETEmail info@tallink.ee **Websites** www.tallinksilja.com *(17 languages, see the internet page)*, www.tallink.com (corporate site) *(English)*

INTERNETEmail info@tallink.ee **Websites** www.tallinksilja.com *(English, Danish, Estonian, Finnish, German, Latvia, Norwegian, Swedish, Russian)*, www.tallink.com (corporate site)

ROUTES OPERATED Tallink branded services *Passenger Ferries* Helsinki – Tallinn: **Shuttle** (2 hrs; **STAR, SUPERSTAR**; up to 6 per day), *Cruise Ferries* (3 hrs 30 – 4hrs 30 mins; **BALTIC QUEEN, SILJA EUROPA***; normally 2 per day), Stockholm – Mariehamn (Åland) – Tallinn (14 hrs; **ROMANTIKA, VICTORIA I**; daily), Stockholm – Riga (Latvia) (16 hrs; **ISABELLE**; alternate days), *Freight-only Ferries* Kapellskär – Paldiski (9 hrs – 11 hrs; **REGAL STAR,** alternate days (round trip on Sunday)), Helsinki – Tallinn (3 hrs 30 mins; **SEA WIND**; 2 per day). *During summer 2016 SILJA EUROPA has 6 cruises Helsinki – Tallinn – Visby.

Silja Line branded services Helsinki (Finland) – Mariehamn (Åland) – Stockholm (Sweden) (16 hrs; *SILJA SERENADE, SILJA SYMPHONY*; 1 per day), Turku (Finland) – Mariehamn (Åland) (day)/Långnäs (Åland) (night) – Stockholm (11 hrs; *BALTIC PRINCESS, GALAXY*; 2 per day).

1	ATLANTIC VISION	30285t	02	27.9k	203.3m	728P	695C	110L	BA2	CA	9211509
2	BALTIC PRINCESS	48300t	08	24.5k	212.0m	2800P	300C	82T	BA	FI	9354284
3	BALTIC QUEEN	48300t	09	24.5k	212.0m	2800P	300C	82T	BA	EE	9443255
4	GALAXY	48915t	06	22.0k	212.0m	2800P	300C	82T	BA	SE	9333694
5	ISABELLE	35154t	89	21.5k	170.9m	2420P	364C	30T	BA	LV	8700723
6F	REGAL STAR	15281t	00	17.5k	156.6m	100P	-	120T	A	EE	9087116
7	ROMANTIKA	40803t	02	22.0k	193.8m	2178P	300C	82T	BA	EE	9237589
8F	SEA WIND	15879t	72	17.5k	154.4m	260P	55C	88Tr	BAS	EE	7128332
9	SILJA EUROPA	59912t	93	21.5k	201.8m	3000P	400C	68T	BA	EE	8919805
10	SILJA SERENADE	58376t	90	21.0k	203.0m	2641P	450C	70T	BA	FI	8715259
11	SILJA SYMPHONY	58377t	91	21.0k	203.0m	2641P	450C	70T	BA	SE	8803769
12	STAR	36249t	07	27.5k	185.0m	1900P	450C	120L	BA	EE	9364722
13	SUPERSTAR	36000t	08	29.0k	175.0m	1800P	600C	140T	BA	EE	9365398
14	VICTORIA I	40975t	04	22.0k	193.8m	2500P	300C	823T	BA	EE	9281281

ATLANTIC VISION Built as the SUPERFAST IX by Howaldtswerke Deutsche Werft AG, Kiel, Germany for *Attica Enterprises* for use by *Superfast Ferries*. She operated between Rostock and Södertälje from January until April 2002. In May 2002 she began operating between Rosyth and Zeebrugge (with the SUPERFAST X (now the STENA SUPERFAST X)). In 2004 fitted with additional cabins and conference/seating areas. In 2005 transferred to the Rostock – Hanko (later Helsinki) route. In 2006 sold to *Tallink*. In October 2008 chartered to *Marine Atlantic* of Canada to operate on the North Sydney-Port aux Basques service and renamed the ATLANTIC VISION.

BALTIC PRINCESS Built by Aker Yards, Helsinki. A large part of the hull was built at St Nazaire, France. In August 2008 replaced the GALAXY on the Tallinn – Helsinki route. In February 2013 transferred to the Stockholm – Turku service.

BALTIC QUEEN Built by STX Europe, Rauma, Finland. Operates between Helsinki and Tallinn.

GALAXY Built by Aker Yards, Rauma, Finland to operate as a cruise ferry on the Tallinn – Helsinki route. In July 2008 transferred to the Stockholm – Turku route and rebranded as a *Silja Line* vessel.

ISABELLE Built as the ISABELLA by Brodogradevna Industrija, Split, Yugoslavia for *SF Line*. Used on the *Viking Line* Stockholm – Naantali service until 1992 when she was switched to operating 24-hour cruises from Helsinki and in 1995 she was transferred to the Stockholm – Helsinki route. During 1996 she additionally operated day cruises to Muuga in Estonia during the 'layover' period in Helsinki. In 1997 she was transferred to the Stockholm – Turku route. in January 2013 she was replaced by the VIKING GRACE. After covering for the AMORELLA during her refit period she was laid up. In April 2013 sold to *Hansa Link Limited*, a subsidiary of *AS Tallink Grupp* and renamed the ISABELLE. In May placed on the Stockholm – Riga service, replacing the SILJA FESTIVAL.

REGAL STAR Partly built by Sudostroitelnyy Zavod Severnaya Verf, St Petersburg. Work started in 1993 (as a deep-sea ro-ro) but was never completed. In 1999 the vessel was purchased, taken to Palumba SpA, Naples and completed as a short-sea ro-ro with accommodation for 80 drivers. In 2000 she was delivered to *MCL* of Italy and placed on a route between Savona and Catania. In September of that year she was chartered to *Grimaldi Ferries* and operated on a route Salerno – Palermo – Valencia. In late 2003 she was sold to *Hansatee Shipping* of Estonia and, in 2004, placed on the Kapellskär – Paldiski route, replacing the KAPELLA. From February 2006 she was transferred to the Helsinki – Tallinn service, replacing the KAPELLA due to the hard ice conditions. She continued in this service for the summer, but the returned to the Paldiski – Kapellskär service. In June 2010 moved to the *SeaWind Line* Stockholm – Turku service for the summer seasons and returned to the Kapellskär – Paldiski route in the autumn.

ROMANTIKA Built by Aker Finnyards, Rauma, Finland for *Tallink Grupp* to operate for *Tallink* between Tallinn and Helsinki. In Spring 2006 moved to the Tallinn – Stockholm route. In May 2009 transferred to the Stockholm – Riga route. In August 2014 moved to the Stockholm – Tallinn service.

SEA WIND Train/vehicle ferry built as the SVEALAND by Helsingørs Skipsværft, Helsingør, Denmark for *Stockholms Rederi AB Svea* and used on the *Trave Line* Helsingborg (Sweden) – Copenhagen (Tuborg Havn) – Travemünde freight service. In 1981 she was sold to *TT-Saga Line* and operated between Travemünde and Malmö. In 1984 she was rebuilt to increase capacity and renamed the SAGA WIND. In 1989 she was acquired by *Silja Line* subsidiary *SeaWind Line*, renamed the SEA WIND and inaugurated a combined rail freight, trailer and lower-priced passenger service between Stockholm and Turku. This route later became freight-only. In January 2015 transferred to the Tallinn – Helsinki freight service.

SILJA EUROPA Built by Jos L Meyer, Papenburg, Germany. Ordered by *Rederi AB Slite* of Sweden for *Viking Line* service between Stockholm and Helsinki and due to be called EUROPA. In 1993, shortly before delivery was due, *Rederi AB Slite* went into liquidation and the order was cancelled. A charter agreement with her builders was then signed by *Silja Line* and she was introduced onto the Stockholm – Helsinki route as SILJA EUROPA. In early 1995 she was transferred to the Stockholm – Turku service. In January 2013 she was transferred to the Helsinki – Tallinn route. In August 2014 chartered to an Australian company as an accommodation vessel. In March 2016 joined the BALTIC PRINCESS as second vessel on the Helsinki – Tallinn 'Cruise' service.

SILJA SERENADE, SILJA SYMPHONY Built by Masa-Yards Oy, Turku, Finland for *Silja Line* for the Stockholm – Helsinki service. In 1993, SILJA SERENADE was transferred to the Stockholm – Turku service but in early 1995 she was transferred back to the Helsinki route.

STAR Built by Aker Yards, Helsinki, Finland for *Tallink* to operate on the Tallinn – Helsinki route.

SUPERSTAR Built by Fincantieri-Cantieri Navali Italiani SpA, Riva Trigoso, Italy to operate on the Tallinn – Helsinki route. In December 2015 sold to *Medinvest SpA (Corsica Ferries Group)* and chartered back. She will be delivered in early 2017 when she will be replaced by the MEGASTAR.

VICTORIA I Built by Aker Finnyards, Rauma, Finland for *Tallink*. Operates between Tallinn and Stockholm.

Under Construction

| 15 | MEGASTAR | 49000t | 17 | 27.0k | 212m | 2800P | - | - | BA | EE | - |

MEGASTAR Under construction by Meyer Turku, Turku, Finland to operate on the Tallinn – Helsinki Shuttle. She will be LNG/diesel dual powered. An option on a second vessel was allowed to lapse in March 2016.

AS Tallink Grupp also own the STENA SUPERFAST VII and STENA SUPERFAST VIII, currently on charter to *Stena Line (UK)*.

TESO

THE COMPANY *TESO* is a Dutch private company, with most shares owned by inhabitants of Texel. Its full name is *Texels Eigen Stoomboot Onderneming*.

MANAGEMENT Managing Director Cees de Waal.

ADDRESS Pontweg 1, 1797 SN Den Hoorn, The Netherlands.

TELEPHONE Administration +31 (0)222 36 96 00, **Reservations** Not applicable.

FAX Administration +31 (0)222 36 96 59.

INTERNET Email info@teso.nl **Website** www.teso.nl *(Dutch, English, German)*

ROUTE OPERATED Den Helder (The Netherlands) – Texel (Dutch Frisian Islands) (20 minutes; *DOKTER WAGEMAKER*, *TEXELSTROOM*; hourly).

| 1 | DOKTER WAGEMAKER | 13256t | 05 | 15.6k | 130.0m | 1750P | 320C | 44L | BA2 | NL | 9294070 |
| 2• | SCHULPENGAT | 8311t | 90 | 13.6k | 110.4m | 1750P | 156C | 25L | BA2 | NL | 8802313 |

Galaxy *(Kalle Id)*

Nils Dacke *(John Bryant)*

3	TEXELSTROOM	16400t	16	15.0k	135.4m	1750P	350C	44L	BA2	NL	9741918

DOKTER WAGEMAKER Built at Galatz, Romania (hull and superstructure) and Royal Schelde, Vlissingen (fitting out) for *TESO*.

SCHULPENGAT Built by Verolme Scheepswerf Heusden BV, Heusden, The Netherlands for *TESO*. In June 2016 laid up.

TEXELSTROOM Built by LaNaval Shipyard, Sestao, Spain to replace the SCHULPENGAT in June 2016.

TT-LINE

THE COMPANY *TT-Line GmbH & Co KG* is a German private sector company.

MANAGEMENT Managing Directors Hanns Heinrich Conzen & Jens Aurel Scharner, **Sales Manager** Dirk Lifke.

ADDRESS Zum Hafenplatz 1, 23570, Travemünde, Germany.

TELEPHONE +49 (0)4502 801 81.

INTERNET Email info@ttline.com **Website** www.ttline.com *(English, German, Swedish)*

ROUTES OPERATED *Passenger Ferries* Travemünde (Germany) – Trelleborg (Sweden) (8 hrs 30 mins/9 hrs 30 mins; *NILS HOLGERSSON, PETER PAN*; 2 per day). *Ro-pax Ferries* Travemünde (Germany) – Trelleborg (Sweden) (7 hrs 30 mins/8 hrs 15 mins; *ROBIN HOOD*; 1 per day), Rostock (Germany) – Trelleborg (Sweden) (5 hrs 30 mins/6 hrs 30 mins/7 hrs 30 mins; *HUCKLEBERRY FINN, TOM SAWYER*; 3 per day, Świnoujście (Poland) – Trelleborg (Sweden) (7 hrs; *NILS DACKE*; 1 per day).

1	HUCKLEBERRY FINN	26391t	88	18.0k	177.2m	400P	280C	121T	BAS2	SE	8618358
2	NILS DACKE	26796t	95	18.5k	179.7m	300P	-	157T	BA	CY	9087465
3	NILS HOLGERSSON	36468t	01	18.0k	190.8m	744P	-	171T	BAS2	DE	9217230
4	PETER PAN	36468t	01	18.0k	190.8m	744P	-	171T	BAS2	SE	9217242
5	ROBIN HOOD	26790t	95	18.5k	179.7m	317P	-	157T	BA	DE	9087477
6	TOM SAWYER	26478t	89	18.0k	177.2m	400P	280C	121T	BAS2	DE	8703232

HUCKLEBERRY FINN Built as the NILS DACKE by Schichau Seebeckwerft AG, Bremerhaven, Germany, as a ro-pax vessel. During Summer 1993 rebuilt to transform her into a passenger/car ferry and renamed the PETER PAN, replacing a similarly named vessel (31356t, 1986). On arrival of the new PETER PAN in Autumn 2001 she was renamed the PETER PAN IV. She was then converted back to ro-pax format, renamed the HUCKLEBERRY FINN and, in early 2002, transferred to the Rostock -Trelleborg route.

NILS DACKE, Ro-pax vessels built as the ROBIN HOOD by Finnyards, Rauma, Finland. She operated on the Travemünde – Trelleborg and Travemünde – Helsingborg routes. In December 2014 she was renamed the NILS DACKE and transferred to Cypriot registry. Moved to the Trelleborg – Świnoujście route.

NILS HOLGERSSON, PETER PAN Built by SSW Fähr und Spezialschiffbau GmbH, Bremerhaven, Germany for the Travemünde – Trelleborg route.

TOM SAWYER Built as the ROBIN HOOD by Schichau Seebeckwerft AG, Bremerhaven, Germany, as a ro-pax vessel. During Winter 1992/93 rebuilt to transform her into a passenger/car ferry and renamed the NILS HOLGERSSON, replacing a similarly named vessel (31395t, 1987) which had been sold to *Brittany Ferries* and renamed the VAL DE LOIRE. In 2001 converted back to ro-pax format and renamed the TOM SAWYER. Transferred to the Rostock – Trelleborg route.

ROBIN HOOD Ro-pax vessels built as the NILS DACKE, by Finnyards, Rauma, Finland. She operated on the Travemünde – Trelleborg and Travemünde – Helsingborg routes. In January 2014, she was transferred to a new Trelleborg – Świnoujście service and changed to Polish registry. In December 2014 she was renamed the ROBIN HOOD and transferred German Registry. Moved to the Travemünde – Trelleborg route.

UNITY LINE

THE COMPANY Unity Line is a Polish company owned by Polish Steamship Company (Polsteam). The operator manages seven ferries on two routes: Świnoujście – Ystad and Świnoujście – Trelleborg. Three ships are owned by Euroafrica Shipping which was previously a partner in the company; the ships continue to be operationally managed by to Unity Line.

MANAGEMENT Managing Director Jarosław Kotarski.

ADDRESS Plac Rodla 8, 70-419 Szczecin, Poland.

TELEPHONE Administration& Reservations +48 91 35 95 600.

FAX Administration +48 91 35 95 885.

INTERNET Email promy@unityline.pl **Website** www.unityline.pl (Polish, Swedish)

ROUTES OPERATED Passenger Service Świnoujście (Poland) – Ystad (Sweden) (6 hrs 30 mins (day), 9 hrs (night); **POLONIA, SKANIA**; 2 per day). **Freight Services** Świnoujście (Poland) – Ystad (Sweden) (8 hrs (day), 9 hrs (night); **JAN ŚNIADECKI, KOPERNIK**; 2 per day), Świnoujście (Poland) – Trelleborg (Sweden) (6 hrs 30 mins (day), 9 hrs (night); **GALILEUSZ, GRYF, WOLIN**; 3 per day).

1F+	GALILEUSZ	15848t	92	17.0k	150.4m	160P	-	115L	A	CY	9019078
2F+	GRYF	18653t	90	16.0k	158.0m	180P	-	125L	BA	BS	8818300
3F+	JAN SNIADECKI	14417t	88	17.0k	155.1m	57P	-	70Lr	SA2	CY	8604711
4F+	KOPERNIK	13788t	77	18.0k	160.1m	360P	-	60Lr	SA2	CY	7527887
5	POLONIA	29875t	95	17.2k	169.9m	920P	440C	145Lr	SA2	BS	9108350
6	SKANIA	23933t	95	22.5k	173.7m	1400P	430C	140L	BA	BS	9086588
7F+	WOLIN	22874t	86	17.5k	188.9m	370P	-	110Lr	SA	BS	8420842

GALILEUSZ Built as the VIA TIRRENO by Van der Giessen-de Noord, Krimpen aan den IJssel, The Netherlands for Viamare di Navigazione SpA of Italy. Initially operated between Voltri and Termini Imerese. In 1998 transferred to the Genoa – Termini Imerese route and in 2001 to the Genoa – Palermo route. In 2006 sold to Euroafrica Shipping, renamed the GALILEUSZ and in November introduced onto the Unity Line Świnoujście – Ystad service. In February 2007 transferred to the new Świnoujście – Trelleborg route.

GRYF Built as the KAPTAN BURHANETTIN ISIM by Fosen Mekaniske Verksteder, Fevag, Norway for Turkish Cargo Lines of Turkey to operate between Trieste (Italy) and Derince (Turkey). In 2002 chartered to Latlines to operate between Lübeck and Riga (Latvia). In 2003 chartered to VentLines to inaugurate a new service between Travemünde and Ventspils. In 2004 sold to Polsteam, managed by Unity Line and renamed the GRYF. Entered service in 2005. In February 2007 transferred to the new Świnoujście – Trelleborg route.

JAN SNIADECKI Built by Falkenbergs Varv AB, Falkenberg, Sweden for Polish Ocean Lines to operate between Świnoujście and Ystad. Now operates for Unity Line on this route.

KOPERNIK Train/vehicle ferry built as the ROSTOCK by Bergens Mekaniske Verksted A/S, Bergen, Norway for Deutsche Reichsbahn of Germany (DDR). Used on freight services between Trelleborg and Sassnitz. In 1992 modified to increase passenger capacity in order to run in passenger service. In 1993 ownership transferred to DFO and in 1994 she opened a new service from Rostock to Trelleborg. In 1997 she was used when winds precluded the use of the new MECKLENBURG-VORPOMMERN. Following modifications to this vessel in late 1997, the ROSTOCK continued to operate to provide additional capacity until the delivery of the SKÅNE of Scandlines AB, after which she was laid up. In 1999 she was sold to SeaWind Line, renamed the STAR WIND and operated in freight-only mode between Stockholm and Turku. Initial plans to bring her passenger accommodation up to the standards required for Baltic night service were dropped. In October 2002 replaced by the SKY WIND and transferred to the Helsinki – Tallinn route. She carried a limited number of ordinary passengers on some sailings. In May 2005 returned to the Stockholm – Turku service, no longer carrying ordinary passengers, but was laid up after a few weeks. In October sold to Euro Shipping OÜ of Estonia, a company linked to Saaremaa Laevakompanii, and renamed the VIRONIA. In 2006 inaugurated a new service between Sillamäe (Estonia) and Kotka (Finland). In 2007 sold to Euroafrica

Kopernik *(Miles Cowsill)*

Polonia *(Miles Cowsill)*

Shipping, renamed the KOPERNIK and, in April 2008, placed on the Świnoujście – Ystad route, replacing the MIKOLAJ KOPERNIK.

POLONIA Train/vehicle ferry built by Langsten Slip & Båtbyggeri A/S, Tomrefjord, Norway for *Polonia Line Ltd* and managed by *Unity Line.*

SKANIA Built as the SUPERFAST I by Schichau Seebeckwerft, Bremerhaven, Germany for *Superfast Ferries* of Greece. Operated between Patras and Ancona (Italy). In 1998 transferred to the Patras – Igoumenitsa (Greece) – Bari (Italy) route. In 2004 sold to a subsidiary of *Grimaldi Lines,* renamed the EUROSTAR ROMA and placed on the Civitavecchia (Italy) – Barcelona (Spain) service. In 2008 sold to *Polsteam* and renamed the SKANIA. After modifications, she was placed on the *Unity Line* Świnoujście – Ystad service as second passenger vessel. In during the peak summer period in 2010 will operate a round trip between Ystad and Rønne for *Bornholmstrafikken.*

WOLIN Train/vehicle ferry built as the ÖRESUND by Moss Rosenberg Værft, Moss, Norway for *Statens Järnvägar (Swedish State Railways)* for the 'DanLink' service between Helsingborg and Copenhagen. Has 817 metres of rail track. Service ceased in July 2000 and vessel laid up. In 2001 sold to *Sea Containers Ferries* and in 2002 converted at Gdansk, Poland to a passenger ferry. She was chartered to *SeaWind Line,* renamed the SKY WIND and in Autumn 2002 replaced the STAR WIND on the Stockholm – Turku service. In 2007 sold to *Polsteam,* renamed the WOLIN and placed on the *Unity Line* Świnoujście – Trelleborg service.

VIKING LINE

THE COMPANY *Viking Line Abp* is a Finnish company Listed on the Helsinki Stock Exchange since 1995.

MANAGEMENT President & CEO Jan Hanses, **Executive Vice President/Deputy CEO and Chief Financial Officer at Viking Line Abp** Andreas Remmer.

ADDRESS Norragatan 4, 22100 Mariehamn, Åland.

TELEPHONE Administration +358 (0)18 27000, **Reservations** +358 (0)9 1235300.

FAX Administration +358 (0)18 16944.

INTERNET Email international.sales@vikingline.com **Websites** www.vikingline.fi *(Finnish, English, Swedish)* www.vikingline.ee *(Estonian)* www.vikingline.de *(German)*

ROUTES OPERATED Stockholm (Sweden) – Mariehamn (Åland) – Helsinki (Finland) (14 hrs; **GABRIELLA, MARIELLA**; 1 per day), Stockholm – Mariehamn (day)/Långnäs (Åland) (night) – Turku (Finland) (9 hrs 10 mins; **AMORELLA, VIKING GRACE**; 2 per day), Kapellskär (Sweden) – Mariehamn (Åland) (2 hrs 15 mins; **ROSELLA**; up to 3 per day), Helsinki – Tallinn (2 hrs 30 mins; **GABRIELLA, MARIELLA, VIKING XPRS,** 3 per day), Cruises from Stockholm to Mariehamn (21 hrs – 24 hrs round trip (most 22 hrs 30 mins); **VIKING CINDERELLA**; 1 per day).

1	AMORELLA	34384t	88	21.5k	169.4m	2450P	450C	53T	BA	FI	8601915
2	GABRIELLA	35492t	92	21.5k	171.2m	2420P	400C	50T	BA	FI	8917601
3	MARIELLA	37799t	85	22.0k	176.9m	2500P	400C	60T	BA	FI	8320573
4	ROSELLA	16850t	80	21.3k	136.0m	1700P	340C	40T	BA	AL	7901265
5	VIKING CINDERELLA	46398t	89	21.5k	191.0m	2500P	100C	-	BA	SE	8719188
6	VIKING GRACE	57000t	13	23.0k	214.0m	2800P	556C	90L	BA	FI	9606900
7	VIKING XPRS	34000t	08	25.0k	185.0m	2500P	250C	60L	BA	EE	9375654

AMORELLA Built by Brodogradevna Industrija, Split, Yugoslavia for *SF Line* for the Stockholm – Mariehamn – Turku service.

GABRIELLA Built as the FRANS SUELL by Brodogradiliste Industrija, Split, Croatia for *Sea-Link AB* of Sweden to operate for subsidiary company *Euroway AB,* who established a service between Lübeck, Travemünde and Malmö. In 1994 this service ceased and she was chartered to *Silja Line,* renamed the SILJA

SCANDINAVIA and transferred to the Stockholm – Turku service. In 1997 she was sold to *Viking Line* to operate between Stockholm and Helsinki. She was renamed the GABRIELLA. In 2014, a daytime sailing during summer from Helsinki to Tallinn was introduced.

MARIELLA Built by Oy Wärtsilä Ab, Turku, Finland for *SF Line*. Used on the Stockholm – Helsinki service. During 1996 additionally operated short cruises to Muuga in Estonia during the 'layover' period in Helsinki. In 2014, a daytime sailing during summer from Helsinki to Tallinn was introduced.

ROSELLA Built by Oy Wärtsilä Ab, Turku, Finland for *SF Line*. Used mainly on the Stockholm – Turku and Kapellskär – Naantali services until 1997. From 1997 operated 21 to 24-hour cruises from Stockholm to Mariehamn under the marketing name 'The Dancing Queen', except in the peak summer period when she operated between Kapellskär and Turku. In Autumn 2003 transferred to a new twice-daily Helsinki – Tallinn ferry service. In May 2008 placed on the Mariehamn – Kapellskär route under the Swedish flag. In 2011 she was extensively rebuilt at Balti Laevaremondi Tehas in Tallinn, Estonia. Cabin capacity was lowered from 1184 to 418 and the restaurant and shop areas were increased. In January 2014 placed under the Finnish flag.

VIKING CINDERELLA Built as the CINDERELLA by Wärtsilä Marine Ab, Turku, Finland for *SF Line*. Until 1993 provided additional capacity between Stockholm and Helsinki and undertook weekend cruises from Helsinki. In 1993 she replaced the OLYMPIA (a sister vessel of the MARIELLA) as the main Stockholm – Helsinki vessel after the OLYMPIA had been chartered to *P&O European Ferries* and renamed the PRIDE OF BILBAO. In 1995 switched to operating 20-hour cruises from Helsinki to Estonia in the off peak and the Stockholm – Mariehamn – Turku service during the peak summer period (end of May to end of August). From 1997 she remained cruising throughout the year. In Autumn 2003 she was transferred to the Swedish flag, renamed the VIKING CINDERELLA and transferred to Stockholm – Mariehamn cruises. She operates these cruises all year round.

VIKING GRACE Built by STX Europe, Turku, Finland. She operates between Stockholm and Turku. She is powered by LNG. Entered service in January 2013.

VIKING XPRS Built by Aker Yards, Helsinki to operate between Helsinki and Tallinn. In January 2014 placed under the Estonian flag.

WAGENBORG PASSAGIERSDIENSTEN

THE COMPANY *Wagenborg Passagiersdiensten BV* is a Dutch private sector company.

MANAGEMENT Managing Director Ger van Langen.

ADDRESS Reeweg 4, 9163 ZM Nes, Ameland, The Netherlands.

TELEPHONE Administration & Reservations *International* +31 85 4011008, *Netherlands* 0900 9238.

FAX Administration & Reservations +31 (0)519 542905.

INTERNET Email info@wpd.nl **Website** www.wpd.nl *(Dutch, English, German)*

ROUTES OPERATED *Car Ferries* Holwerd (The Netherlands) – Ameland (Frisian Islands) (45 minutes; *OERD, SIER*; up to 14 per day), Lauwersoog (The Netherlands) – Schiermonnikoog (Frisian Islands) (45 minutes; *MONNIK, ROTTUM*; up to 6 per day).

1	MONNIK	1121t	85	12.2k	58.0m	1000P	46C	9L	BA	NL	8408961
2	OERD	2286t	03	11.2k	73.2m	1200P	72C	22L	BA	NL	9269673
3	ROTTUM	1121t	85	12.2k	58.0m	1000P	46C	9L	BA	NL	8408959
4	SIER	2286t	95	11.2k	73.2m	1200P	72C	22L	BA	NL	9075761

MONNIK Built by Scheepswerf Hoogezand, Hoogezand, The Netherlands for *Wagenborg Passagiersdiensten BV* as the OERD. In 2003, on delivery of the new OERD, she was renamed the MONNIK. Used on the Lauwersoog – Schiermonnikoog route.

OERD Built by Scheepswerf Bijlsma Lemmer, Lemmer, The Netherlands for *Wagenborg Passagiersdiensten BV*. Used on the Ameland – Holwerd route.

Amorella *(Matthew Punter)*

Viking XPRS *(Miles Cowsill)*

ROTTUM Built as the SIER by Scheepswerf Hoogezand, Hoogezand, The Netherlands for *Wagenborg Passagiersdiensten BV* and used on the Holwerd – Ameland route. In 1995 renamed the ROTTUM and transferred to the Lauwersoog – Schiermonnikoog route.

SIER Built by Shipyard Bijlsma, Wartena, The Netherlands for *Wagenborg Passagiersdiensten BV*. Used on the Ameland – Holwerd route.

WASALINE

THE COMPANY *Wasaline* is the trading name of *NLC Ferry Oy Ab*, a Finnish company, jointly owned by the cities of Vaasa and Umeå.

MANAGING DIRECTOR Peter Ståhlberg,

ADDRESS *Finland* Skeppsredaregatan 3, 65170 Vasa, Finland *Sweden* Blå Vägen 4, 91322 Holmsund, Sweden.

TELEPHONE Administration & Reservations *Finland* +358 (0)207 716 810, *Sweden* +46 (0)90 185 200.

FAX Administration & Reservations

INTERNET *Email* info@wasaline.com *Website* www.wasaline.com *(English, Finnish, Swedish)*

ROUTE OPERATED Vaasa (Finland) – Umeå (Sweden) (4 hrs; *WASA EXPRESS*; 1/2 per day).

1	WASA EXPRESS	17053t	81	17.0k	140.8m	1100P	450C	84T	BAS2	FI	8000226

WASA EXPRESS Built by Oy Wärtsilä AB, Helsinki, Finland as the TRAVEMÜNDE for *Gedser-Travemünde Ruten* of Denmark for their service between Gedser (Denmark) and Travemünde (Germany). In 1986 the company's trading name was changed to *GT Linien* and in 1987, following the takeover by *Sea-Link AB* of Sweden, it was further changed to *GT Link*. The vessel's name was changed to the TRAVEMÜNDE LINK. In 1988 she was purchased by *Rederi AB Gotland* of Sweden, although remaining in service with *GT Link*. Later in 1988 she was chartered to *Sally Ferries* and entered service in December on the Ramsgate – Dunkerque service. She was renamed the SALLY STAR. In 1997 she was transferred to *Silja Line*, to operate between Vaasa and Umeå during the summer period, and operated under the marketing name WASA EXPRESS (although not renamed). She returned to *Rederi AB Gotland* in Autumn 1997, was renamed the THJELVAR and entered service with *Destination Gotland* in January 1998. Withdrawn and laid up in December 2003. In 2004 chartered to *Color Line* to inaugurate a new service between Larvik and Hirtshals. Renamed the COLOR TRAVELLER. Operated in reduced passenger mode on this service but in summer peak period operated between Frederikshavn and Larvik in full passenger mode. In December 2006 returned to *Rederi AB Gotland*. In 2007 renamed the THJELVAR, chartered to *Scandlines* and placed on the Gedser – Rostock route. Renamed the ROSTOCK. In Autumn 2008 withdrawn and laid up. In June 2009 sub-chartered to *Comarit* of Morocco for two months. In September she resumed the name THJELVAR. In August 2008 she was chartered to *Fred. Olsen SA* of Spain, renamed the BETANCURIA and placed on the Las Palmas – Puerto del Rosario – Arrecife service. In September 2012 laid up. In October 2012 purchased by *NLC Ferry Oy Ab* and, in November, renamed the WASA EXPRESS. Entered service in January 2013.

WYKER DAMPFSCHIFFS-REEDEREI

THE COMPANY *Wyker Dampfschiffs-Reederei* is a German company

MANAGEMENT CEO Axel Meynköhn

ADDRESS PO Box 1540, 25933 Wyk auf Föhr, Postfach 1540, Germany.

TELEPHONE Administration & Reservations +49 (0) 46 67 – 9 40 30.

INTERNET *Email* info@faehre.de *Website* www.faehre.de *(Danish, English, German)*

ROUTES OPERATED Dagebüll – Föhr (50min; *NORDFRIESLAND, RUNGHOLT, SCHLESWIG-HOLSTEIN, UTHLANDE*; up to 14 per day), Dagebüll – Amrun (90 min (120 min via Föhr); *NORDFRIESLAND, RUNGHOLT, SCHLESWIG-HOLSTEIN, UTHLANDE*; 7 per day), Föhr – Amrun (1 hr; *NORDFRIESLAND,*

RUNGHOLT; SCHLESWIG-HOLSTEIN, UTHLANDE; up to 4 per day), Schlüttsiel – Hooge – Langeness (2 hrs; *HILLIGENLEI*; up to 2 per day).

1	HILLIGENLEI	467t	85	19.0k	38.3m	200P	22C	-	BA	DE	8411217
2	NORDFRIESLAND	2287t	95	12.0k	67.0m	1200P	55C	-	BA	DE	9102758
3	RUNGHOLT	2268t	92	12.5k	67.9m	975P	55C	-	BA	DE	9038660.
4	SCHLESWIG-HOLSTEIN	3202t	11	12.0k	75.9m	1200P	75C	-	BA	DE	9604378
5	UTHLANDE	1960t	10	12.0k	75.9m	1200P	75C	-	BA	DE	9548407

HILLIGENLEI Built as the PELLWORM by Husumer Schiffswerft, Husum, Germany for *Neue Pellwormer Dampfschiffahrtsgesellschaft* of Germany and operated between Pellworm and Strucklahnungshörn. In 1996 sold to Sven Paulsen, Altwarp, Germany and renamed the ADLER POLONIA. Operated between Altwarp and Novo Warpno (Poland). In 2002 sold to *Wyker Dampfschiffsreederei* and renamed the HILLIGENLEI I. In February 2010 renamed the HILLIGENLEI.

NORDFRIESLAND, RUNGHOLT Built by Husumer Schiffswerft, Husum, Germany for *Wyker Dampfschiffsreederei*.

SCHLESWIG-HOLSTEIN Built by Neptun Werft GmbH, Rostock, Germany for *Wyker Dampfschiffsreederei*.

UTHLANDE Built by J.J. Sietas GmbH & Co KG, Hamburg, Germany for *Wyker Dampfschiffsreederei*.

Under Construction

6	NEWBUILDING		-	18	12.0k	75.9m	1200P	75C	-	BA	DE	-

NEWBUILDING Under construction by Neptun Werft GmbH, Rostock, Germany for *Wyker Dampfschiffsreederei*.

Viking Grace *(Bruce Peter)*

SECTION 8 – OTHER VESSELS

The following passenger vessels are, at the time of going to print, not operating and are owned by companies which do not currently operate services or are used on freight -only services. They are therefore available for possible re-deployment, either in the area covered by this book or elsewhere. Passenger vessels operating freight-only services outside the scope of this book are also included here. Exceptionally we have included two freight-only vessels possibly to be chartered to an operator serving the UK. Withdrawn vessels not yet disposed of and owned by operating companies are shown under the appropriate company and marked '∴'.

CROMARTY FERRY COMPANY

1	CROMARTY QUEEN	68t	10	9.0k	17.3m	50P	4C	-	B	UK

CROMARTY QUEEN Built by Southampton Marine Services for *Cromarty Ferry Company*. Withdrawn at the end of the 2015 summer season and laid up.

REDERI AB GOTLAND

1	GUTE	7616t	79	15.0k	138.8m	88P	-	60T	BA	SE	7802794

GUTE Built as the GUTE by Falkenbergs Varv AB, Falkenberg, Sweden for *Rederi AB Gotland* of Sweden. Used on service between Gotland and the Swedish mainland. In 1988 chartered to *Brambles Shipping* of Australia and used between Port Melbourne (Victoria) and Burnie (Tasmania). In 1992 she was renamed the SALLY SUN and chartered to *Sally Ferries*, operating between Ramsgate and Dunkerque. In 1994 she inaugurated a Ramsgate – Vlissingen service, which was later changed to Dartford – Vlissingen. In 1995 she was chartered to *SeaWind Line*, renamed the SEAWIND II and operated between Stockholm and Turku. In 1997 she was chartered to *Nordic Trucker Line* for the Oxelösund – St Petersburg service and in 1998 she returned to *SeaWind Line*. In 1998, after *Rederi AB Gotland*-owned *Destination Gotland* regained the franchise to operate to Gotland, she was renamed the GUTE and resumed her summer role of providing summer freight back-up to the passenger vessels, but with a number of short charters during the winter. In Autumn 2002 chartered to *Amber Lines* for the Karlshamn – Liepaja service. In February 2003 chartered to *NATO* for the Iraq crisis. Returned to *Destination Gotland* in Summer 2003. In Autumn 2003 chartered to *Scandlines Amber Lines* to operate between Karlshamn and Liepaja. In 2004 lengthened by 20.3m by Nauta Shiprepair, Gdynia, Poland. In Autumn 2004 chartered to *Riga Sea Line* to inaugurate a freight service between Riga and Nynäshamn. In Autumn 2005 the service ended and the vessel was laid up. In January 2006 chartered to *Lisco* and placed on the Klaipėda – Karlshamn route, also undertaking two trips from Klaipėda to Baltiysk. In May 2006 chartered to *SeaWind Line*. In March 2007 chartered to *Baltic Scandinavian Line*. Charter ended September 2007. Apart from a trip to Cameroon, conveying Swedish UN Troops for Chad, she remained laid up until October 2008 when she was chartered to *Baltic Scandinavian Line* to operate between Härnösand and Kaskinen. In 2009 this service closed and she was laid up. At the end of March 2015 she was chartered to *Færgen* to operate between Køge and Rønne covering for the HAMMERODDE. She returned to layup in May.

SECTION 9 – SISTERS – A LIST OF SISTER (OR NEAR SISTER) VESSELS IN THIS BOOK

The following vessels are sisters or near sisters. This refers to 'as built' condition; some ships will subsequently have been modified and become different from their sister vessels.

ÆRØSKØBING, MARSTAL *(Ærøfærgerne)*

AMORELLA, GABRIELLA *(Viking Line)*, ISABELLE *(Tallink Silja Line)*, CROWN OF SCANDINAVIA *(DFDS Seaways)*.

ARGYLE, BUTE *(Caledonian MacBrayne)*.

ATLANTIC VISION *(Tallink)*, STENA SUPERFAST VII, STENA SUPERFAST VIII, STENA SUPERFAST X *(Stena Line)*.

AURORA AF HELSINGBORG, HAMLET, TYCHO BRAHE *(Scandlines – Helsingborg – Helsingør)*.

BALTIC QUEEN, BALTIC PRINCESS, GALAXY *(Tallink Silja Line)*.

BASTØ I, BASTØ II *(Bastø Fosen)*.

BASTØ IV, BASTØ V, BASTØ VI *(Bastø Fosen)*.

BEN-MY-CHREE *(Isle of Man Steam Packet Company)*, COMMODORE CLIPPER *(Condor Ferries)*, HAMMERODDE *(Bornholmstrafikken)* (Near sisters).

BERGENSFJORD, STAVANGERFJORD *(Fjord Line)*.

BERLIN, COPENHAGEN *(Scandlines)*.

BERLIOZ, RODIN *(MyFerryLink)*.

CANNA *(Rathlin Island Ferry Ltd)*, CLEW BAY QUEEN *(Clare Island Ferry Company)*, COLL *(Arranmore Island Ferries)*, EIGG *(Caledonian MacBrayne)*, MORVERN *(Arranmore Fast Ferries)*, RAASAY *(Caledonian MacBrayne)*, RHUM *(Arranmore Island Ferries)*.

CARRIGALOE, GLENBROOK *(Cross River Ferries)*.

CATRIONA, HALLAIG, LOCHINVAR *(Caledonian MacBrayne)*

COLOR FANTASY, COLOR MAGIC *(Color Line)*.

COLOR VIKING *(Color Line)*, STENA NAUTICA *(Stena Line)*.

CÔTE D'ALBATRE, SEVEN SISTERS *(DFDS Seaways)*.

CÔTE DES DUNES, CÔTE DES FLANDRES *(DFDS Seaways)*.

DAGALIEN, DAGGRI *(Shetland Islands Council)*.

DELFT SEAWAYS, DOVER SEAWAYS, DUNKERQUE SEAWAYS *(DFDS Seaways)*.

DEUTSCHLAND, SCHLESWIG-HOLSTEIN *(Scandlines)*.

EARL SIGURD, EARL THORFINN *(Orkney Ferries)*.

ECKERÖ *(Eckerö Linjen)*, POVL ANKER *(Bornholmstrafikken)*.

ERNEST BEVIN, JAMES NEWMAN, JOHN BURNS *(Woolwich Free Ferry)*.

EPSILON *(Irish Ferries)*, ETRETAT *(Brittany Ferries)*, SCOTTISH VIKING, STENA HORIZON, STENA LAGAN, STENA MERSEY, STENA FLAVIA *(Stena Line)*.

EUROPEAN CAUSEWAY, EUROPEAN HIGHLANDER *(P&O Ferries)*.

FENJA, MENJA *(Færgen)*.

FINNCLIPPER, FINNEAGLE, FINNFELLOW *(Finnlines)*, STENA GERMANICA *(Stena Line)*.

FINNLADY, FINNMAID, FINNSTAR, NORDLINK *(Finnlines)*.

FINNPARTNER, FINNTRADER *(Finnlines)*.

FRISIA I, FRISIA V *(Reederei Norden-Frisia)*.

GOTLAND, VISBY *(Destination Gotland)*.

HARILAID, KÖRGELAID *(Saaremaa Laevakompanii)*.

HIIUMA, MUHUMAA, SAAREMAA *(Saaremaa Laevakompanii)*.

HJALTLAND, HROSSEY *(NorthLink Ferries)*.

HUCKLEBERRY FINN, TOM SAWYER *(TT-Line)*.

KAUNAS SEAWAYS *(DFDS Seaways)*, VILNIUS SEAWAYS *(DFDS Seaways)*.

KING SEAWAYS, PRINCESS SEAWAYS *(DFDS Seaways)*.

KONG HARALD, NORDLYS, RICHARD WITH *(Hurtigruten)*.

KRONPRINS FREDERIK, PRINS JOACHIM *(Scandlines)*.

LANGELAND, LOLLAND *(Færgen)*.

LOCH DUNVEGAN, LOCH FYNE *(Caledonian MacBrayne)*.

LOCH LINNHE, LOCH RANZA, LOCH RIDDON, LOCH STRIVEN *(Caledonian MacBrayne)*.

LYNHER II, PLYM II, TAMAR II *(Torpoint Ferries)*.

MARIELLA *(Viking Line)*, PRINCESS ANASTASIA *(St. Peter Line)*.

MERCANDIA IV, MERCANDIA VIII *(Stena Line)*.

MIDNATSOL, TROLLFJORD *(Hurtigruten)*.

MIDSLAND, WESTFALEN *(Rederij Doeksen)*.

MONNIK, ROTTUM *(Wagenborg)*.

MÜNSTERLAND, OSTFRIESLAND *(AG Ems)*.

NILS DACKE, ROBIN HOOD *(TT-Line)*.

NILS HOLGERSSON, PETER PAN *(TT-Line)*.

NORBANK, NORBAY *(P&O Ferries)*.

NORDKAPP, NORDNORGE, POLARLYS *(Hurtigruten)*.

OERD, SIER *(Wagenborg)*.

OILEAN NA H-OIGE, SANCTA MARIA *(Bere Island Ferries)*.

PRIDE OF BRUGES, PRIDE OF YORK *(P&O Ferries)*.

PRIDE OF CANTERBURY, PRIDE OF KENT *(P&O Ferries)*.

PRIDE OF HULL, PRIDE OF ROTTERDAM *(P&O Ferries)*.

PRINCESS MARIA *(St. Peter Line)*, STENA SAGA *(Stena Line)*.

PRINS RICHARD, PRINSESSE BENEDIKTE *(Scandlines)*.

RED EAGLE, RED FALCON, RED OSPREY *(Red Funnel Ferries)*.

ROMANTIKA, VICTORIA I *(Tallink Silja Line)*.

SILJA SERENADE, SILJA SYMPHONY *(Tallink Silja Line)*.

SOUND OF SCARBA, SOUND OF SHUNA *(Western Ferries)*.

SOUND OF SEIL, SOUND OF SOAY *(Western Ferries)*.

SPIRIT OF BRITAIN, SPIRIT OF FRANCE *(P&O Ferries)*.

ST CECILIA, ST FAITH *(Wightlink)*.

STENA ADVENTURER, STENA SCANDINAVICA *(Stena Line)*.

STENA BRITANNICA, STENA HOLLANDICA *(Stena Line)*.

STENA GOTHICA, URD *(Stena Line)*.

STENA SPIRIT, STENA VISION *(Stena Line)*.

SUPERSPEED 1, SUPERSPEED 2 *(Color Line)*.

WIGHT LIGHT, WIGHT SKY, WIGHT SUN *(Wightlink)*.

Fast Ferries

FJORD CAT *(Fjord Line)*, MAX MOLS *(Mols-Linien)*.

KATEXPRESS 1, KATEXPRESS 2, KATEXPRESS 3 *(Mols-Linien)*.

RED JET 1, RED JET 2 *(Red Funnel Ferries)*.

WIGHT RYDER I, WIGHT RYDER II *(Wightlink)*.

Freight Ferries

ADELINE, WILHELMINE *(CLdN/Cobelfret Ferries)*,

AEGEAN BREEZE, ARABIAN BREEZE, ASIAN BREEZE, BALTIC BREEZE *(UECC)*.

AMANDINE, OPALINE *(CLdN/Cobelfret Ferries)*.

ANVIL POINT, EDDYSTONE *(Foreland Shipping)*, FINNMERCHANT *(Finnlines)*, HARTLAND POINT *Foreland Shipping)*, HURST POINT*(Foreland Shipping)*, MASSIMO MURA *(CLdN/Cobelfret Ferries)*.

ARROW *(Isle of Man Steam Packet)*, CLIPPER RANGER *(Seatruck Ferries)*, HELLIAR, HILDASAY *(NorthLink Ferries)*.

AUTO BANK, AUTO BAY *(UECC)*.

AUTOPREMIER, AUTOPRESTIGE, AUTOPRIDE, AUTOPROGRESS *(UECC)*.

AUTOSKY, AUTOSTAR, AUTOSUN *(UECC)*.

BALTICBORG, BOTHNIABORG *(Smurfit Kappa Group)*

BEGONIA SEAWAYS, FICARIA SEAWAYS, FREESIA SEAWAYS *(DFDS Seaways)*.

BOTNIA SEAWAYS, FINLANDIA SEAWAYS *(DFDS Seaways)*, FINNHAWK, FINNKRAFT *(Finnlines)*.

BRITANNIA SEAWAYS, SELANDIA SEAWAYS, SUECIA SEAWAYS *(DFDS Seaways)*.

FINNCARRIER, FINNMASTER *(Finnlines)*, MN PELICAN *(Brittany Ferries)*, SC CONNECTOR *(Sea-Cargo)*.

CAPUCINE, SEVERINE *(Stena Line)*.

CELANDINE, CELESTINE, CLEMENTINE, MELUSINE, VALENTINE, VICTORINE *(CLdN/Cobelfret Ferries)*.

CLIPPER PENNANT *(Seatruck Ferries)*, CLIPPER POINT *(DFDS Seaways)*, SEATRUCK PACE, SEATRUCK PANORAMA *(Seatruck Ferries)*.

CORONA SEAWAYS *(DFDS Seaways)*, FINNBREEZE, FINNMILL, FINNPULP, FINNSEA, FINNSKY, FINNSUN, FINNTIDE, FINNWAVE *(Finnlines)*, FIONIA SEAWAYS, HAFNIA SEAWAYS, JUTLANDIA SEAWAYS *(DFDS Seaways)*.

Stena Scanrail *(Nick Widdows)*

Red Jet 5 *(Andrew Cooke)*

CYMBELINE, UNDINE *(CLdN/Cobelfret Ferries).*

ELISABETH RUSS *(SOL Continent Line)*, PAULINE RUSS, SEAGARD *(Transfennica).*

GENCA, KRAFTCA, PLYCA, PULPCA, TIMCA, TRICA *(Transfennica).*

MAGNOLIA SEAWAYS, PETUNIA SEAWAYS, PRIMULA SEAWAYS *(DFDS Seaways).*

MAZARINE, PALATINE, PEREGRINE, VESPERTINE *(CLdN/Cobelfret Ferries).*

NORSKY, NORSTREAM *(P&O Ferries).*

OBBOLA, ORTVIKEN, ÖSTRAND *(SCA Transforest).*

PAULINE, YASMINE *(CLdN/Cobelfret Ferries).*

SCHIEBORG, SLINGEBORG *(SOL Continent Line)*, SOMERSET *(CLdN/Cobelfret Ferries).*

SEATRUCK POWER, SEATRUCK PROGRESS *(Seatruck Ferries)*, STENA PERFORMER, STENA PRECISION *(Stena Line).*

STENA FORERUNNER *(Transfennica)*, STENA FORETELLER *(Mann Lines).*

STENA TRANSIT, STENA TRANSPORTER *(Stena Line).*

SECTION 10 – CHANGES SINCE FERRIES 2016- BRITISH ISLES AND NORTHERN EUROPE

DISPOSALS

The following vessels, listed in *Ferries 2016 – British Isles and Northern Europe* have been disposed of – either to other companies listed in this book or others. Company names are as used in that publication.

AUTO BALTIC *(UECC)* Charter ended at the end of December 2015. In January 2016 chartered to *Flota Suardiaz.*

AUTORACER *(UECC)* In September 2015 sold to breakers in Denmark for scrap.

AUTORUNNER *(UECC)* In December 2015 sold to *Astra Express* (Liberian registered company) and renamed the ASTRA EXPRESS.

BALTICA *(Finnlines)* In November 2015 chartered to *SOL Continent Line.*

BERLIOZ *(MyFerryLink)* In July 2015 chartered to *DFDS Seaways.* In November renamed the CÔTE DES FLANDRES. Re-entered service in February 2016.

CARRIER *(Transfennica)* During 2015 sold to *Finnlines* and delivered at the end of the year. In January 2016 renamed the FINNCARRIER.

CLIPPER POINT *(DFDS Seaways)* In June 2015 charter ended and returned to *Seatruck Ferries.*

EXPRESS *(P&O Ferries)* In October 2015 charter ended. Chartered to *Gotlandsbåten* of Sweden. Not renamed.

FOYLE VENTURE *(Lough Foyle Ferry Company)* In November 2015 sold to *Frazer Ferries* of The Irish Republic. Resumed operation for them in July 2016.

FRIEDRICH RUSS *(Transfennica)* In December 2015 charter ended.

MALO SEAWAYS *(DFDS Seaways)* Withdrawn from traffic in February 2016 and laid up. In June 2016 chartered ended. Renamed the STENA NORDICA and chartered to *GNV* of Italy to operate between Sicily and the Italian mainland.

MARFRET NIOLON *(Sea-Cargo)* In November 2015 charter ended.

MISANA *(Finnlines)* In December 2015 charter ended. Long-term chartered to *Stena RoRo* and time chartered by them to *Transfennica*.

MISIDA *(Finnlines)* In December 2015 charter ended. Long-term chartered to *Stena RoRo* and time chartered by them to *Transfennica*.

NORD PAS-DE-CALAIS *(MyFerryLink)* In 2015 laid up. In May 2016 chartered to *FRS Iberia* of Spain and renamed the AL ANDALUS EXPRESS. Operates between Spain and Morocco.

PORTSMOUTH QUEEN *(Gosport Ferry)* In February 2016 sold for use as a party cruise boat on the Thames. Renamed the LONDON QUEEN.

PRINS JOACHIM *(Scandlines)* In May 2016 sold to *European Seaways* of Greece to operate between Italy and Albania. Renamed the PRINCE for delivery voyage. May be further renamed.

RED JET 5 *(Red Funnel Ferries)* In May 2016 sold to *Tirrenia Di Navigazione Spa* of Italy.

RENFRE ROSE *(Arranmore Island Ferry Services)* In June 2016 sold to *Highland Ferries* to reopen the Cromarty – Nigg service.

RODIN *(MyFerryLink)* In July 2015 chartered to *DFDS Seaways*. In November renamed the CÔTE DES DUNES. Re-entered service in February 2016.

SPATHOEK *(Rederij Doeksen)* In May 2016 sold to the *Atlantides Group* of Greece. Renamed the LISA I.

ST SORNEY *(Rathlin Island Ferry)* Disposed of during 2015.

STENA EXPLORER *(Stena Line)* In October 2015 sold to *Karadeniz Holding* of Turkey. Renamed the ONE WORLD KARADENIZ and it eas announced that she would be converted to act as office space at the Karmarine Shipyard in Yalova. However, she is no for sale again.

STENA SCANRAIL *(Stena Line)* In September 2015 sold to *Istanbul Lines* of Turkey. Renamed the BIRDENIZ.

THE PRINCESS ANNE *(Sea Containers Ferries)* Having been out of action for 16 years, this craft can no longer be regarded as laid-up but rather as a historic relic. Now owned by *Homes and Communities Agency*, on whose land at Lee on Solent she is situated. She is likely to be preserved.

THE PRINCESS MARGARET *(Sea Containers Ferries)* As the PRINCESS ANNE. However she is more likely to be scrapped as the land on which she is sited is required.

THORA *(Shetland Islands Council)* During 2015 sold.

TRADER *(Transfennica)* During 2015 sold to *Finnlines* and delivered at the end of the year. In January 2016 renamed the FINNMASTER.

TRELLEBORG *(Stena Line)* In April 2015 sold to *Go Shipping & Management Inc* of Greece and renamed the SUNNY.

VANGUARD, VENTURER *(Knoydart Seabridge)* Now operated by *Western Isles Cruises*.

VESSELS RENAMED

The following vessels have been renamed since the publication of *Ferries 2016 – British Isles and Northern Europe* without change of owner/operator.

ASK *(Stena Line)* In September 2015 renamed the STENA GOTHICA.

BASTØ IV *(Bastø Fosen)* In February 2016 renamed the BASTØ VII.

BASTØ V *(Bastø Fosen)* In February 2016 renamed the BASTØ VIII.

HELGOLAND *(AG Ems)* In January 2016 renamed the WESTFALEN.

KANHAVE *(Færgen)* In August 2015 renamed the SAMSØ.

OBBOLA *(SCA Transforest)* In May 2016 renamed the SCA OBBOLA.

Nord Pas-de-Calais *(John Hendy)*

Stena Explorer *(Gordon Hislip)*

ÖSTRAND *(SCA Transforest)* In June 2016 renamed the SCA ÖSTRAND.

ORTVIKEN *(SCA Transforest)* In July 2016 renamed the SCA ORTVIKEN.

WILLIAMSBORG *(CLdN/Cobelfret Ferries)* In January 2016 renamed the MASSIMO MURA.

COMPANY CHANGES

Cromarty Ferry Company This operator has ceased trading.

Kynoydart Seabridge The operation of this company (and two vessels) has been taken over by the new operator of *Western Isles Cruises*. A passenger only service is operated.

Lough Foyle Ferry Company This operator has ceased trading. The Lough Foyle ferry is now operated by *Frazer Ferries*.

MyFerryLink This operator has ceased trading.

Passage East Ferry This operator has been acquired by *Frazer Ferries* and is now listed under their name.

Sea Containers Ferries The ownership of the two hovercraft THE PRINCESS ANNE and the PRINCESS MARGARET changed some years ago. They are now owned by *Homes and Communities Agency*, owners of the land on which they are parked. However they must now be regarded as historic relics rather than laid up vessels.

FERRIES ILLUSTRATED

LATE NEWS

INDEX

Other books from Ferry Publications

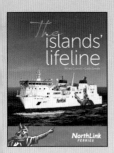

NorthLink
The Islands' Lifeline

This new book covers the history of ferry services to Orkney and Shetland and includes a wealth of outstanding and historical pictures. It also includes the development of Nothlink and the major improvements on ferry operations to the Islands over the last 10 years. Features on the refits of NorthLink vessels, distribution and freight services from Shetland and Orkney, and Willie MacKay, a long standing master, gives the readers an insight to the passage from mainland Scotland to the Islands. 128 pages. Price £18.00 plus p&p.

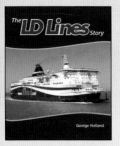

LD Lines

The LD Lines Story looks back over a colourful decade of ferry services in Northern Europe. The company was not afraid to experiment and innovate. It brought routes and vessels to ports that would have previously been considered totally inconceivable in a ferry industry that was going through painful adjustments to external factors outside of its control. 48 pages. Price £9.95 plus p&p.

The Townsend Thoresen Years

Following public demand we have reprinted this title in its original form. The book features the history of Townsend Thoresen up until the demise of the company in 1987. It includes a wealth of interesting pictures and also includes an overview of Thoresen Car Ferries at Portsmouth, ASN at Felixstowe and subsequently Townsend Thoresen operations at Felixstowe. The Belgium operations are also included. The final chapter includes the final months of this famous iconic company. A Fleet List and a Masters and their Ships list. Limited print run of 200 copies. Price £9.99 plus p&p.

Order online from
www.ferrypubs.co.uk
By telephone on
+44 (0)1624 898445
By post from
PO Box 33, Ramsey, Isle of Man IM99 4LP
Please telephone or email for current postage costs.

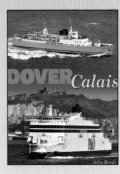

Dover-Calais

This will be an updated versic of the Dover-Calais 2009 edit Written by John Hendy, it cov the history of the most famo ferry crossing in the world bu looks in detail at the development and expansion the ferry operations and the new tonnage which has bee introduced since the openin the tunnel. The book is richly illustrated in colour and blac and white. It also includes DFDS and Myferrylink operations. Pr £18.95 plus p&p.

Holyhead-Dun Laoghaire

In February 2015, just s of its 190th anniversary Stena Line withdrew the link to Holyhead. This b covers the history and development of the po Dun Laoghaire and its l with Holyhead. Throug two world wars and beyond, the Dun Laogh Holyhead service beca part of Irish life, millions of emigrants said goodbye to Ireland they passed through the gates of the Carlisle Pier, the mailboa terminal. In happier times, emigration traffic gave way to touri and the first car ferries appeared in 1965. Thirty years later anc route was selected by Stena Line to receive the first of its revolutionary HSS vessels. Price £19.50 plus p&p.

Trans Europa Years

TransEuropa Ferries commenc ferry operations on the Englis Channel between Ramsgate a Ostend in 1998, following the demise of Sally Ferries. The company started its own passenger service during 200 and has used a variety of ship their services on the English Channel, most of which have operated for other operators. April 2013 the company ceased operations and the service wa closed. In this book Dean Smith traces the rise and fall of this Slovenian shipping company.. Price £9.95 plus p&p.